THE CLIMATE PANDEMIC

HOW CLIMATE DISRUPTION THREATENS HUMAN SURVIVAL

DENNIS MEREDITH

Glyphus

For information about this title or to order other books and/or electronic media, contact the publisher:
Glyphus, L.L.C.
2947 Mesa Grove Rd., Fallbrook, CA 92028
www.glyphus.com
editor@glyphus.com

Library of Congress Control Number: 2022916673

ISBNs:
  Print: 978-1-939118-23-3
  Kindle: 978-1-939118-25-7

Printed in the United States of America

Cover and Interior design: 1106 Design

The great enemy of the truth is very often not the lie—deliberate, contrived and dishonest—but the myth—persistent, persuasive and unrealistic. Too often we hold fast to the clichés of our forebears. We subject all facts to a prefabricated set of interpretations. We enjoy the comfort of opinion without the discomfort of thought.

—JOHN F. KENNEDY

Table of Contents

Preface

It was a run-of-the-mill traffic jam that first triggered my revelation of our seemingly inevitable extinction from a climate pandemic. We had just moved into a house near Temecula, California, north of San Diego. As an habitual hiker, I had immediately plotted a route that took me up to a mountain ridge overlooking the freeway that runs north-south. The highway winds its way across a stark scrub landscape of low mountains strewn with boulders and splashed with the green of avocado groves.

On one of my afternoon hikes, I was mulling whether I might write a book about climate change and what it could contribute to the field. I reached the overlook to see a massive freeway traffic jam stretching away into the distance, as a phalanx of thousands of rush-hour cars surged northward from San Diego toward Temecula. I knew that nearly every car carried a single person. The cars inched forward, uselessly burning gasoline and spewing carbon dioxide.

Such mass commuter migrations are by no means a San Diego phenomenon. Gargantuan traffic jams play out daily throughout urban areas worldwide. Each person in these daily trips has made an individual decision to undertake what is often an onerous commute. Each person has decided that expending time and gasoline and wearing out a car is worth it. And each person ignores the broader consequences of that commute.

And so does the government. In San Diego, as in so many cities, the government hasn't mustered the support, the will, or the funds to create a mass transit system that could alleviate the terrible congestion of this lemming-like migration.

Of course, I'd seen traffic jams before. But my witnessing the jam on this freeway came at a particularly critical time in history. Even as those masses of cars streamed north and south each day, I was aware that a wealth of new scientific discoveries was documenting unequivocally that their emissions were contributing to an inexorable global climatic deterioration—with effects from catastrophic wildfires to ocean acidification.

And I realized that, as dire as these findings were, they were receiving far too little attention. Unlike the round-the-clock coverage of the COVID-19 pandemic, climate discoveries were being engulfed by the daily flood of news. And, they were appearing piecemeal in the media; not integrated into the frightening, tragic mosaic that revealed a global environmental catastrophe that could lead to human extinction.

I decided to gather those findings into this book and to seek to make sense of their implications. In the process, I discovered to my surprise that much of what I believed about climate disruption were myths. For example, as discussed later, there is scientists' inaccurate claim that limiting global temperature rise to 1.5°C would help avoid climate catastrophe. And also as discussed later, there is the erroneous, hyped belief that renewable energy will offer a major clean energy source.

Once I decided to cover the science, I realized I needed to cover how our own human nature is leading to a global catastrophe. After all, such a tragedy will be due not just to our exploitation of fossil fuels, but more basically to our own failings as a species to wisely manage that exploitation.

Hard truth to power

Some may criticize the book as encouraging what climatologist Michael Mann has termed "doomism"—injecting apocalyptic pessimism into a society that needs optimism to combat climate disruption.[1][2] This criticism of pessimism, however, begs two questions: whether this book accurately portrays a dire climate future for our species; and whether it presents a truth that is preferable to the myth that we will ultimately survive climate disruption.

Mann has been quoted as asserting, "There is no evidence of climate change scenarios that would render human beings extinct."[3] However, absence of evidence is not evidence of absence, as the saying goes. Given the profound limitations of climate disruption scenarios that this book reveals, the fact that they don't allow for the possibility of human extinction means nothing.

On the other hand, it is well known that vast numbers of species have gone extinct over the eons when their environment no longer supported them. Humans are certainly no different from any other species—utterly dependent on our environment for survival. In fact, Earth is already undergoing an ecological unraveling (see Mass Extinction).

I leave it to you, after reading this book, to decide whether I am a cockeyed pessimist or a climate Cassandra. However, before dismissing the possibility of human extinction from climate disruption, I would ask you to honestly ask yourself whether you really believe that our species can survive long term, given the profound environmental damage we have done, and continue to do, to the planet.

This book's stark predictions may engender the kind of ad hominem attacks that have plagued the emotion-charged controversy over climate disruption. The attacks might be intensified by the anger people may feel at being confronted by the traumatic prospect of human extinction.

However, I could not let the prospect of such attacks deter me, especially given my background. I have spent my professional life at universities, where the pursuit of truth was a foremost duty and a moral imperative. I have worked at medical centers, where I saw that physicians' sense of their duty to truth demanded that they face the bleak necessity of telling patients of the most heart-rending prognoses—that they are terminal.

I was also inspired by those government leaders who, during the COVID-19 pandemic, took the moral responsibility to give the public the unvarnished truth—in contrast to a president who minimized the danger, grasped at unproven treatments, and dubbed himself a "cheerleader."

And, of course, I have subscribed to the tenets of responsible journalism, which demand that I follow the story wherever the evidence leads—regardless of how painful the revealed truth. Thus, when I came to understand the ultimate consequences of climate disruption, I could not ignore what I saw as my responsibility to explain them.

All that said, I did have an intense debate with myself about whether to write a book that would so severely disrupt the comfortable shared fiction that humans will somehow manage to prevail in the climate pandemic. As historian Yuval Noah Harari so insightfully wrote:

> The advantages of increased social cohesion are often so big that fictional stories routinely triumph over the truth in human history. Scholars have known this for thousands of years, which is why scholars often had to decide whether they served the truth or social harmony. Should they aim to unite people by making sure everyone believes in the same fiction, or should they let people know the truth even at the price of disunity?[4]

In the end, I decided that those who need the truth should have it. So, this book tells a hard, even devastating, truth—a *really* inconvenient truth, if you will. If you are not prepared to confront this truth, do not read this book. Give it away, donate it to a library, or put it on a high shelf—out of sight, out of mind.

Besides explaining the science of climate disruption, this book also includes editorializing. So, I should describe my qualifications for presuming to advance these opinions.

I spent some four decades in news offices writing releases and articles about scientists at the Universities of Wisconsin and Rhode Island, MIT, Caltech, Cornell, and Duke. In those posts, I could observe scientists' personalities, their ambitions, and the arduous process they go through to secure funding, do research, and advance their careers.

Looking back on that experience, I've come to realize how the nature of the scientific process, and of the scientists themselves, contributed to the failure to alert the world to a looming global environmental disaster.

My experience as a public information officer (PIO) has also given me insight into the nature of the scientific process and how scientists communicate their research. That experience informed my book *Explaining Research.*[5] It also enabled me to understand the inherent flaws and shortcomings of even the best science.

Even given those flaws, however, science remains the most reliable source of insight into climate disruption. This book's discussions of that disruption and its dire consequences rely on the best available science.

It is that science that builds what I believe to be a credible case that our current course is leading us toward extinction.

My experience as a PIO working with the media enabled me to understand how journalism—as responsible as reporters are—can misrepresent scientific discoveries, and in turn how the public can misperceive science.

Climatology is a complex and ever-changing science, and this book represents my best effort to explain it clearly and accurately, and to reflect the latest knowledge. Although this book has been independently and rigorously fact checked, any errors of fact or interpretation are entirely my own.

To enable readers to explore further the research cited in this book, I have included on the website ClimatePandemic.com and in the e-book, hyperlinks to the cited references—books, scientific papers, lay articles, reports, and websites. However, some articles will require a fee or subscription to access.

I have tried to include only scientific papers, reports, and books vetted by the scientific community. However, some questionable studies may have crept into the mix, given that scientific publishing and peer review are imperfect processes. In fact, in researching this book, I was saved more than once from such error by journalists who published insightful critiques of such studies. I heartily thank them!

A note about units of measure: While the metric system is the system of choice among scientists, some of the references in this book cite English measures. I have elected to cite measures in whatever system they appeared in the literature.

Finally, I will make my best effort to maintain accuracy by including on ClimatePandemic.com addenda, errata, reviews, and critiques of the book.

Acknowledgments

I owe an enormous debt of gratitude to the science, economic, environment, and general assignment writers covering climate disruption, as well as the scientists who write lay-level articles. Their expert reportage led me to key scientific papers and offered invaluable context and insight into the science. They number many hundreds, a list far too long to include in the print book, so I have posted it on ClimatePandemic.com.

Special thanks to the people who helped shepherd this book from draft to finished work. Insightful comments from my longtime friend and esteemed colleague David Salisbury helped me focus on and remedy the manuscript's weaknesses. Without the meticulous, tireless fact-checking by Dr. Alka Tripathy-Lang, this book would have been infested with errors large and small. And Megan Sever's virtuoso editing skills and deep knowledge of climate science contributed enormously to the book's quality.

Above all, I'd like to express my deepest gratitude to my dear wife, Joni. She has supported my work for more than five decades, and is a canny editor, wise counsel, and best friend.

Introduction

The COVID-19 pandemic created a massive health and economic catastrophe that reverberated throughout society for years. However, society has learned to live with an endemic viral threat. In tragic contrast, this book proposes that we are experiencing an infinitely more serious "climate pandemic" that poses an existential threat to humanity. Its nature is precisely like that of a viral pandemic, in that it is global and relentless. And just as the pandemic behaves only according to the biological principles governing the spread of infectious organisms, the climate obeys only the principles of geoscience.

Like the COVID-19 pandemic, the climate pandemic, in a sense, mutates to unpredictably generate new forms. That is, climate disruption is so very complex—with interacting environmental, social, economic, and political elements—that attempting to mitigate it creates unexpected consequences.

Also like the COVID-19 pandemic, the climate pandemic has been marked by the tragic failure of society's leaders to understand its nature and to institute policies to stop it. Both pandemics have also been heavily politicized, with the tragic ignoring of science by partisan factions. Politically motivated "climate hesitancy" can be just as lethal as has been vaccine hesitancy.

However, unlike the COVID-19 pandemic, the climate pandemic has no ready solutions. People will not become immune to its effects. Nor will there be the technological equivalent of vaccines, antiviral drugs, or simple practices like social distancing and mask-wearing to protect people from its ravages.

As horrific as the COVID-19 pandemic has been, its effects pale in comparison to the coming catastrophe from climate disruption. In fact, the climate pandemic will steadily worsen, even bringing our species to extinction, unless we launch a global revolution to abandon our carbon-dependent energy system.

Given the evidence in this book, I see only a vanishingly small possibility of such a revolution. And I do not see a pathway for our species' survival.

However, it is my fervent hope that those who read this book *will* somehow see such a pathway. I even hope that they will identify flaws in my reasoning and/or my interpretation of the science that will render my opinion invalid.

I must emphasize that my agonizing conclusion did not arise from my own personal predilection. Rather, it emerged from the vast trove of credible research detailed in this book documenting the devastation to the global environment that we are causing. I do not consider myself an advocate for this conclusion, but rather its reluctant messenger.

Our failed response to climate disruption has been the environmental equivalent of the devastating 1986 Chernobyl nuclear accident, but writ far larger.

In the case of Chernobyl, scientists knew well and documented the fatal design flaws of the Soviet nuclear power plants. They—as well as the Soviet political leaders—knew that cost-cutting, shoddy workmanship, political pressure, and willful ignorance had led to the building of power plants that were unstable, unpredictable, and accident-prone.[6] Their egregious failure to remedy those flaws led to the cataclysmic explosion that exposed millions to hazardous radiation and rendered vast regions uninhabitable.

Similarly, our scientists and political leaders have well known of the profound dangers of climate disruption. But, as this book shows, for the same economic and political motivations at work in Chernobyl, they have minimized, even ignored those dangers.

Climate disruption is, indeed, humanity's Chernobyl.

Given our failures, it would be tempting to extend this book's pandemic metaphor to depict us as unthinking infectious agents responsible for the climate catastrophe. But such a metaphor would be simplistic and demeaning. True, we are the causative agents of the climate pandemic. And our spread has, indeed, been viral. But unlike viruses, we are no biological automatons. We are a stunning, intelligent evolutionary achievement, albeit a flawed one.

As this book will show, those flaws have brought us to a point where we are draining the life out of the very planet that gave *us* life, with tragic consequences for our species' future. It will explore why those flaws in our human nature are driving us toward extinction. While this book's account of our potential future may read like an apocalyptic drama, its portent of an extinction-level threat is no science fiction.

I recognize that, in the words of Carl Sagan, "extraordinary claims require extraordinary evidence." So, in this heavily referenced book, I have sought to document the evidence for the extraordinary claim that we face extinction. My journalistic approach has been: "Don't take my word for it."

The book is also extensively referenced because it aims to give readers access to the important scientific and policy literature on climate disruption. I hope the book and the resources it offers serve to inform researchers and policymakers about the daunting scientific, economic, and political realities of climate disruption. I have read so many articles and books in which the authors propose climate-rescue policies that are little more than vague, naive hand-waving, with little understanding of those realities.

Also, the hundreds of meticulously researched scientific papers and reports this book cites make it obvious how utterly absurd are climate "de-nihilists'" claims that climate research is flawed, sloppy, or dishonest.

I have so named this misguided cadre because of their nihilistic rejection of established science, and for their destructiveness (see Co-infection by De-nihilism). (I should note that the term was independently coined by Mary Annaïse Heglar of the Natural Resources Defense Council.)

This book also explains why groups key to conveying climate disruption's cataclysmic potential have muted their voices. The mainstream media, scientists, and politicians failed to sound the alarm over decades during which they knew of climate disruption's dangers. I will explore the psychological, social, and economic reasons for this failure.

Besides covering the research that has revealed the looming climate catastrophe, I explain why that research has not prompted global action beyond a weak, nonbinding agreement to try to combat the problem (see Paris Agreement: Blind and Toothless).

The book will show that we are not equipped to meet the challenges of climate disruption because its fundamental properties place it far beyond the realm of threats that we evolved to cope with that (see I. The Climate Pandemic, a Super-Wicked Problem).

It details how our embrace of technology and our desire for the most comfortable life have led us to create a massive, global fossil fuel infrastructure whose momentum renders it impossible for us to evolve our society to become sustainable (see II. The Carbon Contagion). Nevertheless, we cling to an unfounded belief that decarbonization to achieve a zero-carbon world is a realistic possibility (see Decarbonization Delusion).

It explores how global heating from fossil-fuel-produced greenhouse gases is triggering tipping points—irreversible environmental changes that exacerbate the heating in a feedback loop. Such feedback processes include the melting of icy methane clathrates on the ocean floor, decomposition of global permafrost deposits, combustion of immense peat deposits, and emissions from the world's warming soils (see Climate Monsters).

Some tipping points will take more than a century to become hazardous; other will take mere decades. But all will ultimately add to the rising concentration of carbon dioxide (CO_2).

The book details how our carbon-fouling of the planet has produced a plague on the environment. This plague comprises melting polar ice, mass extinctions, a rise in global temperature, heat waves, wildfires, disappearing forests, intensified storms, and severe droughts. The scientific studies cited in this book predict that these terrestrial phenomena will only become worse (see III. Plague on the Environment).

The world's oceans are also suffering a relentless worsening of climate-disruption-caused impacts—including warming waters, oxygen depletion, acidification, rising sea levels, devastated coral reefs, disappearing ocean life, and disruption of critical ocean currents (see Sea Change).

The consequences of these catastrophes include a more toxic and disease-ridden Earth, famine, environmental exodus, global conflict, and perhaps even nuclear war (see IV. Viral Human Consequences).

Climate disruption is only secondarily a technological problem. It is primarily an institutional and human problem. The fundamentally flawed nature of our institutions has driven development of the energy technology that could be the means to our end. Every segment of our society failed that should have played a role in avoiding our fate—including the media, scientists, environmentalists, corporations, and politicians (see V. The Epidemiology of Society's Failure).

This book also explores how our individual psychology, misperceptions, and biases laid the groundwork for our potential extinction (see Why We Failed). The neural machinery we evolved to survive—which enabled us to become Earth's dominant species—contains the seeds of our destruction. For example, we all have a natural tendency to act according to our own rational, immediate interests. But our individual interests can become irrational when it comes to ensuring our survival as a species.

Many believe that the political and technological equivalent of a vaccine will inoculate us against our fate. But this hope is currently but a comforting mirage. As this book shows, there will be no rescue by global agreements, renewable energy, carbon capture, or geoengineering (see VI. Grasping at Climate Panaceas).

The evidence this book offers reveals that climate disruption threatens extinction of the human species—part of a vast ecological tragedy for the planet.

This book is not a wake-up call.

It may well be taps.

I
The Climate Pandemic, a Super-Wicked Problem

A disease pandemic—as frightening and catastrophic as it is—is a solvable problem. We can use our medical technology to create vaccines to protect us and drug treatments to cure us of the microbe. And eventually, our own immune systems mobilize to fight infection by the invading microbe, ultimately making us resistant.

In sharp contrast, climate disruption has been dubbed a "super-wicked" problem by policy analysts.[7] They wrote that a super-wicked problem comprises four features:

> Time is running out; those who cause the problem also seek to provide a solution; the central authority needed to address it is weak or nonexistent; and . . . policy responses discount the future irrationally. These four features combine to create a policymaking "tragedy" where traditional analytical techniques are ill-equipped to identify solutions, even when it is well recognized that actions must take place soon to avoid catastrophic future impacts.

In his book *Don't Even Think About It: Why Our Brains Are Wired to Ignore Climate Change,* author George Marshall wrote, "by definition, it defies having a clear definition because it keeps evolving according to the solutions we evolve to solve it." Climate disruption has "no deadlines, no geographic location, no single cause, solution, or enemy. Our brains, constantly scanning for the cues that we need to process and categorize information, find none, and we are left grasping at air," he wrote.[8]

The COVID-19 pandemic garnered continual headlines, not just because of its catastrophic nature, but also because we perceived it as simple, fast, immediate, major, alien, and certain. In contrast, climate disruption is a super-wicked problem because we perceive it as too complex, slow, distant, minor, ordinary, and uncertain.

Too complex to fear

Both a viral pandemic such as the COVID-19 outbreak and the climate pandemic have identifiable culprits. A new virulent virus strain caused the COVID-19 pandemic, and greenhouse gas emissions has caused the climate pandemic. Both also have a defined array of symptoms.

The viral infection causes headache, fever, lung congestion, and so forth. Similarly, the climate pandemic produces higher temperatures—a global fever—and chemical effects such as ocean acidification.

However, the climate pandemic's symptoms interact and spread through the environment and society in more complex ways than a viral pandemic. It does not provide what policy analyst Alice Hill calls a "no more" moment. In her book *The Fight for Climate after COVID-19*, she wrote that:

> With climate change there is no single "no more" moment to galvanize public support and thus political will. The very nature of climate change dulls a sense of urgency. Because climate impacts manifest in different locations at different times in seemingly unrelated ways, they can seem episodic to the casual observer. Their variety, temporal variation, and geographic sprawl act to disguise their global cumulative growth.[9] Climate disruption's complexity also overwhelms us emotionally.

As journalist Amanda Hess wrote eloquently in *The New York Times*:

> Global warming represents the collapse of such complex systems at such an extreme scale that it overrides our emotional capacity. This creates its own perverse flavor of climate denial: We acknowledge the science but do not truly accept it, at least not enough to urgently act . . . .

As global warming cooks the Earth, it melts our brains,
fries our nerves and explodes the narratives that we like
to tell about humankind—even the apocalyptic ones.[10]

It is dizzying to trace just a single thread of the climate pandemic's effects. Some examples:

- Higher greenhouse gas levels trap more heat in the atmosphere ... which melts glaciers ... which causes sea-level rise ... which floods coastal cities ... which devastates economies ... which triggers political upheaval ... which sparks wars.
- Glaciers melt ... which shifts ocean circulation ... which disrupts local climates ... which devastates fisheries and farming ... which causes famine ... which impairs public health ... which triggers epidemics.
- Higher temperatures dry the land and exacerbate droughts ... which drive bark beetle outbreaks ... which kill millions of acres of trees ... which fuel wildfires ... which emit even more CO_2 ... which help destroy forest ecosystems that support local economies.[11]

How these threads interweave insidiously in the fabric of society was dramatically revealed in one study of Arctic heating over 47 years. The study found complex interactions among physical changes such as melting sea ice and reduced snow cover, and biological changes such as the mismatched timing of flowers blooming and insects pollinating those flowers.

The study concluded that the region had entered into an "unprecedented state, with implications not only within but beyond the Arctic."[12]

Indeed, ecosystem tipping points could interact to trigger unpredictable cascade effects. One analysis of more than a thousand scientific papers on such tipping points found evidence that almost half could interact with one another. The researchers said their work "suggests that current approaches to environmental management and governance underestimate the likelihood of cascading effects."[13] (For more on tipping points, see Climate Monsters.)

What's more, the climate pandemic has arisen because of a complex, interacting mix of failures of key segments of society: the media, scientists, environmentalists, corporations, and politicians (see V. The Epidemiology of Society's Failure).

Too slow to fear

While the COVID-19 pandemic was rapid, sweeping across the globe in months, the climate pandemic has come on too slowly to fear. Climate disruption's impacts accumulate gradually over decades. Rising temperatures, acidifying oceans, dying forests—all advance slowly and insidiously.

There is also a time lag in the effects of CO_2 emissions that adds to our perception of slowness. The effects of a given increase in CO_2 do not occur for perhaps decades.[14]

A viral pandemic is also dramatic in its cycle, producing a spike in infections followed by a drastic fall. Psychologically, such a dramatic evolution is easier for us to respond to than the climate pandemic, which presents as a steadily worsening phenomenon.

Climate disruption's slowness, lag time, and gradualness threaten to produce in our psyches a shifting baseline—aka a new normal. We become literally acclimatized to each new global temperature level and the resulting environmental disasters. Journalist David Roberts has dubbed the phenomenon the "scariest thing about global warming," writing:

> No moment of reckoning arrives. The atmosphere becomes progressively more unstable, but it never does so fast enough, dramatically enough, to command the sustained attention of any particular generation of human beings. Instead, it is treated as rising background noise. . . . Put more bluntly: The public may never notice that it's getting warmer. . . . And so, little by little, a hotter, more chaotic, and more dangerous world is becoming normal to us, as we sleepwalk toward more tragedies.[15]

With the climate pandemic, we are the proverbial frog in slowly heating water, failing to react to gradually more dire circumstances.

Too distant to fear

While some recent impacts of climate disruption have become unavoidably close—such as droughts, wildfires, hurricanes, and floods—many impacts are geographically and psychologically distant from our daily lives.

We do not see as relevant to our lives the extinction of geographically remote polar bears or inundation of the Maldives, an island chain in the Indian Ocean.[16] [17]

While people's perception of the local risk of climate disruption is rising, it is still far from universal. For example, only about half of US respondents in a Yale/George Mason University survey believe global heating will harm them or their family.[18]

This illusory and dangerous perception of distance contributes to the inaction that threatens our survival. We simply do not grasp the impact of global climate disruption on our own lives. As an article in Yale's *Journal of Industrial Ecology* asserted:

> Everything, from the food we eat to the clothes we wear to cars we drive, has global implications, requiring resources from distant places and generating pollution far from our homes ... our understanding of the complex ripple effect throughout the global economy and on natural and social systems remains rudimentary.[19]

Climate disruption also seems distant in time—at least its most catastrophic effects. While we already suffer record temperatures, storms, and droughts, the true cataclysms are likely decades away. So, "global warming doesn't trigger our concern [because] we see it as a threat to our futures—not our afternoons," wrote psychologist Daniel Gilbert.[20]

Especially dangerous is climate disruption's psychological distance for political leaders. They are responsible for developing long-term environmental policies, but their careers revolve around the short-term process of getting reelected (see Why the Politicians Failed). Their engagement with global deterioration is mainly abstract. They don't experience firsthand such global environmental catastrophes as droughts that lead to famines, which might make them personally appreciate the urgency.

Psychological distance renders climate disruption unfamiliar, which also makes it less urgent. We have a tendency to confuse the *unfamiliar* with the *improbable*, pointed out Nobel-Prize-winning economist Thomas Schelling: "The contingency we have not considered seriously looks strange; what looks strange is thought improbable; what is improbable need not be considered seriously," he wrote.[21]

Too minor to fear

Climate disruption may seem minor because it involves warming of only a few degrees Celsius—surely not a trigger of ecological disaster. After all, we experience temperature fluctuations far larger than that over a day, not to mention over the seasons.

But the delicately balanced global ecology that is our lifeline evolved within an incredibly narrow range of temperatures (see Six Degrees to Termination).

Current global temperature increases are triggering profound, often unpredictable changes in that ecology. These changes impact our food, health, economy, and political stability, and as this book shows, could end our species.

For example, even slightly warmer temperatures affect the spread of disease. Global heating enables the spread of notorious mosquito-borne viruses such as Zika, West Nile virus, and dengue fever.[22] [23] The mosquitoes' invasive northern spread is enabled by higher temperatures and humidity, as well as lengthening their season, and spurring them to feed more actively (see Diseased Earth).

In the ocean, even slightly warmer waters enable disease-causing *Vibrio* bacteria to thrive in waters farther north than their historical range.[24] The bacteria cause infections such as cholera and gastroenteritis-like symptoms from eating raw shellfish or even just playing in the water. One study calculated that even a 1°C increase in sea-surface temperature nearly doubled the number of *Vibrio* cases.[25]

Similarly, the slight increase in ocean acidity from higher amounts of dissolved CO_2 profoundly damage marine life, even unraveling the ocean food chain (see Acidified Waters).

While these effects seem subtle, they are lethal. CO_2's role in climate disruption is analogous to poisoning by the radioactive isotope polonium in the human body. Both poisons infuse insidiously through the system, tearing apart the fabric of life. In polonium's case, the effects are vomiting, hair loss, immune collapse, and death. In CO_2's case, the effects are collapse of ecosystems and mass extinctions (see Mass Extinction).[26]

Too ordinary to fear

A viral pandemic constitutes an invasion by an alien species. Viruses are exotic organisms that exist on the divide between living and nonliving. They are biological automatons—unthinking, relentlessly proliferating molecules. What's more, they comprise a vast menagerie whose many species can pose drastically different threats.

The SARS-COV-2 virus is about twice as infectious as the influenza virus. About ten times more unvaccinated victims require hospitalization, and the fatality rate is about ten times larger. So, we have deeply, and rightfully, dreaded its appearance.

On the other hand, we have tended to accept sizzling summers, crop-killing droughts, raging forest fires, rainfall deluges, surging floods, and lethal hurricanes and tornadoes as part of the ordinary vicissitudes of nature. They are familiar because we have seen, or even experienced them, from our childhood.

"Malignant normality" is the term psychiatrist Robert Jay Lifton used to denote such an acceptance. He coined the term when studying Nazi doctors who normalized their duty to select Jews for the gas chamber. The same malignant normality applies to nuclear weapons and climate disruption, he wrote. In the case of nuclear weapons, the normality takes the form of stockpiling masses of weapons and a willingness to use them.[27]

"With climate, climate normality was in the everyday practice," wrote Lifton. "We were born into climate normality. This is the world which we entered and in which we live now and which continues. If we allow it to continue as it is now, it will result in the end of human civilization within the present century."

Such normality produces desensitization in the context of climate disruption—the tragedy of the "too-commons." In fact, one study found that people can come to accept weather extremes—in this case unusual temperatures—as normal in only a couple of years.[28]

When we suffer such disasters, we come to accept as a standard response grieving for those killed, rebuilding what was shattered, and recovering from the loss.

But that response to what are really *unnatural* disasters has only recently included a call for the major restructuring of our energy economy to alleviate future such tragedies.

If only climate disruption spawned zombies.

Too uncertain to fear

We reserve our panic for perils that are immediate and certain—whether it's the droplet-spewing cough of an infected person or an oncoming truck barreling toward us.

We also prefer predictability in our lives, from the regular appearance of a paycheck, to the comfort of a daily schedule, to the reliable cuisine at a favorite restaurant.

But climate science is both uncertain and unpredictable. That is, even with vast amounts of knowledge about climate disruption, scientists always seek more—to fill in gaps and refine their understanding (see Why the Scientists Failed). Scientists know that predicting climate disruption and global heating depends on a disparate range of environmental factors such as ocean chemistry, atmospheric physics, and ice properties.

This uncertainty may make you question the validity of the science, since scientists are making constant discoveries of new climate threats and adjusting their predictions.

For example, scientists have been reluctant to pin a particular hurricane, flood, tornado, or heat wave on climate disruption. They have been more willing to say that the likelihood or intensity of such extreme events is increased by global heating. But such statements sound to our ears like weasel-wording—even though the scientists are being scientifically precise.

Similarly, scientists are willing to say that climate disruption helps spawn political upheaval and wars, although no scientist would pin a given conflict on it (see Climate War Outbreak).

De-nihilists of climate disruption use such tentativeness and caution as purported evidence that climate science is unreliable. It is a ploy that often resonates with nonscientists, even though it is wrong (see Co-infection by De-nihilism).

Later, we will explore how scientists' tentative language is fundamental to the scientific culture, but how it has compromised society's ability to appreciate the profound hazard of climate disruption (see Why the Scientists Failed).

Given our skewed perception of climate disruption, we cope with its super-wickedness by not doing very much. We are not making significant changes to our lifestyles to make them more eco-friendly, according to a statistical analysis of American's energy-related lifestyles. The analysis revealed that we are using somewhat less electricity and water and are recycling. But it concluded that our actual changes in behavior are "very much a mixed bag."[29]

And most of us in the US are still commuting alone—more than three-quarters of us, in fact—rather than carpooling or taking public transit, found a US Census Bureau study.[30]

We also prefer to drive gas-powered cars. Globally, today only a small percentage of vehicle sales are electric or gas-electric hybrids.[31] Buyers are currently opting more for gas-guzzling SUVs, trucks, and vans (see Fossilized Transportation). In the US, 2050 will still see battery and hybrid vehicles only a small fraction of total sales, compared to those powered by fossil fuels, projects the US Energy Information Administration.[32]

All these misperceptions lead us to rank climate disruption far too low in our list of fears, given its profound existential danger. Ranking highest on Americans' perception of threats are infectious diseases, terrorism, and nuclear weapons spread, found a Pew Research Center survey. Climate disruption ranked lower on the list than China's power and influence, and cyberattacks from other countries.[33]

Even worse, a Pew survey of Americans' priorities found that climate disruption ranked below such issues as the budget deficit, the criminal justice system and problems of poor people.[34] However, in reality climate disruption profoundly impacts all the public's priorities.

II
The Carbon Contagion

It seems impossible that carbon dioxide (CO_2) is the principal instrument of a climate disaster. It is a benign, non-toxic gas—the bubbles in sodas, the gas exhaled in our every breath, a life-giving substance for plants. Its atmospheric concentration seems entirely trivial: 0.04%, or around 400 parts per million (ppm).

However, CO_2 is the central culprit in the bleak consequences of climate disruption. This section will explore the "carbon contagion" of unchecked fossil fuel production and what scientists know about its consequences.

Carbon-Fevered Planet

The pernicious property of both CO_2 and its hydrocarbon cousin methane (CH_4) is that they trap more heat than other atmospheric gases, such as oxygen and nitrogen. They are so-called "greenhouse gases"—along with water vapor, nitrous oxide (N_2O), and ozone.

So, the higher the atmospheric concentration of these gases, the more solar heat is trapped. And they are high. Said the 2021 report of the UN Intergovernmental Panel on Climate Change (IPCC):

> In 2019, atmospheric CO_2 concentrations were higher than at any time in at least 2 million years, and concentrations of CH_4 and N_2O were higher than at any time in at least 800,000 years.[35]

The oceans currently suck up much of that heat, as well as absorbing CO_2. However, that carbon sink is not infinite. As the oceans warm, they absorb less CO_2, like a warm soda losing its fizz. This loss in ocean absorption is exacerbated by stratification of surface waters separate from the colder deep waters. Thus, those waters warm even more, becoming even less able to absorb CO_2.[36]

One reason that unchecked fossil fuel burning will prove so catastrophic is that a large fraction of emitted CO_2 has a hellishly long atmospheric lifetime—measured in centuries.[37] The complexity of CO_2 processing in the environment means that millennia will pass before the carbon emitted today will be thoroughly absorbed.[38]

This longevity means that the Earth would continue to experience so-called "committed warming" long after greenhouse gas emissions ended.[39]

It is true that if CO_2 levels magically stopped rising, global temperature would eventually level off. However, there are two major catches:

First, atmospheric CO_2 levels and global temperatures *would not go down*, meaning a continued polar ice melting, sea level rise, and other effects. And secondly, the chances are zero of CO_2 concentrations leveling off (see Decarbonization Delusion).

Even the unprecedented temporary plunge in emissions due to the COVID-19 pandemic did not reduce atmospheric concentrations. So concentrations will continue to rise and so will unrelenting heating.

Relentless rise, irreversible effects

And so will the effects of those emissions. Said the 2021 IPCC report: "Many changes due to past and future greenhouse gas emissions are irreversible for centuries to millennia, especially changes in the ocean, ice sheets and global sea level." These changes include ocean acidification (see Acidified Waters), melting ice (see Inexorable Melt), and sea-level rise (see Flood Warning).

CO_2 rise is unequivocally due to the burning of fossil fuels. Before such combustion began with the Industrial Revolution in the 19th century, the level was 278 parts per million. The 400 parts-per-million level was reached in 2016, and it has continued to rise.[40] [41] See the graph on the next page for the dramatic recent history of that rise.

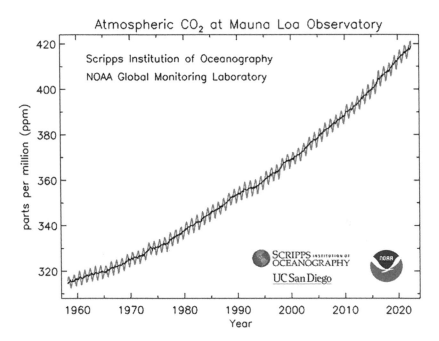

Atmospheric carbon dioxide has seen a drastic rise since 1960.

Source: Scripps Institution of Oceanography, NOAA Global Monitoring Laboratory

Ancient conditions revisited

When the 400-ppm CO_2 level last existed about 3 million years ago, global temperatures were 3–4°C above modern preindustrial levels, which is where the Earth is headed now by the end of the century, according to computer models (see Six Degrees to Termination).[42][43][44] Sea levels were about 15 to 20 meters above modern levels—which would swamp coastal regions today (see Flood Warning).[45]

The current rate of CO_2 increase is unprecedented in geologic history. The average CO_2 concentration continues to set records each year, concluded the American Meteorological Society's *State of the Climate* report. Their analysis is based on modern measurements and in ice core records dating back as far as 800,000 years. The growth rate of CO_2 levels has tripled since the early 1960s, said the report.[46]

Emissions are driven in part by economic growth; and despite the temporary economic downturn from the COVID-19 pandemic, that growth could be higher than expected, found an analysis by economists. They concluded that there is a greater than 35% probability that emissions in 2100 will exceed even the most extreme predicted CO_2 concentrations.[47] Thus, given the current trends, it is fair to assume that emissions growth will continue unabated.

Overall, there is no credible evidence that global society can undergo the necessary radical technological and political transformation to slow, much less halt, emissions (see VI. Grasping at Climate Panaceas).

Given trends as of 2021, continuing CO_2 emissions will fall far short of meeting climate goals, concluded climatologists. They found that, at current emission rates, the "carbon budget" for limiting global heating to 1.5°C will be used up within only about ten years.[48]

Heat-trapping methane will also add to global heating (see Mounting Methane). While methane lasts only about a decade in the atmosphere, it traps up to 25 times more heat over a century than does CO_2.[49] And, it degrades to CO_2.

The most powerful heat-trapping greenhouse gas is N_2O, popularly known as laughing gas. Largely produced by manure application and soil microbes breaking down farm fertilizers, N_2O traps some 300 times more heat than does CO_2. And it lasts more than a century in the atmosphere. However, N_2O concentrations are about one-thousandth that of CO_2.[50]

The carbon contagion also will not abate because of the stunning momentum of emissions. Fossil-fuel-burning and industrial processes release about 37 billion tons of CO_2 a year. In 2020, the top emitters were China (28%), the US (15%), the European Union (8%), India (7%), Russia (5%), and Japan (3%). All these countries' emissions continue to increase, according to the Global Carbon Project.[51]

These emission statistics, however, mask a huge amount of uncertainty. There are serious deficiencies in countries' reporting of their emissions. For example, China has refused to allow outside scientists to monitor its emissions, admitting that its emissions greatly increased over the last decades.[52][53][54] And in the past, China has significantly underreported the amount of energy it produced from coal (see Fossil Fools).

Fossil Fools

Houston, Texas, is a doomed city and an alarming lesson for cities worldwide.

You wouldn't believe so when you enter Houston's Museum of Natural Science Wiess Energy Hall, a relentlessly upbeat celebration of the oil industry.[55] As you enter, you first encounter a full-size model of a drilling rig floor operated by animatronic roughnecks, sponsored by ExxonMobil. From there, you move into the sprawling main hall, almost the size of a football field. Largely funded by oil companies, the Energy Hall is a Disneyesque "petroland" of colorful exhibits touting the wonders of oil and gas exploration and refining. For example, on my visit, I rode the simulated Eagle Ford Shale Experience, a virtual thrill ride that plunged deep into an oil well, revealing the wonders of fracking technology.

But when I asked a docent whether I could see any exhibits on climate change, she paused and cannily replied that I *could* ask questions about climate change. But there were no exhibits as such. Today, Energy Hall only obliquely addresses climate change, via a few touchscreen monitors displaying images of melting glaciers. The accompanying text declares only that hydrocarbon energy "is both finite and unsustainable at our current rate of consumption."

And while the museum's online courses exhaustively cover the energy industry, there is no apparent mention of its climate consequences.[56]

The Energy Hall is only one example reflecting Houston's status as an epicenter of tragic irony about climate disruption, and an instructive one. It is an archetypal example of a city, like so many worldwide, that has fostered an unbridled fossil fuel industry, while ignoring its looming climate consequences.

The area is home to massive oil refineries, the largest of which—ExxonMobil's and Marathon Petroleum's—each refine more than half a million barrels of oil a day.[57]

Such facilities are one reason Texas has the highest CO_2 emissions—almost twice as high as California's despite having about 10 million fewer people.[58]

Houston is also home to many oil company headquarters. Perhaps the largest such corporate center is ExxonMobil's 385-acre campus, which accommodates more than 10,000 employees and visitors. The company's website declares that the campus "was constructed to the highest standards of energy efficiency and environmental stewardship."[59]

That statement is ironic, given that in nearby Baytown ExxonMobil's refinery is one of the top three US refinery emitters of soot pollution. The other two are its refineries in Beaumont, Texas, and Baton Rouge, Louisiana. Marathon's Baytown refinery ranks number seven.[60] The Marathon refinery has also emitted levels of cancer-causing benzene far above EPA's "action level."[61]

Houston residents also pay a health price for the oil industry in their exposure to chemical pollutants. The Houston Health Department has recorded levels of cancer-causing formaldehyde in neighborhoods near the Houston Ship Channel more than 13 times the Environmental Protection Agency's minimum health threat level.[62]

Houston's transportation system is fossil-fueled. Some 600 miles of freeways crisscross the region, including the world's widest, the Katy freeway, at 26 lanes over many stretches. In contrast, the region has only 23 miles of light rail transit.

In a split civic personality, Houston celebrates fossil fuels, while recognizing the foolishness of continuing to depend on them.

For example, the City of Houston has launched a Climate Action Plan that aims to power municipal operations with renewable energy by 2025 and achieve carbon neutrality by 2050.[63] However, the plan is unenforceable, comprising only a series of recommendations. Also, it does not address the polluters outside the city limits, including the refineries and petrochemical plants along the Houston Ship Channel.[64]

Houston's looming catastrophes

Despite such efforts, climate disruption will make Houston nearly unlivable by the end of the century. Sea-level rise will inundate large expanses of the coastal region, including the sites of the aforementioned oil refineries.[65]

And even before sea-level rise wreaks its damage, the area may well be hit by a category 4 or 5 hurricane, such as Hurricanes Harvey in 2017 and Ida in 2021 (see Superstormy Weather). The storm surge from such a storm could overtop protective barriers—creating what severe storm researcher Jim Blackburn has called "the worst environmental disaster in United States history." The surge could cause the failure of storage tanks that could release nearly 90 million gallons of oil and hazardous chemicals into adjacent neighborhoods and the estuary of Galveston Bay. Such a disaster would also be a "staggering blow to the U.S. economy and national security, because of the potential loss of military grade jet fuel production," Blackburn wrote.[66]

The Houston area has about 900 facilities at flood risk that hold toxic chemicals, found an investigation by the *Bulletin of the Atomic Scientists*.[67] Tanks at those facilities contain flammable and toxic chemicals that are feedstocks for plastics, solvents, and gasoline. Those tanks risk being ruptured in a major flood by impacts from the thousands of shipping containers stacked along the Houston Ship Channel. These ruptures would release chemicals that would transform the region into a toxic wasteland. Such a disaster would have nationwide effects, closing a major shipping port for weeks or months.

The state and the US Army Corps of Engineers have proposed a $26-billion plan to protect the coastal region from hurricane flooding. The plan involved erecting miles of seawalls and huge gates across the main inlet to the bay from the Gulf of Mexico. But this project, if it is ever built, would not be completed until around 2042.[68] More likely than not, the region would already have suffered devastating storms.

Aside from hurricane surges, Houston will see severe flooding from increasingly intense storms, poor flood management, and subsidence from groundwater pumping (see Flood Warning).[69] [70] [71] At the same time, the state of Texas will face the most arid conditions in the last thousand years.[72]

Houston's temperatures will soar to lethal levels, their effects exacerbated by the region's high humidity and the urban heat island effect (see Hellscape Earth). Houston has experienced the fastest rise in temperature among major cities since 1986.[73] By mid-century, Houston is projected to suffer 109 days a year of temperatures above 100°F, versus 36 days today.[74] The higher temperatures and increased flooding will spawn an increase in mosquito-borne and water-borne diseases (see Diseased Earth).

Strategic corporate ignorance

Despite such grim climate realities, Houston's ExxonMobil has largely ignored climate disruption in its aggressive production plans over decades. Its strategy entailed continual massive exploration and growth.[75] Nor have most oil and gas companies invested in renewable energy, to become low-carbon energy providers. Those investments have amounted to only a few percent of their total investments, asserted a 2020 International Energy Agency (IEA) report.[76]

In contrast, a sharp divide has arisen in such investment between European and American oil companies, including ExxonMobil. While European companies such as BP instituted climate-aware investment policies, American companies ". . . are doubling down on oil and natural gas and investing what amounts to pocket change in innovative climate-oriented efforts . . ." wrote *The New York Times* reporter Clifford Krauss.[77]

Fossil fuel companies will thus continue their high production levels. In 2020, that production, globally, amounted to more than 32 billion barrels of oil and almost 4 trillion cubic meters of natural gas. Coal mining produced some 2.6 trillion metric tons of oil equivalent—the measure of the heat energy in the coal.[78]

While the COVID-19 pandemic caused a temporary oil and gas production drop, the long term will see continuing high levels, with a concomitant continuation of CO_2 emissions. An IEA report forecast a demand that levels off in the mid-2030s and begins only a slight decline to 2050.[79] In particular, expanded oil production will take place in countries not known for high levels of production, including Brazil, Canada, Norway, and Guyana.[80]

Global energy consumption will increase by nearly 50% between 2020 and 2050 without significant policy or technology changes, found a report of the US Energy Information Administration (USEIA).[81] Thus, the pre-pandemic declaration of one past IEA report is still valid:

> For the moment, the collective signal sent by governments in their climate pledges . . . is that fossil fuels, in particular natural gas and oil, will continue to be a bedrock of the global energy system for many decades to come.[82]

Coal remains a king

Coal remains one of the largest global energy sources, with 27% of the total as of 2019, according to the IEA. The other major energy sources are oil at 31% and natural gas at 23%.[83]

While globally coal-fired power generation declined in 2019 and 2020, it rose after that, projected to hit all-time highs during the following years, according to the IEA.[84]

Over the longer term, coal demand will decline only slowly, reducing by 25% below the 2020 level by 2050, predicted an IEA report.[85] However, that's not enough to meet IEA's Net Zero Emissions by 2050 Scenario limits. To meet those limits, coal-fired electricity generation would need to decline by 11% a year to 2030, with a complete phase-out by 2040, according to the IEA.[86]

The number of new coal-fired plant under construction will continue to rise, albeit slowly, found one report.[87] Coal-fired plants are being planned or built in countries including China, India, Turkey, and the Republic of Korea, noted a 2020 UN report.[88]

More than 400 energy-related companies globally are planning to expand their coal operations, found the environmental group Urgewald. If their projects are built, more than 500 gigawatts would be added to the global coal-fired capacity. Fewer than 25 companies are adopting a coal phase-out date.[89]

Coal-producing countries are readily increasing their output to fuel the growing number of plants. For example, India's coal plants will be supplied by massive coal exports from Australia—which as of this writing refuses to commit to reining in production.[90] India receives nearly half of its energy consumption from coal, and it will continue to burn vast, and growing, amounts of coal to fuel its rapid economic growth.[91]

Since 2005, China and India have accounted for 85% of the new coal plants.[92] China is the largest driver of the growth of coal, continuing construction of plants within its borders even as it retires plants, according to the website Global Energy Monitor.[93] And although outside its borders China has many coal plants under construction, it has announced a commitment to build no new plants abroad.[94]

China would have to shut down nearly 600 of its coal-fired plants to meet its declared goal of reaching becoming carbon-neutral before 2060, according to an analysis by the group TransitionZero.[95] [96]

Economy trumps climate

There is near-zero likelihood that the world will significantly reduce, much less abandon, its use of fossil fuels. Besides the world's deep dependence on fossil fuels, there is the immense political and economic impact of loss of vast numbers of jobs that depend on the industry—more than one million in the US alone.[97]

Transitioning away from fossil fuels would produce wrenching economic change, even though it would ultimately yield major economic, environmental, and health advantages, as detailed later (see Why the Corporations Failed and Viral Human Consequences). A mild version of that change was the economic impact of even the temporary collapse in oil prices during the COVID-19 pandemic.[98]

Russia represents a prime example of a country that fully recognizes the consequences of climate disruption, but will not rein in its carbon emissions. The country has experienced storms, heat waves, floods, wildfires, and disease outbreaks that the government acknowledges are linked to climate disruption. However, neither the Russian government nor its oil and gas industry will adopt emission-limiting policies that would compromise an industry critical to its economy.

A prime example of the country's intransigence is the huge array of wind turbines constructed on Russia's Sakhalin Island. The purpose of this clean energy? To mine more coal.[99] Also, Russia recognizes the advantages of a warmer climate in opening new ice-free shipping lanes and rendering vast areas of its northern regions amenable to crop production.[100] [101] [102]

Indeed, the Climate Action Tracker has rated as "critically insufficient" Russia's Paris Agreement emission reduction targets. The analysis found that Russia's Paris Agreement goal is based on business-as-usual emission policies (see Paris Agreement: Blind and Toothless).[103]

Nor will China abandon its lucrative oil and gas deposits, continuing to explore for new resources. For example, it announced in 2021 discovery of a major new oil reserve of one billion tons in the Taklamakan Desert, its largest oil and gas-bearing area.[104]

The failure to adopt adequate emission reduction targets by Russia, China, Brazil, and Australia would produce a global temperature increase of 5°C, found an analysis by the Paris Equity Check.[105]

Catastrophic "carbon bombs"

The massive investment in global fossil fuel production has created an enormous gap between planned expansion and that necessary to meet temperature limits, analyses have found.

The year 2030 would see 110% more production than that consistent with a 1.5°C limit, concluded a report by the UN Environment Programme and other groups. By 2040, this production gap would increase to 190% more production than consistent with a 1.5°C pathway and 89% more than consistent with a 2°C pathway, found the report.[106]

Another analysis identified some 425 "carbon bombs"—oil and gas projects that would emit more than a billion tons of CO_2 over their lifetimes. The researchers found that if these projects go forward, their emissions would be twice as large as those required to meet the 1.5°C limit.[107]

US oil and gas production is also on track for massive increases over the next decades, according to an environmental group consortium. The resulting fuel use could release by 2050 the equivalent lifetime emissions of a thousand coal-fired power plants.[108]

In fact, emissions from oil and gas production are greatly underreported, according to the monitoring group Climate TRACE. Their data showed that, of the countries required to report their emissions, actual levels are as much as three times higher. The group found that half of the largest emission sources are oil and gas production fields and their associated facilities.[109]

True, oil companies have reduced their planned exploration investments because of the COVID-19 pandemic and lobbying by climate activists. In 2020, ExxonMobil announced that it would invest about $20–$25 billion annually on exploration and development over the following five years—less than previously projected $30 billion.[110] However, such investment continues to drive major oil and gas production.

A premier example of fossil foolishness is the tar sands in Alberta, Canada. Not really sands, they are a sludge of sand, clay, water, and molasses-like oily bitumen.[111] This mix must be heated to separate the oil before refining. The Alberta tar sands represent the world's third-largest oil reserves, about 166 billion barrels. Total production was about 2.8 million barrels a day in 2017.[112]

Tar sands are notoriously dirty fuel sources. Producing one gallon of gasoline from the sludge emits about 15% more CO_2 than from conventional oil. And producing each gallon requires about 5.9 gallons of water—which is left polluted with heavy metals. While almost all of this process water is recycled for reuse, the toxic storage ponds cover dozens of square miles. Mining the sands also requires clearing vast areas of forest, which would otherwise be a CO_2 sink.

Tar sands are so carbon-polluting that energy economists Christophe McGlade and Paul Ekins concluded that they must be totally abandoned if global temperature increases are to be limited to 2°C.[113] They also aren't a sound investment. ExxonMobil has even removed tar sands from its proven reserves, basically admitting that they are not an economic resource.[114]

Nevertheless, amid considerable controversy, the industry has begun building a $12.6 billion expansion of a pipeline to transport tar sands oil from Alberta to the Canadian West Coast.[115]

Mounting Methane

The remote-sensing satellite made a shocking, even unbelievable, discovery in 2022 as it passed over the Raspadskaya coal mine, the largest in Russia. The mine didn't just produce 5.5 million metric tons of coal a year. In the process it was spewing 95 metric tons of methane (CH_4) an hour. What's more, the scientists who detected the emissions believe they were deliberate—venting methane pockets from the mine to reduce methane buildup. That venting is almost certainly continuing.[116]

As huge as this source is, it constitutes only a small fraction of CH_4 emissions from other coal mines, as well as oil and gas wells, rotting permafrost vegetation, the Amazon flood plain, livestock, wild animals, rice paddies, landfills, reservoirs, and seafloor methane trapped in icy structures called clathrate, or hydrates.

CH_4 is the "other" primary greenhouse gas, with physical properties far different from CO_2. It is dozens of times more potent than CO_2 at trapping heat, although its lifetime in the atmosphere is only about a decade. Then, however, it chemically transforms into longer-lived CO_2.

While CH_4 emissions have grown steadily over many decades, 2007 marked the beginning of a record-setting rise in concentrations—increases not expected in greenhouse gas projections.[117 118 119 120]

Emissions from warming wetlands constitute one worrisome source of the increase. "If natural wetlands, or changes in atmospheric chemistry, indeed accelerate the [CH_4] rise, it may be a climate feedback that humans have little hope of slowing," warned atmospheric scientists Sara Mikaloff Fletcher and Hinrich Schaefe.[121]

CH_4 began particularly drastic and abrupt rises in 2020, reported NOAA—suggesting that such a feedback loop may already have begun.[122] Wildfires may cause one ominous change in atmospheric chemistry that underlies the drastic CH_4 rise, researchers have reported.[123] Their analyses indicated that massive wildfires emitting carbon monoxide may sop up chemicals called hydroxyl radicals from the air. These active substances are "detergents of the atmosphere"—critical in cleaning the atmosphere of methane. Carbon monoxide is a relatively fast reactor with hydroxyl radicals, said the researchers.

"On average, a carbon monoxide molecule remains in the atmosphere for about three months before it's attacked by a hydroxyl radical, while methane persists for about a decade," co-author Simon Redfern told *The Guardian*. "So wildfires have a swift impact on using up the hydroxyl 'detergent' and reduce the methane removal."[124]

The major culprits behind the increase in CH_4 emissions appear to be equally oil and gas production, and agriculture.[125]

Multiple analyses have confirmed major CH_4 leakages from oil production, natural gas pipelines, processing plants, and hydraulic fracturing. In fact, such leakage estimates are approaching—perhaps exceeding—the limit beyond which natural gas will no longer be superior to coal, in terms of greenhouse gas emissions.[126 127 128 129 130 131]

Coal mining from such sources as the Raspadskaya mine is also a major CH_4 source, found an analysis by Global Energy Monitor. In fact, annual CH_4 emissions from coal mining (52.3 million metric tons) rival those of both oil (39 million metric tons) and gas (45 million metric tons).[132]

"Frucking" the Earth

In particular, hydraulic fracturing, or fracking, appears to be producing high CH_4 leakage, researchers have found. Fracking involves releasing natural gas by pumping pressurized fluid into wells to fracture subterranean rock formations to increase their permeability.

One study of satellite data from two fracking regions in the US and Canada found large-scale "fugitive emissions" that in one of the regions corresponded to about 10% of the energy production. The researchers pointed out that fracking wells rapidly deplete, requiring continuous drilling of new wells, increasing leakage.[133] What's more, millions of oil and gas wells are simply abandoned rather than being plugged—left to leak massive amounts of methane.[134 135 136]

Another calculation concluded that "shale-gas production in North America over the past decade may have contributed more than half of all of the increased [CH_4] emissions from fossil fuels globally and approximately one-third of the total increased emissions from all sources globally over the past decade."[137]

Given the magnitude of its environmental damage, the extraction process might be profanely dubbed "frucking." It can contaminate water sources, spread toxic chemicals, and trigger earthquakes.[138][139][140] In some cases, tap water and river water at fracking sites emit so much CH_4 that they can actually be lit on fire.[141][142]

In advocating a ban on fracking, physicians' groups analyzed more than 1,700 scientific papers and media reports on fracking, concluding that:

> From air and water pollution to radioactivity to social disruption to greenhouse gas emissions, the data continue to reveal a plethora of recurring problems and harms that cannot be sufficiently averted through regulatory frameworks. There is no evidence that fracking can operate without threatening public health directly and without imperiling climate stability, upon which public health depends.[143]

Natural gas combustion in itself does emit lower levels of CO_2 than coal burning, so it has been advertised as a "bridge" to cleaner energy sources.[144]

However, declared engineer Anthony Ingraffea, "as a longtime oil and gas engineer . . . I can assure you that this gas is not 'clean'." He cited measurements by the National Oceanic and Atmospheric Administration (NOAA) showing leakage rates of 2.3–17% in gas and oil fields in California, Colorado, and Utah. And he cited a government study indicating that, unless leaks can be kept below 2%, gas "lacks any climate advantage over coal."

Ingraffea said that so many wells leak because:

> . . . pressures under the Earth, temperature changes, ground movement from the drilling of nearby wells and shrinkage crack and damage the thin layer of brittle cement that is supposed to seal the wells. And getting the cement perfect as the drilling goes horizontally into shale is extremely challenging. Once the cement is damaged, repairing it thousands of feet underground is expensive and often unsuccessful.[145]

In the end shale gas production is not a low-carbon alternative and "will not substantially change the course of global [greenhouse gas] concentrations," concluded researchers Richard Newell and Daniel Raimi, who modeled its climate impacts.[146]

In fact, the shale gas era may well end in only a matter of years, according to an analysis by *The Wall Street Journal*. Meanwhile, the large companies will continue to drill hundreds of wells a year to maintain production—abandoning the spent wells to continue to leak methane.[147]

Dam surprising

Reservoirs behind dams are also a CH_4 source, and they represent an example of how such sources can be both insidious and unexpected. One study of CO_2, CH_4, and nitrous oxide (N_2O) emitted from hundreds of dams around the world found that the gases emanate from

- Microbes digesting organic sediment
- The rise and fall of the reservoirs which enhances bubbling of methane; and
- The reservoirs collecting and breaking down organic matter flowing from the surrounding land.

The researchers estimated that the reservoirs could be emitting up to billions of tons a year of carbon-dioxide-equivalent.[148]

Dam-related CH_4 will increase because at least 3,700 major dams are either planned or under construction. And while it might be argued that these dams will replace some fossil fuel plants, according to a study, "even such a dramatic expansion in hydropower capacity will be insufficient to compensate for the increasing electricity demand. Furthermore, it will only partially close the electricity gap [and] may not substantially reduce greenhouse gas emission."[149] [150]

Dams also can cause ecological damage. Amazon River Basin dams—with 428 proposed, under construction, or built—prevent sediment transport that provides nutrients and sustain wildlife. In one study, researchers concluded that "the accumulated negative environmental effects of existing dams and proposed dams, if constructed, will trigger massive hydrophysical and biotic disturbances that will affect the Amazon Basin's floodplains, estuary and sediment plume."[151]

Said lead researcher Edgardo Latrubesse: "The dimension of the impacts can be not only regional, but also on an interhemispheric scale. . . . If all the planned dams in the basin are constructed, their cumulative effect will trigger a change in sediment flowing into the Atlantic Ocean that may hinder the regional climate."[152]

Wrote ecologist Philip Fearnside of the Amazonian dam construction:

> Dams are not economically attractive if their true environmental and social costs are considered . . . hydropower is already unreliable and is projected to become much more so in light of climate change and projected shifts in rainfall patterns, and dams also emit significant quantities of methane, a greenhouse gas, from hydropower reservoirs.[153]

Lakes and ponds also emit CH_4, and their emissions will increase as temperatures rise, according to an experimental study by ecologists. They artificially warmed ponds over a period of seven years, and found that the waters emitted more CH_4 and showed greatly reduced ability to absorb CO_2.

"Lakes and ponds cover only about 4 percent of the Earth's non-glaciated surface, yet they represent disproportionately large sources of methane and carbon dioxide," wrote the researchers.[154]

International efforts to curb methane emissions have been weak at best. An example of this weakness is the Global Methane Pledge agreed to by more than 100 nations in 2021.[155] The agreement is nonbinding and commits only to reducing CH_4 emissions by at least 30% by 2030. And it did not include three of the heaviest methane-emitting countries—China, India, and Russia.

Bankrolling the Contagion

The carbon contagion is powered not only by its own overwhelming momentum, but by massive investment and subsidies. International banks have provided some $2.7 trillion in fossil fuel financing in the years 2016–2019.[156]

Governments directly subsidize the fossil fuel industry, giving hundreds of billions of dollars a year, according to the International Energy Agency.[157] The G20 nations alone subsidized fossil fuels with more $3 trillion between 2015 and 2019, according to a BloombergNEF analysis. The report noted that, "given varying levels of transparency nations provide on such funds, these figures are probably an under-count."[158]

The subsidy figure is even larger when indirect subsidies—almost $6 trillion a year—are taken into account, according to the International Monetary Fund.[159] These indirect subsidies arise from:

- The fact that people and businesses pay less than the costs of supplying the energy
- The cost of the industry's favorable tax treatments, and
- The cost of the damage to environment and health.

Many governments, including the US, subsidize oil and gas as a political tool to maintain popular support.[160][161] The US provides more than $20 billion each year in direct and indirect subsidies to oil, gas, and coal producers, according to Oil Change International. These subsidies include exemptions, deductions, credits, preferential tax rates, and reduced liability. The group wrote:

> Subsidizing oil companies with public handouts can . . . "pick winners," by making oil extraction and development economically viable where it wouldn't have been otherwise, thus influencing a private company's decisions to invest in ramping up oil production.[162][163]

The greater production enabled by subsidies "means oil prices are forced down and oil consumption goes up—and so does the carbon pollution emitted when that oil is burned," the group wrote.

Three of the largest insurance companies—Aviva, Aegon, and Amlin—have called on the G20 to stop such subsidies.[164] Together, these companies manage some $1.2 trillion in assets.

Aviva CEO Mark Wilson was quoted as saying, "Climate change in particular represents the mother of all risks—to business and to society as a whole. And that risk is magnified by the way in which fossil fuel subsidies distort the energy market. These subsidies are simply unsustainable."[165]

However, ending subsidies will not necessarily reduce greenhouse gas emissions, found a study by energy analysts. Economists had assumed that without subsidies, reduction in emissions would occur because higher fuel prices would discourage inefficiencies and encourage renewable energy. However, the researchers' computer modeling revealed that ending subsidies would deliver only small emission benefits. In fact, ending subsidies would even increase emissions in some regions because coal would replace oil and natural gas.[166]

Road to climate ruin

Besides subsidizing the carbon contagion, we have also literally built the road to our own destruction. In the US, enormous investment in the interstate highway system has shaped the country into a sprawling, energy-hungry society. In contrast, Japan and European countries invested in efficient mass transit.

The vast highway network ". . . made the US a country of commuters, utterly dependent on fossil fuels to drive their vehicles, and to heat and cool their big houses," wrote author McKay Jenkins. She wrote:

> The myriad problems associated with our dependence on fossil fuels (warfare in oil-producing countries; climate change; rising sea levels, ocean acidification, species loss) can all, in large measure, be traced to the explosion of growth that sprouted along the American interstate highway system.[167]

Ultimately, the massive investment in fossil fuels and their huge subsidies will cause a global climate-caused financial crisis that dwarfs even that caused by the COVID-19 pandemic (see Why the Corporations Failed). The crisis will be triggered by an unexpected environmental disaster that one group of economists dubbed a "Green Swan." The term is derived from the concept of the "Black Swan"—an extremely disruptive, unexpected event. The economists asserted that traditional risk assessments and existing models "cannot anticipate accurately enough the form that climate-related risks will take."[168]

Decarbonization Delusion

"Decarbonizing" the economy—reducing or eliminating carbon pollution—has been touted to avoid catastrophic global heating. Decarbonization can involve efforts ranging from increasing solar and wind energy production to capturing CO_2 emissions from fossil-fueled power plants.

The realistic outlook for decarbonization, however, reveals it to be a delusion borne of desperation and ignorance.

For one thing, few decarbonization technologies are mature enough to be deployed on a significant scale, according to a report from the International Energy Agency (IEA). Some such technologies include:

- Low-carbon hydrogen and hydrogen-derived fuel
- Electrification of end-use sectors like heating and transportation
- Carbon capture, utilization, and storage
- Bioenergy[169]

Development of energy-related technologies is a long road, the report pointed out. Even the fastest such technologies, like LEDs and lithium-ion batteries, "took 10–30 years to go from the first prototype to the mass market."

And many of these technologies face insurmountable obstacles to *ever* being commercially deployed (see Fossilized Transportation, Carbon Capture Snake Oil, and "Hydrogen pipe dream" below).

The IEA report charged that there is a "stark disconnect between these high-profile pledges" by governments and companies to reach sustainability goals and "the current state of clean energy technology."

Still at the prototype and demonstration level are decarbonizing technologies for heavy industry such as chemicals, steel, and cement, found another IEA report.[170] The decarbonization challenges they face include their:

- Long-lived 30-to-40-year plant lifetimes
- High temperature heat requirements
- Unavoidable process emissions, for example from cement production
- A competitive global market that yields thin profit margins.

A report by the Energy Transitions Commission—a coalition of corporate leaders—concluded that overall, there is no real acceleration toward decarbonization.[171] The authors analyzed the policies required to jump-start a decarbonizing transition in ten sectors of the economy that account for 80% of the world's emissions, including steel, cement, plastics, heavy road transport, aviation, and shipping.

"The low carbon transition has barely begun" in most sectors, the report concluded. Decarbonization technologies in a few areas, like power generation, cars, and buildings are only in the "diffusion" stage, beginning to change the technology. None are at the "reconfiguration" stage where they are changing the whole sector.

Fantasy decarbonizing scenarios

Decarbonization computer models are little more than technological fantasies that spin out unrealistic 1.5°C and 2°C scenarios—as detailed in a 2022 report by the UN Intergovernmental Panel on Climate Change (IPCC).[172] All the models depend on massive reductions in fossil fuel production and greenhouse gases. They depend on transitioning to renewable energy (see Renewable Energy Hype). And they depend on unproven and uneconomic carbon capture technology to remove CO_2 from the air (see Carbon Capture Snake Oil).

For example, one modeling study found that limiting heating to 1.5°C by 2050 would mean leaving in the ground nearly 60% of oil and gas and 90% of coal reserves.[173] Another study found that 40% of even *existing* fossil fuel production must be shut down to give a 50–50 chance of staying below 1.5°C.[174]

Even a higher 2°C limit requires stranding a third of oil reserves, almost half of gas reserves, and over 80% of coal reserves, found another economists' analysis.[175]

Such resource stranding would be political suicide for any government seeking to impose such limits. And it would be financially disastrous. One study found that aggressive energy policies to limit warming to 2°C would cause massive financial losses to investors. Tracing the risk of ownership of more than 40,000 oil and gas assets, the researchers calculated that such a move would mean that $1.4 trillion in existing projects would lose their value. Private investors would suffer the most through their pension funds and investments.[176]

Stranding oil, gas, and coal deposits would mean as much as $28 trillion in lost revenue for energy companies over the next two decades, asserted historian Adam Tooze in 2019. Besides impacting investors, decarbonization would damage the companies that depend on those resources—chemical, construction, and industrial companies and power utilities—causing trillions of dollars in lost asset values.[177]

What's more, attempts at stranding resources will be thwarted by legal claims from investors seeking compensation under international treaties. Countries offer such treaties to encourage foreign investment, and if they are violated, those investors can demand arbitration. One analysis estimated that such arbitration could lead to government liabilities up to $340 billion for oil and gas projects. Risks would be even greater if coal mining and fossil fuel infrastructure were included. What's more, governments fearing such liabilities could abandon climate commitments and roll back regulations.[178]

Nature won't help

Some climate models assume that a significant amount of CO_2 will be naturally absorbed, which is also unrealistic.[179] As one group of environmental researchers commented:

> The resilience of natural carbon sinks is deteriorating, and some key biomes, such as rainforests, may cross tipping points to becoming sources of carbon. Keeping well below 2°C will require creating a new carbon sink on the scale of the natural ocean sink.[180]

Study after study has projected an inexorable march toward disastrous CO_2 levels (see Carbon-Fevered Planet). The curve of increasing CO_2 shows that, unless the current growth rate is drastically slowed, levels will reach 500 ppm within 50 years. That level would raise the global temperature increase to more than 3°C—a level that would trigger vast climate disruption (see Six Degrees to Termination). The world would see superstorms, major sea-level rise, famine-level agriculture disruption, and other disasters (see III. Plague on the Environment).[181]

Preposterous decarbonizing plans

Just as decarbonization models are breathtakingly unrealistic, so are decarbonization plans. They are entirely academic, in the sense of being theoretical and impractical. They are technocratic solutions to a societal problem—neglecting the political, economic, and sociological barriers to their implementation.

In assessing these barriers, one large-scale analysis concluded that they are, indeed, insurmountable. The *Hamburg Climate Futures Outlook* study was developed by more than 40 academic researchers in sociology, macroeconomics, and the natural sciences.[182]

The study sought to determine whether "a scenario is not merely feasible, but also that there is enough societal momentum and political will to make that future materialize," wrote three of the authors. "Our final assessment: even if a partial decarbonisation is currently plausible, deep decarbonisation by the year 2050 is not."[183]

A notable example of an unrealistic global plan is the IEA's "Net Zero Emissions by 2050" plan. The plan, in fact, directly contradicts the IEA's own forecasts, including the IEA's report on decarbonization technologies, discussed above.

Among the IEA net zero plan's requirements and implications:
- A 45% drop in total CO_2 emissions by 2030 from 2010 levels
- A 17% drop in primary energy demand by 2030 to a 2006 level, even though the global economy is twice as large
- A 60% drop in coal demand by 2030, to a level last seen in the 1970s
- No coal plants operating in 2030 without carbon capture and storage
- A fivefold increase in solar photovoltaic generation by 2030
- A rise in renewable's share of global electricity supply from 27% in 2019 to 60% in 2030

- Retrofitting nearly half of buildings in advanced economies to be energy efficient by 2030, and one-third retrofitted elsewhere
- Making more than 50% of passenger cars sold in 2030 be electric, up from 2.5% in 2019
- Doubling global battery manufacture every two years
- Generating about 25% of heat used in industry in 2030 from electricity and low-carbon fuels such as hydrogen, versus a negligible amount today
- Replacing airline flights under one hour with low-carbon alternatives
- Walking or cycling for car trips under 3 kilometers.[184]

Another such unrealistic plan is Princeton University's "Net-Zero America" plan. The plan proposes by 2030:

- Roughly 50 million electric cars on the road
- More than double the electric heat pumps for home heating and triple the number in commercial buildings
- A fourfold increase in solar and wind electric generation
- A 60% expansion of high-voltage transmission capacity to deliver renewable electricity
- Eliminating coal-burning and ceasing coal production
- Closing more than 700 coal mines and retiring some 500 coal-fired power plants.

Furthermore, by 2050, the plan proposes having:

- 300 million electric cars on the road
- 130 million homes heated with heat pumps
- More than 1,000 carbon-capture facilities
- Up to 25,000 miles of interstate CO_2 pipelines with thousands of injection wells
- Tens to hundreds of gigawatts of wind and solar power generation added each year
- Hundreds of biomass (wood and other organic material) conversion facilities with a production of 620 million tons per year of biomass feedstock.[185]

One similarly radical scenario, *America's Zero Carbon Action Plan*, does address the political realities of decarbonization. However, it notes that "many of the technological solutions are understood but lack the institutional coordination, political support, and market incentives to scale." The report also noted that some of its proposals "are likely to be controversial and resisted by affected industries, lobbies, and political interests."

Of the report's ambitious proposals for electrification of the US economy, the authors admit that "this section has highlighted that the US power sector is characterized by fragmentation in regulation, ownership, financial incentives, and institutions."[186]

Even plans that aim at less substantial emissions reduction seem wildly unrealistic. One such plan is the International Renewable Energy Agency's "ambitious, yet realistic" Transforming Energy Scenario.[187] It envisions a decline in energy demand of 75% by 2050, roughly the equivalent of China's current energy demand. The plan would require coal use to decline by 41% by 2030, and 87% by 2050. Oil use would drop by 31% by 2030 and 87% by 2050. Natural gas use would decline by 41% by 2050. However, the plan does not address the impact of carbon-polluting industries like aviation and shipping (see Fossilized Transportation).

As detailed later, none of these plans is feasible (see Renewable Energy Hype, Fossilized Transportation, Carbon Capture Snake Oil, Energy Inefficiency, Nuclear Powerless, and "Hydrogen pipe dream" below).

Other analyses have also concluded that achieving net zero emissions by mid-century would require halting construction of fossil-fueled power plants.[188] Those analyses would also require retiring carbon-emitting power plants, boilers, furnaces, and vehicles before the end of their useful life and replacing them with zero-emission technology.[189] Such construction halts or early retirements would be considered absurd by any electrical utility.

Currently operating generation facilities already commit the world to emissions some 300 billion tons *above* that compatible with average 1.5–2.0°C reduction scenarios, according to an analysis by economists. What's more, planned plants would add almost an equal amount to emissions. The researchers concluded that about 20% of global generating capacity would have to be stranded to meet Paris Agreement goals.[190]

Basically, concluded MIT energy researchers, a net-zero-carbon-emitting world is unrealistic. Their analysis that showed that fossil fuels will continue to account for about 78% of global energy by 2050.[191]

Bursting the bubble of overshoot

Many scenarios have conceded an inevitable temperature overshoot above 1.5°C, but claim that carbon capture could bring that temperature back down. However, the idea of overshoot is the equivalent of a soap bubble—alluring, but fatally fragile.

First of all, avoiding overshoot in the first place offers enormous environmental and economic advantages, studies have shown.[192] [193] Secondly, carbon capture is not a viable technology (see Carbon Capture Snake Oil).

But the conceptual bubble of overshoot was conclusively burst by the 2022 IPCC report on climate disruption's impacts. The report concluded that:

> Additional warming, e.g., above 1.5°C during an overshoot period this century, will result in irreversible impacts on certain ecosystems with low resilience, such as polar, mountain, and coastal ecosystems, impacted by ice-sheet, glacier melt, or by accelerating and higher committed sea level rise. . . . such impacts are already observed and are projected to increase with every additional increment of global warming, such as increased wildfires, mass mortality of trees, drying of peatlands, and thawing of permafrost, weakening natural land carbon sinks and increasing releases of greenhouse gases.[194]

Hydrogen pipe dream

Hydrogen has been touted as the ultimate carbon-free fuel, given that it produces only water when burned. Advocates have envisioned a "hydrogen economy," in which hydrogen is generated by renewable energy for home and industry use, for energy storage, and for transportation. However, an investment of more than $11 trillion by 2050 would be required for hydrogen to provide just 24% of the world's energy needs, according to the research firm BloombergNEF.[195]

A massive hydrogen production, storage, and transportation infrastructure would have to be created from scratch. Existing infrastructure like natural gas pipelines cannot be used for pure hydrogen because it tends to embrittle pipeline steel and welds. Also, as a smaller molecule, hydrogen tends to leak from pipelines more than natural gas.[196] What's more, the technology for large-scale storage of compressed hydrogen is largely "immature and under development," found one analysis. The researchers concluded that "Furthermore, the infrastructure and facilities behind some of the technologies are massive, which would require significant resources and costs."[197]

Natural gas furnaces and other appliances cannot burn hydrogen, so they would have to be modified or replaced.[198] Internal combustion engine vehicles could not be converted to hydrogen in any significant way because hydrogen is far less energy-dense than gasoline or natural gas. To be used in vehicles, it would have to be stored at more than 300 times atmospheric pressure or absorbed as a chemical hydride—requiring complex and expensive equipment.[199] And since hydrogen is lower in energy density than natural gas, more volume would be required to yield the same energy output.

Heavy industry like steel, cement, petrochemicals, glass, and ceramics won't likely be converted to hydrogen, either. Its use in heavy industry is limited by economic and technological barriers, for example, the cost and engineering challenges of replacing huge inventories of equipment.

As one study of the economics of converting heavy industry to hydrogen concluded, "All approaches have substantial limitations or challenges to commercial deployment."[200]

Today, almost all hydrogen is "grey hydrogen"—produced from natural gas, releasing large amounts of CO_2. Capturing that CO_2—proposed as one pathway to a clean hydrogen economy—is not feasible, as discussed later (see Carbon Capture Snake Oil).

Producing "green hydrogen" from renewable energy using electrolysis is about four-to-six times more expensive than from natural gas, said an

IEA report.[201] And investment in hydrogen production by countries and private companies is far short of that required for hydrogen production to play a role in a strategy of net-zero greenhouse gas emissions by 2050, said the report. Nor is hydrogen production technology mature, found the report, concluding that "Hydrogen is a key pillar of decarbonisation for industry, although most of the technologies that can contribute significantly are still nascent."

Another major drawback to producing green hydrogen is that huge numbers of electrolyzers would be required, found the IRENA analysis cited earlier.[202] The agency's ambitious Transforming Energy Scenario—which envisions a 75% decline in energy demand by 2050—would require constructing up to 60 gigawatts of electrolyzers per year until then.[203]

Such electrolysis would also require massive amounts of pure water. Each kilogram of hydrogen produced would require 27 gallons of water as a feedstock, found one analysis.[204] Such water would have to be purified at a cost of about $2,400 per ton of hydrogen, calculated journalist Irina Slav—plus the cost of transporting the water.[205] Furthermore, such water demand would arise amid a profound decrease in global water supplies (see Megadrought Era).

Such technological and economic barriers mean that hydrogen could only account for from 1–14% of total US energy demand, according to a Department of Energy analysis. The lower number arises from a "base case" scenario, and the higher from an "ambitious" scenario.[206]

Finally, there is a political barrier in that government policy is inadequate to foster a cost-competitive hydrogen economy, concluded the BloombergNEF study referenced above.

Decarbonization policies won't work

Successful decarbonization policies would require a drastic improvement in energy intensity—the energy consumption per unit of economic input. However, it is highly unlikely that policies can improve energy intensity enough to spur decarbonization, according to one analysis. [207] The researchers explored 17 decarbonization scenarios aimed at stabilizing CO_2 levels or global heating by reducing emissions between 50% and

90% by 2050. Their conclusion: "All of the scenarios examined envision *historically unprecedented* improvements in the energy intensity of the global economy [emphasis added]."

Basically, such obstacles mean that researchers spinning out decarbonization scenarios are hoping for an energy-intensity miracle to bail them out.

In fact, according to a concept called the Green Paradox, decarbonizing policies can actually accelerate fossil fuel extraction. The Green Paradox holds that carbon-reducing policies force fossil fuel producers to face lower future prices as demand drops for oil, gas, and coal. So, to maximize short-term profits, the industry ramps up production.[208]

"In my view, the Green Paradox is not simply a theoretical possibility," wrote economist Hans-Werner Sinn Sinn, who identified the concept. "I believe it explains why fossil fuel prices have failed to rise since the 1980s, despite decreasing stocks of fossil fuels and the vigorous growth of the world economy." He wrote that carbon-reduction policies "alarmed resource owners. In fact, while most of us perceived these developments as a breakthrough in the battle against global warming, resource owners viewed them as efforts that threatened to destroy their markets."

Delayed, inadequate decarbonization effects

Even if decarbonization magically achieved a drop to zero emissions, the effect on global temperature would not occur for decades, found one modeling study. The researchers analyzed the impact of reducing not only CO_2, but also CH_4, N_2O, and carbon soot. They concluded that for all of those substances, even strong mitigation would have such a delayed effect.[209]

In fact, deep cuts in all non-CO_2 emissions would be necessary to limit global warming, concluded researchers. They compared the effects of reducing just CO_2 with also reducing substances including CH_4 and N_2O. The role of such emissions has been "underappreciated" by planners, wrote the researchers. They concluded that "Absent deep cuts in non-CO_2 emissions, CO_2 abatement alone is unable to keep warming below even the 2°C threshold by 2050."[210]

Decarbonization might not even slow global heating over future centuries, concluded researchers who modeled how the climate would adjust to zero-CO_2 emissions. They found that warmer oceans could overcompensate for the decreasing CO_2 levels, driving a centuries-long global temperature increase after an initial century of decrease.[211]

"If our results are correct . . . limiting the warming to 2°C would require keeping future cumulative carbon emissions below 250 billion tons, only half of the already-emitted amount of 500 billion tons," co-author Thomas Frölicher told the Climate News Network.[212]

In a perverse twist, if governments managed to miraculously decarbonize the world, the reduction in air pollution would actually increase near-term global heating. Atmospheric aerosols such as sulfates have so far helped limit temperature rise by reflecting sunlight back into space. Their disappearance would trigger a global mean surface heating of 0.5–1.1°C, calculated physicists.[213] [214] [215]

"We've been polluting ourselves toward a slightly cooler climate," researcher Bjørn Hallvard Samet told *Yale Climate 360*. He said that cleaning up air pollution would result in an immediate increase in global temperature, compared with the far slower temperature reduction from reducing greenhouse gases.[216]

The bottom line is that the Earth is carbonizing, not decarbonizing, and it is projected to do so for the rest of the century. The rate of rise in the CO_2 level is accelerating, according to data produced by the National Oceanic and Atmospheric Administration (NOAA). Their data for the measurements between 1990 and 2020 come from some 80 air sampling sites around the globe.[217]

Thus, the carbon contagion continues unchecked. Even if the rising emissions curve is turned downward, massive amounts of CO_2 will still be pumped into the atmosphere to remain for centuries.

The resulting global heating will trigger positive feedback loops that will add even more CO_2 and CH_4—generating sea-level rise, drought, superstorms, and lethal temperatures (see Climate Monsters).

The stark reality is that there currently exists neither the global political structure nor the political will to prevent extraction of the vast majority of potential fossil fuel reserves, which will drive a carbonization level that threatens human survival.

Climate Monsters

Given the steady rise of atmospheric CO_2 over the last decades, one might expect a steady increase in temperature—perhaps gradual enough for our species to adjust to survive. However, self-reinforcing feedback loops are accelerating climate disruption. These loops, dubbed "climate monsters," by journalist Graham Readfearn, are triggered when global heating reaches a tipping point.[218]

A tipping point is an intuitively obvious concept. To demonstrate it, gradually tip over an object like a stack of blocks. As the object's imbalance increases, it reaches a point where the slightest additional tap will send it abruptly crashing down on its own.

Scientists have only a vague idea of when most environmental tipping points may occur. And computer models aren't built to predict such sudden changes (see "Their models are blind to abrupt changes" under Why the Scientists Failed).

However, scientists have identified numerous climate disruption effects that are essentially irreversible for centuries to millennia. The effects include forest loss; permafrost carbon loss; Greenland and Antarctic ice loss; and, ocean heating, sea level rise, deoxygenation, and acidification, concluded the 2021 report of the UN Intergovernmental Panel on Climate Change (IPCC).[219]

Up to 15 tipping points are now "active," concluded an analysis by researchers using data on ancient climates, modern observations, model predictions, and best estimates.[220] They sought to peg the minimum temperature increase that might trigger a given tipping point; the maximum temperature increase that a system could take before tipping; and where each tipping point might lie between those extremes.

Their analysis indicated that parts of the West Antarctic ice sheet may have already passed a tipping point. Their study also detected "early warning signals" of destabilization of the Greenland ice sheet, the Atlantic

Meridional Overturning Circulation (AMOC), and the Amazon rainforest (see Inexorable Melt, Ruining AMOC, and Ghost Forests).

The analysis revealed that the current level of global heating lies within the lower end of five tipping point ranges, and six others become "likely" at 1.5°C of heating.

"The world is heading towards 2–3°C of global warming," said co-author Johan Rockström. "This sets Earth on course to cross multiple dangerous tipping points that will be disastrous for people across the world."[221]

Tipping points may even interact, creating domino effects, in which one tipping point lowers the temperature threshold of others, researchers have found. In one study, climatologist Ricarda Winkelmann and colleagues modeled the tipping point effects of interactions among the Greenland and West Antarctic ice sheets, the Atlantic Meridional Overturning Circulation, and the Amazon rainforest. They concluded that, "the interactions tend to destabilise the network of tipping elements."[222]

"We provide a risk analysis, not a prediction, but our findings still raise concern," Winkelmann told *The Guardian*. She said that the findings "might mean we have less time to reduce greenhouse gas emissions and still prevent tipping processes."[223]

Among the major global feedback loops that could release vast amounts of greenhouse gases are clathrates melting and releasing methane, permafrost thawing and releasing greenhouse gas, burning peat bogs releasing greenhouse gas, and emissions from warming soils.

Clathrate Gun

Methane clathrates, or methane hydrates, seem like stuff from another planet—comprising CH_4 molecules imprisoned in cages of crystalline ice. They're only stable at very specific temperatures and pressures. Saturn's moon Titan is thought to hold vast deposits of methane clathrate that spew as a frozen slush from ice volcanoes.[224] Clathrates are so rich with CH_4 that setting a match to one causes it to erupt in flame.

On Earth, this "fire ice" was produced by bacteria breaking down organic matter. In the near-freezing ocean depths, the resulting CH_4

was trapped in ice, rather than escaping. Frozen permafrost in the polar tundra regions also harbors large amounts of clathrates.

These deposits are believed to hold trillions of metric tons of clathrate, containing hundreds of times more carbon than is released into the atmosphere annually by burning coal, oil, and gas.[225][226]

The rise in global temperatures has spawned the "clathrate gun hypothesis," which holds that global warming can trigger a sudden methane release as warmer water temperatures destabilize the delicate crystal structures. The theory holds that in the past this methane has produced rapidly increased global temperatures, creating a feedback loop that produced runaway global heating. The release of methane clathrates has been theorized as one possible cause of the Paleocene-Eocene Thermal Maximum (PETM) about 56 million years ago, which saw a global temperature increase of 5–8°C over some 20,000 years.

The question is whether the destabilizing of methane clathrates, causing them to release their gases, could cause major global warming today. There is some evidence that CH_4 from melting clathrates is already bubbling up from relatively shallow US and Canadian Pacific coastal areas. Off these coasts, oceanographers have documented some 168 bubble plumes emanating from relatively shallow depths.[227]

"We see an unusually high number of bubble plumes at the depth where methane hydrate would decompose if seawater has warmed," according to oceanographer Paul Johnson. "So it is not likely to be just emitted from the sediments; this appears to be coming from the decomposition of methane that has been frozen for thousands of years."[228]

Along a broader region out to sea, an analysis found that warming at those depths could destabilize CH_4 deposits extending from Northern California to British Columbia to Alaska. The study calculated that just off the Washington coast, today's ocean warming could cause about a 100,000 metric tons a year to be released—about the same amount of CH_4 as was released by the 2010 blowout of the Deepwater Horizon oil rig in the Gulf of Mexico.[229]

The Atlantic Ocean's outer continental shelf is also seeing widespread CH_4 leakage, found another survey—which documented about 570 such seeps between North Carolina and Massachusetts.[230]

These discoveries suggest that methane hydrate deposits are vulnerable to destabilization worldwide in the shallowest ocean depths where they have formed. Fortunately, at depths greater than 100 meters, most of the CH_4 released when methane clathrates destabilize doesn't reach the surface. (It does, however, transform into CO_2 that could acidify the ocean water and reduce oxygenation.)

But such CH_4 seeps are not evidence for the dreaded clathrate gun, say scientists. Their consensus is that the vast majority of the methane clathrates are in such deep water—about a thousand meters—that they will remain stable over millennia, even with major global heating.[231][232]

Permafrost Bomb

The thick, green Siberian forest is scarred by a massive crater that stretches for about a kilometer, reaching a depth of up to 100 meters. The locals call the Batagaika Crater a "gateway to the underworld." Indeed, its depths do appear hellish, as the crater reveals decaying corpses of ancient mammoths, musk oxen, and horses.

Scientists call the crater a "megaslump," where the permafrost beneath has thawed and collapsed the ground above it. The crater is growing rapidly, as the permafrost around it continues to thaw.[233][234]

Such craters, which pockmark frozen tundra worldwide, are the most visible evidence of melting permafrost due to global heating. Researchers have estimated that massive permafrost deposits hold some 1.6 trillion tons of frozen carbon.[235][236]

Significant thawing is already happening, multiple studies have found, including one of the Canadian Arctic that shows thawing occurring 70 years earlier than predicted.[237]

Faster thawing was also discovered by researchers who reported the results of field samples and satellite imaging across Russia, Alaska, and Canada. They found that the "ice-wedges" that penetrate permafrost were melting faster than previously known.[238]

"At the places where we have sufficient amounts of data, we are seeing this process happen in less than a decade and even after one warm summer," the study's lead author Anna Liljedahl told *The Washington*

Post. "The scientific community has had the assumption that this cold permafrost would be protected from climate warming, but we're showing here that the top of the permafrost, even if it's very cold, is very sensitive to these warming events," she said.[239]

Estimates from another study suggest that one-quarter of Alaska permafrost will be thawed by 2100.[240] Russian officials estimate that Russia may lose 30% of its permafrost by 2050.[241] Globally, one analysis has estimated that between one-quarter and two-thirds of permafrost will be gone by 2200.[242]

The warming Arctic tundra has already become a net source of CO_2, according to Alaskan field measurements. In one study, atmospheric scientists analyzed CO_2 measurements from aircraft and an Alaska research station. They found a 73% increase in CO_2 emissions from the tundra since 1975, "supporting the view that rising temperatures have made Arctic ecosystems a net source of CO_2."[243]

Despite such field data and researchers' estimates, scientists still have little idea exactly how fast permafrost will thaw because of its complex structure. As one group of permafrost researchers wrote:

> Frozen soil doesn't just lock up carbon—it physically holds the landscape together. Across the Arctic and Boreal regions, permafrost is collapsing suddenly as pockets of ice within it melt. Instead of a few centimetres of soil thawing each year, several metres of soil can become destabilized within days or weeks. The land can sink and be inundated by swelling lakes and wetlands.[244]

The researchers reported that when they returned to Alaskan field sites, they often found that areas that were forested only a year before were now covered with lakes. They declared that "permafrost is thawing much more quickly than models have predicted, with unknown consequences for greenhouse-gas release."

What's more, thawing of permafrost beneath such lakes could significantly accelerate carbon emissions, according to a study led by aquatic ecologist Katey Walter Anthony. The researchers discovered the phenomenon by modeling and taking observations at such lakes in Alaska, Siberia, and Sweden.[245]

Anthony and her colleagues' radiocarbon dating of CO_2 and CH_4 seeping from Arctic lakes in Alaska, Siberia, and Canada revealed that in some cases, the gases came from carbon stored tens of thousands of years.[246]

How much thawing with temperature rise?

In addition to how fast, scientists are also far from certain just how *much* permafrost will thaw with a given rise in global temperature. Researchers led by climate modeler Sarah Chadburn sought to quantify that thawing, using data on the current distribution of permafrost and air temperature. They calculated that about 4 million square kilometers (1.6 million square miles) of permafrost could thaw for every 1°C of global temperature increase. This amount is 20% more than researchers had previously theorized. Chadburn and her team found that even stabilizing the climate at 2°C would eventually reduce permafrost area by more than 40%—causing a massive influx of CO_2.[247]

There's also a permafrost "lid" under the East Siberian Arctic Shelf that has already begun leaking huge amounts of methane into the atmosphere. The ice shelf sprawls over some 2 million square kilometers (800,000 square miles) beneath the Arctic Ocean. The lid was thought to be an impermeable barrier sealing in methane.[248] [249] [250]

"When this lid loses its integrity, this is when we start worrying," said Natalia Shakhova, part of a team sampling Arctic Ocean waters and drilling into permafrost there. "The amount of methane currently releasing makes us think it will increase as a result of the disintegration of this permafrost body. The most important consequence could be in terms of growing methane emissions . . . a linear trend becomes exponential."[251]

Despite the potential impact, none of the effects of permafrost carbon feedback have been included in IPCC assessment reports, pointed out Joseph Romm, in his 2018 book *Climate Change: What Everyone Needs to Know*.[252]

"The bottom line is that any time this book or any news report cites an IPCC projection of future warming or future climate impacts, it is almost certain that projection represents an underestimate of what is to come," Romm wrote.

Thus, the threat is quite real of a "permafrost bomb"—a rapid melting with release of massive amounts of greenhouse gases. "It's a lit fuse, but the length of that fuse is very long," Katey Walter Anthony told *The Canadian Press.* "According to the model projections, we're getting ready for the part where it starts to explode. But it hasn't happened yet."[253]

Peat Megafires

Global heating will cause massive deposits of peat worldwide to burn more frequently, with profound consequences. Peat, the accumulation of partially decayed vegetation, is found in massive deposits in the Arctic tundra, as well as tropical regions such as Africa and Indonesia.

The carbon emissions from a peat fire can be immense. The 1997 Indonesian fire season may have released 2.5 billion metric tons of carbon, possibly 40% of all fossil fuel emissions that year, researchers calculated.[254] And in 2015, smoldering peat megafires in Indonesia burned uncontrollably over vast areas of forest, producing a pall of acrid smoke that shrouded much of the country, reaching neighboring Malaysia and Singapore. Estimates are that those fires caused some 100,000 premature deaths in the region.[255] In Indonesia, most of these fires are set by people, primarily to clear land for farming. But they dramatically illustrate what will be far more common under future global heating, as the massive global peat deposits elsewhere dry out and catch fire.

An international survey of peat bogs found that they contain more carbon than all the world's vegetation, and about as much as the atmosphere today—totaling 850 billion metric tons.[256] And new deposits are still being discovered. Researchers led by Greta Dargie reported mapping a previously unknown peat bog covering 56,000 square miles, an area larger than England, in the Central Congo Basin. They noted that the bog—which contains carbon the equivalent of two decades of current US fossil fuel emissions—is among those vulnerable to drying from global heating.[257] [258]

The future will be far worse, according to researchers who used satellite data and modeling to forecast the future of peat fires with drying due to El Niño. They found a "strong *nonlinear* [emphasis added] relationship . . . between fire emissions and cumulative water deficit"—meaning that fires increase greatly with drying. They forecast that the massive carbon release would create a "significant positive feedback to climate warming."[259]

Fiery tipping point

Peat in the Arctic tundra will also release CO_2 by catching fire through human- or lightning-caused fires, or those that continually smolder beneath the ground. The fires also remove protective insulation and produce charred earth that absorbs more solar heat than reflective snow and ice. That heat increases drying and makes the tundra more vulnerable to fires.

Tundra fires are already increasing, but nobody knows how severe this future burning will be. However, researchers analyzing charcoal in Alaskan tundra sediments for clues to past fires have found indications that the future could be more fiery for the Arctic. The researchers found that drier areas—expected with future heating—burned far more frequently than cooler, moister ones.[260] [261]

"Our work illustrates that some tundra regions can burn frequently, implying that future warming could certainly result in more frequent tundra burning," said co-author Philip Higuera.[262]

Respiring Soils

Besides peat deposits, the other major terrestrial carbon repository—the buried organic remains of plants and roots in soils—will also increase emissions from global heating.

The effects of soil warming could be profound, according to a study by 50 scientists worldwide. For their study, the researchers combined field measurements of soil carbon from 49 experimental plots in North America, Europe, and Asia. Such plots are defined areas of land in which scientists calculate the amount of carbon emitted at different temperatures.

They calculated that the current rate of global heating will lead to the emission of about 55 billion metric tons of carbon by 2050, which comprises 12–17% of the expected carbon emissions over this period.[263]

"By taking this global perspective, we're able to see that there is a feedback, and it's actually going to be massive," lead author Thomas Crowther told *The Washington Post*. "It's of the same order of magnitude as having an extra US on the planet," he said.

Despite the impact of such release, said Crowther, "the entire magnitude of this feedback was removed from several of the Earth system models," the models that inform the IPCC, because of the massive uncertainty surrounding the feedback potential.[264]

In an article in *Yale News*, Crowther pointed out that the Arctic region constitutes the largest potential source of soil carbon emissions. Carbon has built up over centuries there because microbes are less active.[265]

"But as you start to warm, the activities of those microbes increase, and that's when the losses start to happen," said Crowther. "The scary thing is these cold regions are the places that are expected to warm the most under climate change."

Soil-warming triggers carbon loss

In studying carbon loss from soil warming, researchers heat plots of soil by a precise amount and measure the resulting emissions. In one 26-year experiment, ecologists used heating cables to artificially warm plots of soil in Harvard Forest in Massachusetts. They found that over the period the top layer of the soil lost a significant amount of carbon—the equivalent of 17% of the soil carbon.[266]

"This magnitude of loss could amount to hundreds of petagrams—billions of metric tons—of carbon fluxing from the world's forest soils to the atmosphere, if those soils responded to warming like the Harvard Forest soils have done over the experimental period," research leader Jerry Melillo told *The Washington Post*. Extrapolating the findings to the world's forests suggests that carbon loss of the top meter of soil over this century could be the "equivalent to the past two decades of carbon emissions from fossil fuel burning."[267]

In fact, carbon release from soils may be far greater than such studies show because the researchers literally didn't probe deep enough into their subject. In previous warming studies, researchers had only heated the top soil layer. But in an experiment that did go deeper, soil biochemists inserted warming rods one meter into coniferous forest soils to heat them over two years. When the researchers measured the CO_2 emissions from 4°C warming, they found more than a third greater emissions than previous studies. Given the level of emissions they measured, they estimated that 4°C warming could cause soils worldwide to emit carbon the equivalent of roughly 30% of current human-caused emissions.[268]

As previously noted, soil microbes become more active with rising temperatures. One study by biologists demonstrated this rise in activity. The researchers analyzed the results of 27 soil-warming studies in climates ranging from the equatorial desert to the Arctic. They found that soil microbes increased activity with temperature up to about 25°C (77°F). Above that temperature, soil respiration begins to decrease, reducing their emissions. Importantly, Arctic soils were most responsive to warmer temperatures, found the researchers.[269]

"That means the Arctic latitudes, where soil temperatures rarely, if ever, reach 25°C, will continue to be most responsive to climate warming," according to research leader Joanna Carey. "Because there is so much carbon stored in frozen soils of the Arctic, this has really serious repercussions for future climate change."[270]

Thus, as global temperatures rise, loss of soil carbon will constitute another major climate monster.

Besides their role in causing permafrost and soil emissions, microbes will play a central role in multiple climate disruption impacts. A consensus statement by 30 microbiologists cited impacts ranging from disease epidemics to ruined crops.[271]

"Across marine and terrestrial biomes, microbially driven greenhouse gas emissions are increasing and positively feeding back on climate change," the scientists said. "Ignorance of the role of, effects on and feedback response of microbial communities to climate change can lead to our own peril," they said (see Mounting Methane, Toxic Earth, Diseased Earth).

III
Plague on the Environment

As the World Meteorological Organization has documented, Earth is suffering a relentless rise in temperatures and sea level, producing profound environmental impacts—including melting glaciers, heat waves, droughts, floods, wildfires, dying forests, superstorms, floods, and a ravaged ocean.[272] This section explores these environmental and human impacts.

Six Degrees to Termination

The global temperature rise since the beginning of the Industrial Revolution has been relentless and dramatic, as depicted in the graph on the next page. The 2021 report of the UN Intergovernmental Panel on Climate Change (IPCC) said that:

> Global surface temperature has increased faster since 1970 than in any other 50-year period over at least the last 2000 years. Temperatures during the most recent decade (2011–2020) exceed those of the most recent multi-century warm period, around 6500 years ago.[273]

That temperature increase shows no indication of stopping, much less reversing course, as we continue pumping carbon dioxide (CO_2) and methane (CH_4) into the atmosphere.

The IPCC report concluded that by 2100, global temperatures compared to 1850–1900 will be higher by:

- 1.0–1.8°C under a very low emissions scenario
- 2.1–3.5°C under an intermediate scenario
- 2.3–5.7°C under a very high emissions scenario

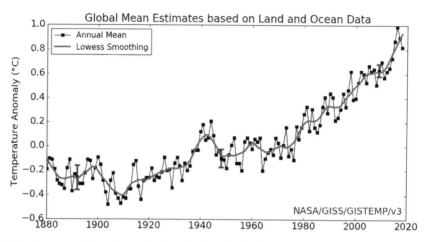

Global temperature since the beginning of the Industrial Revolution has shown a relentless rise among short-term variations.

Source: NASA Goddard Institute for Space Studies

The last time global surface temperature was at or above 2.5°C was over 3 million years ago, said the report.

Dubious Political Numbers

The benchmark temperatures used in climate policy-making—1.5°C, 2°C, 4°C, and 6°C—are political numbers not scientific numbers. Their scientific provenance is highly dubious (see the discussion "2°C fabrication" in Paris Agreement: Blind and Toothless). The conveniently round numbers might even be considered scientifically dishonest because scientists don't really know the consequences of each increase. But for political expediency, they pretend that they do. Nevertheless, the numbers are still used in this book, since the UN Intergovernmental Panel on Climate Change and climate scientists cite them to denote future benchmarks.

Very roughly speaking, the evidence presented in this book indicates that the consequences might be considered to be

- crippling (1.5°C, 2°C)
- devastating (4°C)
- terminal (6°C)

Indeed, some models have estimated global temperature increases of up to 7°C by 2100.[274] [275] [276]

The intervening years will see a relentless temperature rise, models have forecast. By 2050, the red line of 2°C above preindustrial levels could be reached, even if the Paris pledges are fully implemented, estimated a report by the Universal Ecological Fund.[277] In fact, a 2018 MIT report concluded that their model deemed the Paris pledges as inadequate to prevent a 2°C rise.[278]

The upshot of all these predictions: "There is not a cat in hell's chance" of meeting the 2°C limit, declared climatologist Bill McGuire.[279]

In fact, meeting the 2°C limit would require mass-scale *removal* of atmospheric CO_2—deploying technology that does not now exist—as well as achieving net zero emissions by 2085, found one study. "Mass-scale" means removing a gargantuan billions of metric tons of CO_2 a year, according to one analysis (see Carbon Capture Snake Oil).[280]

Temperatures could rise even further in a feedback cycle, because as temperatures rise, the atmosphere becomes more sensitive to CO_2 increases, found an analysis by researchers led by Tobias Friedrich.[281]

In their study, the researchers first reconstructed temperatures for the last 784,000 years. They used computer models, as well as data from coring marine sediments and glaciers. They projected that increased sensitivity would mean that by 2100, global temperatures would reach 5.9°C above preindustrial levels, with a range of 4.78–7.36°C.[282]

Even that devastating increase may not be the upper limit, because of feedbacks like the potential loss of cloud cover triggered by higher CO_2 levels. The levels expected over the next century could cause the evaporation of cooling stratocumulus clouds, triggering a massive 8°C global heating greater than that caused by greenhouse gases alone, found a modeling study led by Tapio Schneider.[283]

The steady temperature rise is causing an increasing imbalance between the Earth's heat gain and loss, according to a NASA/NOAA study. The study, using both satellite and ground-based data, found that the imbalance had doubled from 2005–2019.[284]

"The trends we found were quite alarming in a sense," according to the study's lead author, geophysicist Norman Loeb. "The magnitude of the increase is unprecedented."[285]

Lethal temperature trajectory

While these predictions vary, they show clearly that the world could well be 4°C warmer than preindustrial levels by the end of the century, on an upward trajectory toward 6°C and beyond. (To understand why efforts to prevent this trajectory will fail, see VI. Grasping at Climate Panaceas.) The effects of a 4°C increase would be devastating. Vast areas of the world would become desert or rendered uninhabitable by heat, droughts, or floods (see Hellscape Earth, Megadrought Era, and Flood Warning). These regions include much of the US, South America, Africa, Australia, Europe, and Asia. Huge areas of coastlines around the world would be inundated and island nations would disappear beneath the waves.[286 287 288] As described by environmental biologist Rachel Warren:

> The limits for human adaptation are likely to be exceeded
> in many parts of the world, while the limits for adaptation
> for natural systems would largely be exceeded throughout
> the world. Hence, the ecosystem services upon which
> human livelihoods depend would not be preserved.[289]

In a 6°C average warmer world, the limits for human adaptation would be exceeded throughout the world. But even that 6°C world is by no means the end of global heating.

If fossil fuels continue to be burned at the current rate, an up to 10°C of warming has been forecast by some researchers, including Katarzyna Tokarska and her colleagues.[290] Their models assumed burning just the lower end of the estimated available fossil fuel resources, and without significant efforts to reduce usage. The result, the researchers found, was that 5 trillion metric tons of CO_2 would be added to the atmosphere, in sharp contrast to the 2 million metric tons that is the worst-case scenario of the IPCC.

The time period for a projected 10°C increase seems long—around 200 years. However, it is the blink of an eye in evolutionary terms, making it certain that under such an increase most of the world's organisms, including humans, could not evolve to survive.

Lessons of ancient history

The closest ancient analog to today's global heating is the Paleocene-Eocene Thermal Maximum (PETM) 56 million years ago.[291] The PETM saw the release of up to 1.7 million metric tons per year of CO_2 over thousands of years.[292] The result was a CO_2 level of well over 1,000 parts per million, similar to what is expected by the next century with the current trajectory.[293][294]

Back then, the ancestors of today's elephants and crocodiles managed to adapt, shifting northward to survive. Marine creatures weren't so fortunate, with mass extinctions likely due to ocean warming and acidification.

The catch today, though, is that we are releasing about ten times as much CO_2 a *year*—faster than any rate in 66 million years, according to research led by Richard Zeebe. The researchers analyzed ancient sediments to detect signs of new CO_2 entering the atmosphere.[295] In another study, researchers concluded that CO_2 increases could have been driven by tipping-point feedbacks such as melting methane clathrates (see Climate Monsters).[296]

In reconstructing average land temperatures during the PETM, researchers have calculated that global air temperatures rose 5–8°C, and average sea-surface temperatures rose up to 10°C in less than a couple hundred thousand years, possibly as few as 15,000 years. Such temperatures would produce a tropical Europe and possibly unlivable equatorial regions.[297]

Researchers studying the PETM have concluded that the vast amounts of CO_2 we are injecting into the atmosphere today guarantees a far faster warming than during the ancient rise 56 million years ago.

The consequences of this drastic temperature rise—as listed in numerous reports and detailed in the following sections—will be:

- Melting of Arctic and Antarctic ice
- Slowing and even possible collapse of ocean currents
- Inundating sea-level rise
- Catastrophic floods, droughts, and storms
- Ecosystem-destroying wildfires
- Devastation of northern boreal forests and the Amazon rainforest
- Unraveling of the ocean food web from heating, acidification, and anoxia
- A heat-soaked, disease-plagued, increasingly toxic Earth.[298] [299] [300]

As discussed later, these environmental disasters could lead to widespread famine, mass migration of environmental refugees, governmental collapse, and military conflicts, possibly including nuclear war (see IV. Viral Human Consequences).

Inexorable Melt

Like any typical visitor to the Athabasca Glacier in the Canadian Rockies, I dipped my hand into the ice-cold glacial meltwater flowing from the pristine ice. I cupped it to my mouth and enjoyed a refreshing drink. The crystal-clear water was a treat. But the stream is also an ominous sign of the relentless melting of the massive glacier with rising global temperatures. The vast ice field occupies more than two square miles of the broad mountain valley and is almost a thousand feet deep at its thickest.

Decades ago, the glacier extended to the park's visitor center. But today, to reach the glacier I had to take a precarious 30-minute ride up to the ice in a 27-ton Ice Explorer vehicle, trundling across a barren, gray moonscape of rocky glacial moraine.

The glacier is retreating about 16 feet each year—so fast that the steel markers that rangers drive into the edge of the ice in spring to guide visitors are laying on bare ground by the end of the summer. Park rangers say the glacier could disappear within a generation.

Such melting glaciers in the world's mountains, at the poles, and in Greenland will create profound, widespread impacts, wrote Jorge Daniel Taillant in his book *Meltdown*. The impacts include more global heating, sea level rise, fresh water shortages, ocean warming, unstable and violent weather patterns, habitat destruction, land shifts, and catastrophic glacier tsunamis.

"Melting glaciers aren't the original *cause* of our climate problems, they are a *symptom* of a much greater problem (global warming)," he wrote. "But they are also a force, which in turn feeds back into the problem and makes it even worse."[301]

Global mountain glacier retreat

The Athabasca and the other mountain glaciers—those outside the Greenland and the Antarctic ice sheets—are losing mass at an accelerating rate since 2000. That lost mass contributed to about 20% of sea-level rise between 2000 and 2019, glaciologists determined using satellite imagery.[302] The global glacier retreat since 1950 "is unprecedented in at least the last 2000 years," concluded an IPCC report.[303]

Melting mountain glaciers will reduce water supplies for huge populations. Some 800 million people depend on Himalayan glaciers for water. Those glaciers have lost ice ten times faster over the last decades than during the period of expansion during The Little Ice Age that ended around 400 years ago.[304] And the rate of loss doubled between 2000 and 2016, compared to 1975–2000, found satellite studies.[305] [306]

Even limiting temperature rise to 1.5°C would cause glaciers in Asian mountains to shrink by as much as 64% by century's end, according to a modeling analysis led by physical geographer Philip Kraaijenbrink.[307] The glaciers feed the Yangtze, Ganges, Mekong, and other rivers that more than a billion people depend on for water.

Such highly visited glaciers as the Athabasca are the most visible sign of the melting of the planet's ice. Given the relentless global temperature rise, that melting will continue until global ice cover is all but gone.

Melting will also accelerate because exposed land and open water absorb more heat than reflective, white ice—a process called the albedo effect.

While scientists currently believe that total global melting might take centuries, they are uncertain. For example, they have not taken into account such accelerating factors as absorption of heat by algae growing on melting snow or soot from fossil fuel combustion.[308] [309] These deposits darken the ice, increasing heat absorption and melting.

Melting of land-based glaciers in Alaska, the Arctic, and Greenland will constitute major contributors to the 52–74 centimeter sea-level rise forecast for 2100, noted a report by the Arctic Mapping and Assessment Programme. This rise is double the minimum estimate made by the UN Intergovernmental Panel on Climate Change's (IPCC).[310]

All three major global ice sources—Arctic, Antarctic, and Greenland—are disappearing at unprecedented rates. Analysis of satellite data has revealed that the rate of global ice loss has increased greatly over the decades 1994 to 2017.[311]

Combined ice losses from Greenland and Antarctica have increased six-fold, from 81 billion metric tons a year in the 1990s to 474 billion metric tons a year by the 2010s, according to satellite studies.[312] [313] [314]

"The ice sheets are now following the worst-case climate warming scenarios set out by the [IPCC]," according to Thomas Slater. "Sea-level rise on this scale will have very serious impacts on coastal communities this century," including storm and tidal surges (see Flood Warning).[315]

Arctic melting

The Arctic Ocean faces an "inevitable" loss of summer sea ice, even with the "very lowest emission pathways," concluded the *State of the Cryosphere Report 2022*. In the past, much of the ice remained frozen year-round, and the report called the total loss "a terminal diagnosis for that ecosystem and its essential role reflecting sunlight."[316]

According to a 2021 IPCC report, "In 2011–2020, annual average Arctic sea ice area reached its lowest level since at least 1850. Late summer Arctic sea ice area was smaller than at any time in at least the past 1000 years."[317]

Arctic sea ice is an important influencer of global climate by moderating ocean circulation. For example, melting of Arctic sea-ice weakens critical circulation patterns like the Atlantic Meridional Overturning Circulation (AMOC), which provides a major source of warmth for North America and Western Europe (see Ruining AMOC).[318]

The sea ice also influences atmospheric processes like the polar vortex, a massive band of winds circling the North Pole.[319] Destabilizing disruptions in this circulation, possibly due to reduced sea ice, could trigger the jet stream to become wavy, sending cold air far south and drawing warm air northward.

A warming Arctic could have global impacts, found a report by the Stockholm Environmental Institute. Changes in Arctic sea ice, permafrost, and vegetation could trigger "tropical forests turning to savannas, monsoon systems weakening, mangroves collapsing, coral reefs becoming dominated by algae, and the West Antarctica ice sheet collapsing," warned the report.[320]

The Arctic Ocean is rapidly losing its ice, both in the extent of ice cover and the thickness of the remaining ice. Melting will continue unabated because the Arctic is showing a relentless rise in air temperatures over sea and land—the latter being more than twice as fast as the global average—according to NOAA's *Arctic Report Card*.[321]

Part of the reason for this march toward an ice-free Arctic is a strong feedback loop: Bright sea ice reflects 80% of sunlight that hits it; by contrast, the dark ocean surface absorbs 90% of the sunlight.[322] Thus, at the current rate of CO_2 increase and global heating, researchers say that summer Arctic sea ice will disappear entirely over the next decades.[323] [324]

Some climate de-nihilists have touted the advantages of an ice-free Arctic Ocean. They assert that it will enable shorter shipping routes, increased hydropower, increased tourism, and better access to fishing grounds and oil and mineral deposits. However, an economic analysis of the overall impact by the Arctic Mapping and Assessment Programme showed that the loss of sea ice will cost $7 trillion to $90 trillion between 2010 and 2100. This cost arises from coastal erosion and flooding, increased wildfires, and permafrost thawing. It also arises from global impacts on greenhouse gas emissions, climate, weather, sea-level rise, and world commerce, noted the report.

Modeling studies, in fact, have shown that the region's rapid warming have driven it permanently into a new climate regime in which "extremes become routine."[325] Thus, an Arctic tipping point may already have been reached (see Permafrost Bomb).

Antarctic melting

In the Antarctic, global heating is triggering disintegration of the vast ice shelves—sheets of ice hundreds of meters thick. Unlike the Arctic, in which ice floats on an ocean, the Antarctic is a land continent largely covered with ice.[326]

At the continental edges, the ice shelves act as critical plugs, preventing erosion of glaciers behind them. In shallower waters, the shelves are grounded on the ocean bottom, but in deeper waters they float, making them vulnerable to warming waters.[327]

Global heating has caused these plugs to become unstable, and massive areas of ice shelves are breaking away, exposing the glaciers behind them. In July 2017, an iceberg twice the size of Delaware broke off the Larsen C Ice Shelf in Antarctica.[328] In May 2021, an iceberg bigger than Rhode Island broke off the Ronne Ice Shelf.[329]

Such floating ice shelves break away in large part due to melting from beneath, due to the intrusion of water warmed by global heating.[330][331] The ice shelves are also more vulnerable to disintegration because warmer temperatures create pools of surface meltwater. This meltwater warms via the albedo effect—the same as in the Arctic. Runoff of surface meltwater increases the ice shelves' vulnerability to "hydrofracturing," causing them to crack and disintegrate.[332]

There will be "effectively instantaneous" loss of ice from the grounded ice sheets when floating plugs that stabilize them are lost, researchers have concluded. Their modeling and satellite studies suggest that "we are not protected against the impact of the Antarctic ice sheet on global sea levels by a long response time."[333]

Such disintegration is already seriously undermining the largest Antarctic glacier, Totten Glacier, which acts as a barrier holding back vast areas of ice.[334]

Glaciologists had believed that large-scale collapse of such glaciers would take centuries. However, more recent studies suggest that the collapse of such glaciers as the Thwaites Glacier—the size of Florida—could occur within decades.[335] Sometimes dubbed the Doomsday Glacier, the Thwaites Glacier is a central plug stabilizing the entire West Antarctica ice sheet.[336]

Using underwater robots to measure water temperatures beneath the glacier, the researchers found major inflows of warm water "impinging from all sides on pinning points critical to ice-shelf stability, a scenario that may lead to unpinning and retreat."[337]

Melting of the Antarctic ice sheets, including Thwaites Glacier, has greatly accelerated in recent decades, numerous studies have shown. Such studies used satellite and aerial photography data, as well as computer models.[338] [339] [340] [341] [342]

The current rate of overall ice loss is five times faster than in 1992, one satellite data analysis showed.[343] The ice sheet thinning has been rapid in glaciological terms, study leader Andy Shepherd told *The Guardian*.[344]

"The speed of drawing down ice from an ice sheet used to be spoken of in geological timescales, but that has now been replaced by people's lifetimes," he said.

The West Antarctic ice sheet has collapsed rapidly in the past, causing a huge sea-level rise, as seen in cores of ancient sediments. Some 125,000 years ago, during a brief warm period with temperatures slightly higher than today, the ice sheet collapsed, and sea levels were some 6 to 9 meters higher than today. Such a rise today would cause vast coastal areas to be inundated (see Flood Warning).[345]

A 4°C warming above preindustrial levels could cause more than a third of the vast Antarctic ice shelves to collapse, according to one modeling study.[346]

The glaciers may reach irreversible temperature-driven tipping points, beyond which Antarctic melting is irreversible. Positive internal feedback arises because melting creates secondary effects that trigger more melting. For example, melting ice sheets slump down to lower, warmer elevations, speeding melting. And softer ice slides faster into the ocean, where it melts quicker. As mentioned earlier, the pools of water atop glaciers are also darker, adding to the feedback and speeding melting.

One modeling study identified three levels of Antarctic tipping points:

- At 2°c above preindustrial levels, the West Antarctic ice sheet is committed to partial collapse. Average sea level rises by more than 2 meters.
- Between 6–9°c above preindustrial levels, more than 70% of ice is lost. Average sea level rises more than 12 meters.
- At more than 10°c above preindustrial levels, Antarctica becomes virtually ice free.

"Our results show that if the Paris Agreement is not met, Antarctica's long-term sea-level contribution will dramatically increase and exceed that of all other sources," wrote the researchers.[347]

In a worst-case scenario in which the Antarctic ice sheet melted completely, sea-level rise would be about 60 meters (200 feet).[348]

Greenland melting

The Greenland ice sheet, covering more than 650,000 square miles, is melting both from above and below. The land-based ice sheet is like Antarctica's, with large areas jutting into the ocean. On its surface, huge "supraglacial" lakes are forming and draining into the ice.[349] Beneath the ice, plumes of warm water intrude into Greenland's fjords to melt the ice sheet.[350] [351] Such drainage may lubricate the ice sheet, speeding its slide into the Atlantic.

The ice sheet melting is rapid and accelerating, computer modeling and studies of satellite data and ice records show. The studies concluded that the Greenland ice sheet has already passed the point of no return.[352] [353] [354] [355]

Greenland melting is nonlinear, meaning that the future portends still greater acceleration, found glaciologists' studies of ice cores reflecting prehistoric melting.[356] Geographer Luke Trusel said that his team's studies showed that the melting has "gone into overdrive" and is now "adding to sea level more than any time during the last three and a half centuries, if not thousands of years."[357]

Estimates of long-term sea-level rise from Greenland melting have continued to increase, with one analysis forecasting about 274 millimeters (11 inches) of sea-level rise from Greenland melting alone by 2100.[358] Complete melting of the ice sheet would cause sea level to rise about 6 meters.[359]

Mass Extinction

Why should we care about polar bears or cheetahs or Karner blue butterflies, or any other vulnerable or endangered species? After all, their fate seems unconnected to our own well-being. It may seem irrelevant that this century is seeing a climate- and human-caused "sixth extinction"—a decimation of species that will be as severe as those over the past millions of years.

But it's not irrelevant. Mass extinctions will profoundly affect our lives. Plants and animals are an integral part of the "ecosystem services" necessary for our survival.[360]

"Our economies, livelihoods and well-being all depend on our most precious asset: Nature," was a key headline message asserted by *The Economics of Biodiversity*—a massive review of the economic value of the natural world.[361] It declared that:

> We are part of Nature, not separate from it. We rely on Nature to provide us with food, water, and shelter; regulate our climate and disease; maintain nutrient cycles and oxygen production; and provide us with spiritual fulfilment and opportunities for recreation and recuperation, which can enhance our health and well-being. . . . Nature is therefore an asset, just as produced capital (roads, buildings, and factories) and human capital (health, knowledge, and skills) are assets. . . . Biodiversity enables Nature to be productive, resilient, and adaptable. . . . Reduce biodiversity, and Nature and humanity suffer.

And as Michael Tennesen eloquently wrote in his book, *The Next Species*:[362]

> Ecosystems of multiple species . . . are essential for human life. They represent the genetic diversity of life, providing the raw ingredients for new medicines, new crops, and new livestock.
>
> Forests store more carbon from CO_2 if they have a greater variety of tree species. Streams clean up more pollution if they have a greater variety of microbes. Increasing the diversity of fish means there are greater fishery yields. Increasing plant diversity means they can better fend off invasive plants. Natural enemies better control agricultural pests if they are composed of a variety of predators, parasites, and pathogens. And ecosystems with a greater biodiversity can better withstand stress such as higher temperatures.
>
> On the other hand, less diversity means less carbon capture, more polluted streams, fewer fish, more invasive plants, more agricultural pests, and more of the species that do poorly under stress.

Nature provides services worth about $125 trillion a year, calculated the World Wildlife Fund (WWF) in its 2018 *Living Planet Report*. "As we better understand our reliance on natural systems it's clear that nature is not just a 'nice to have'," the authors wrote.[363]

Climate disruption is only one cause of the extinctions of plants and animals. Much more serious for many species is overexploitation, and habitat loss and degradation, noted the WWF 2016 *Living Planet Report*. The report noted, however, that climate disruption can exacerbate those effects. It warned that people may further unravel the ecological web by plundering natural resources, as they suffer from drought, storms, and other climate disasters.

"Growing evidence suggests that the Earth has already exceeded the Planetary Boundary for climate change," concluded the report, citing melting polar ice and permafrost, and rainforest destruction as prime examples.[364]

Around a million species of plants and animals—an average of 25% of Earth's total—are threatened with extinction, according to a landmark report by the biodiversity group IPBES.[365]

"The global rate of species extinction is already at least tens to hundreds of times higher than the average rate over the past 10 million years and is accelerating," declared the report, the most comprehensive of its kind.

With a 4.5°C temperature increase, almost half of species studied would be at risk of extinction, calculated climatologist Rachel Warren and colleagues.[366] Numerous studies have predicted just such a temperature increase by 2100 (see Six Degrees to Termination).

Ocean life could face a mass extinction event by 2300 on par with the one that wiped out the dinosaurs, if fossil fuel continues its current rate of increase, found one modeling study. Climate disruption's projected impact "is profound, driving extinction risk higher and marine biological richness lower than has been seen in Earth's history for the past tens of millions of years," wrote the researchers.[367]

"Ecological Armageddon"

Climate disruption essentially puts the Earth in a disastrous ecological blender—unpredictably altering temperatures, rainfall, and myriad other factors that species depend on for survival. Given humans' dependence on the environment as discussed, the effects of such ecological catastrophe will directly impact human survival.

"There is likely no hope of ever predicting the detailed consequences of climate disruption to a particular species any more than we can predict the outcome of tossed dice," wrote theoretical ecologist Stuart Pimm.[368] As an example, he called "potentially catastrophic" the inability to predict how a tropical disease or agricultural pest will spread.

Population sizes of mammals, birds, amphibians, reptiles, and fish have dropped by an average of 69% over the last five decades, concluded WWF's 2022 *Living Planet Report*.[369]

Climate disruption's impact on mammals and birds was clearly revealed in an analysis by population ecologists.[370] They found that 47%

of 873 mammals and 23.4% of 1,272 birds show evidence of impact from climate disruption. Mammals most affected were elephants, primates, and marsupials; birds most affected were species that live at high altitudes.

Insects have also been caught in the ecological blender. In a Puerto Rican preserve, the "biomass" of arthropods such as insects and spiders has fallen by up to 60 times the level 30 years ago, found biologists. They also found a decline in lizards, frogs, and birds that eat the arthropods. Given the rise in forest temperature they measured, "our study indicates that climate warming is the driving force behind the collapse of the forest's food web," they wrote.[371]

Similarly, ecologists measured a greater than 75% decline in the biomass of flying insects in nature reserves over the past 27 years. Not only does loss of insects knock out the base of the ecological food chain, it also eliminates such critical insect services as pollination.[372]

"Insects make up about two-thirds of all life on Earth but there has been some kind of horrific decline," study co-author Dave Goulson told *The Independent*. "We appear to be making vast tracts of land inhospitable to most forms of life and are currently on course for ecological Armageddon. If we lose the insects, then everything is going to collapse."[373]

Indeed, with the current trajectory of temperature increase, about half of all insects will lose more than half of their habitat by 2100, according to an analysis of 34,000 species of insects and other invertebrates by biologists.[374]

Rising temperatures alone can reduce male insect fertility, found another study. When biologists exposed beetles to heat in the laboratory, they found a drop by half in the amount of the insects' offspring. And, in females, the laboratory heat waves reduced the number and viability of eggs they laid.[375]

Up to one-third of the world's parasitic worm species could go extinct by 2070, found a study by biologists.[376] Losing parasites such as mosquitoes, ticks, and parasitic worms might not seem a bad thing. But parasites are key to maintaining a healthy ecological balance, for example by regulating the population of their host species. The finding is a good example of how the loss of species can unravel an intricate, interdependent ecological web.

Co-extinction is also an ecological hazard. It occurs when "the loss of one species can make more species disappear . . . and possibly bring entire systems to an unexpected, sudden regime shift, or even total collapse," said a study of co-extinction by biologists.[377] When they subjected "virtual Earths" in a computer model to different trajectories of temperature change, they found that ecological dependencies "amplify the direct effects of environmental change on the collapse of planetary diversity by up to ten times." They concluded that "primary extinctions driven by environmental change could be just the tip of an enormous extinction iceberg."

Drastic ecological disruption could begin within decades, concluded researchers in another analysis.[378] They calculated the impact of past and projected future temperature and precipitation on more than 30,000 marine and terrestrial species. They projected that within any given ecological niche, most species will be abruptly and catastrophically exposed to climate conditions beyond their niche limits—probably before 2030 in tropical oceans and by 2050 for tropical forests and higher latitudes. An ecological niche is the combination of environmental conditions that foster the survival of a plant or animal.

Evolution loses the race

Global heating is happening too fast for most species to evolve to keep up, according to an analysis by climatologists.[379] They modeled the current global heating rate and compared it with historical data revealing change in past eras. Those historical data included chemical analysis of ice cores and of microbes in ancient sediments.

They concluded that current global heating is "at least an order of magnitude—and potentially several orders of magnitude—more rapid than the changes to which terrestrial ecosystems have been exposed during the past 65 million years." This rapidity of heating, as well as pollution and habitat degradation "will present terrestrial ecosystems with an environment that is unprecedented in recent evolutionary history," they wrote.

In another supporting study, biologists analyzed how fast the ecological niches of 56 plant and animal species have changed over time. They found that historically the niches changed about 200,000 times slower than the current rate of climate disruption.[380]

Lethal Earth

Hellscape Earth

After reading "Six Degrees to Termination," you might have puzzled over why scientists are so worried over a few degrees of global heating. After all, over the seasons we experience far more temperature variation—from frigid winters to scorching summers. But seemingly small global temperature changes can trigger debilitating, even lethal, local extremes. The effects of such extreme temperatures were succinctly summarized by environmental economists Tamma Carleton and Solomon Hsiang:

> Heat induces mortality, has lasting impact on fetuses and infants, and incites aggression and violence while lowering human productivity. High temperatures also damage crops, inflate electricity demand, and may trigger population movements within and across national borders.[381]

Average global temperatures have continued to set modern records. As of this writing, summer 2020 was the hottest year on record for the Northern Hemisphere, according to the US National Oceanic and Atmospheric Administration (NOAA).[382] And the decade 2009–2018 was the warmest on record globally, according to the European Environmental Agency.[383] More broadly, annual global temperatures are the hottest in 12,000 years, researchers found when they reconstructed ancient temperatures from marine sediment cores.[384]

The vicious heat waves spawned by such temperatures are exemplified by those in the summer of 2022, in which records were set in Europe,

Africa, and Asia.[385] No doubt, after this book's publication, record heat waves will continue.

Mind-blowing future heat

Multiple studies have predicted an enormous future rise in lethal heating—"not only more intense extremes but also events that break previous records by much larger margins," found one study. The study predicted many-fold increases—compared with the last three decades—in the probability of record extremes over the next five decades.[386]

By 2050, even if the 2°C limit is met, dangerous heat index levels will increase up to 100% across much of the tropics, found another study. The heat index measures the combined effects of temperature and humidity and reflects heat's impact on the body. Such heating will increase by 3 to 10 times in the temperate zones, such as the US and Europe. By 2100, tropical and subtropical countries will experience dangerous heating during most days, and "the kinds of deadly heat waves that have been rarities in the midlatitudes will become annual occurrences," found the study.[387]

By 2070, up to 3.5 billion people could live in heat zones so extreme as to be unsuitable for habitation, found a study that analyzed data on demographics, land use, and climate.[388]

Even with drastic reductions in greenhouse gas emissions, by 2100 48% of the global population might be exposed to lethal heat for at least 20 days a year, versus about 30% today, concluded a study led by biogeographer Camilo Mora. With increasing emissions, the percentage of lethal heat days might reach 74%.[389 390]

"Finding so many cases of heat-related deaths was mind blowing, especially as they often don't get much attention because they last for just a few days and then people moved on," Mora told *The Guardian*.[391]

In the US, a 3°C warming would produce about 15 times as many high-temperature records as low records by century's end, researchers have calculated. By contrast, the current average ratio is about twice as many highs as lows, they found.[392]

An "extreme heat belt" will emerge in the US, stretching from Northern Texas to Illinois, found one modeling study.[393] By 2053, that region will experience days with a heat index above 125°F. Overall, in the US, the population exposed to extreme heat will rise from 8 million today to 107 million over the next three decades, found the report.

Lethal heat waves will have broad economic impacts, said Elfatih Eltahir, co-author of a paper forecasting heat waves in South Asia:[394]

"With the disruption to the agricultural production, it doesn't need to be the heat wave itself that kills people. Production will go down, so potentially everyone will suffer," he said (see "Heat robs labor" below).[395]

Some regions, such as parts of Africa, will experience lethal heat waves sooner than others. African heat waves have become more frequent over the past decades, according to one analysis of temperature records. A team of geophysicists projected that at the current rate of temperature rise, by 2040, African heat waves that are unusual today could occur every season and that heat and drought will render some regions uninhabitable.[396]

Another analysis emphasized that while all regions will face new temperature extremes, "the impacts, in terms of frequency of heat extremes, will become significantly worse for poorer nations when compared with their wealthier counterparts."[397]

Summers worldwide will become steadily hotter if the current pace of CO_2 emission continues unabated, noted an analysis by climatologists. Their modeling revealed that, with unabated heating, global summer temperatures would have an 80% chance of breaking a record each year between 2061 and 2080.[398] [399]

Lethal heat + humidity

The combination of high temperatures and high humidity will be particularly deadly. High humidity can render otherwise tolerable temperatures lethal because the body can no longer cool itself through perspiration, reaching what's called "wet-bulb temperatures." In his interview with *The Guardian* cited above, Mora described the physiological impact of high heat and humidity:

Your sweat doesn't evaporate if it is very humid, so heat accumulates in your body instead. People can then suffer heat toxicity, which is like sunburn on the inside of your body. The blood rushes to the skin to cool you down so there's less blood going to the organs. A common killer is when the lining of your gut breaks down and leaks toxins into the rest of your body.

Populations exposed to dangerous wet-bulb temperatures increase enormously with higher global temperatures. One analysis found that the global population exposed to at least one day of lethal heat-humidity:

- Has increased from 97 million to 275 million with the current temperature rise of about 1°C above preindustrial levels
- Will increase to 508 million with 1.5°C of warming
- Will increase to 789 million with 2°C of warming
- Will increase to 1.22 billion with 3°C of warming.[400]

Brief waves of potentially lethal heat/humidity are already occurring in areas of South Asia, the coastal Middle East, and the coastal Mexican southwest, found an analysis of weather station data. The number of such events more than doubled between 1979 and 2017, found the analysis.[401]

More than a third of recent heat-related deaths can already be attributed to global heating, found an analysis of records during 1991–2018. The study covered 43 countries and found dozens to hundreds of deaths each year evident on every continent.[402]

Future deadly heat waves affecting billions of people will occur throughout Pakistan, Nepal, India, Bangladesh, and Sri Lanka—constituting one-fifth of the world's population—predicted another study of heat/humidity.[403]

Future temperatures, future heat waves

In a future world of a 4°C increase, summers in China and the eastern US would include extreme humid heat waves of 55°C (131°F), found an analysis by ecologists. These high-humidity heat waves would trigger heat strokes in people exposed to them. Such heat waves would be expected as often as every other year in a 4°C world, the scientists said.[404]

In a future 7°C world, frequent heat waves would cripple humans' very ability to survive and render some regions uninhabitable.

An 11–12°C warming—possible if all fossil fuels are burned—would spread lethal temperatures to most human-populated regions, concluded researchers Steven Sherwood and Matthew Huber.[405]

They pointed out that their assumptions likely *overestimate* survivability: "Our limit applies to a person out of the sun, in gale-force winds, doused with water, wearing no clothing, and not working," they wrote.

In the US, more than 1,300 people die every year from heat waves today, according to a statistical estimate cited by the report *The Impacts of Climate Change on Human Health in the United States*. Climate models project that the number will rise to about 27,000 a year by 2100 for 209 US cities, according to the report. In addition, increased heat is projected to worsen respiratory, hormonal, urinary, genital, and renal problems. Heat can also kill indirectly. Extreme heat will cause more wildfires and airborne allergens, which will contribute to premature deaths, the report pointed out.[406]

Climate is the culprit

Extreme temperatures have clearly been linked to climate disruption. Record global temperature increases and Asian and Alaskan heat waves *would not have happened* in a preindustrial climate, according to an American Meteorological Society report on extreme events.[407] The report went beyond previous assessments that climate disruption had only *increased the odds* and intensity of such events.

The report noted that climate scientists had long predicted that global heating "would at some point become sufficiently strong and emergent to push an extreme event beyond the bounds of natural variability alone . . . . It is striking how quickly we are now starting to see such results."

Both heat extremes and heavy rainfall have increased due to even the relatively small global heating since the Industrial Revolution, found a study by climatologists Erich Fischer and Reto Knutti. Their modeling compared the chances of extreme temperatures from preindustrial times to today—the difference being attributable to global heating. Their analysis indicated that 75% of extremely hot days could be attributed to global heating.[408]

"People can argue that we had these kinds of extremes well before human influence on the climate . . . And that's correct. But the odds have changed, and we get more of them," Fischer told *The New York Times*.[409]

Ominously, their analysis indicated that the effect of global heating on hot extremes is "nonlinear." That is, as global temperature rises linearly, hot extremes will soar. For example, they forecast that a 5°C global heating would cause a 62-fold increase in extreme temperatures.

Global heating's influence on record heat waves, downpours, and droughts was also explored using historical data and computer models by climatologist Noah Diffenbaugh and colleagues. Their analysis revealed a clear signature of global heating in more than 80% of record heat events, as well as increasing the probability of the driest and wettest events.[410]

"This suggests that the world isn't yet at a place where every single record-setting hot event has a human fingerprint, but we are getting close to that point," Diffenbaugh told *The Washington Post*.[411]

Heat bakes cities

Heat stress will be higher in cities—home to more than half the world's population—due to the "urban heat island" effect, in which pavement and buildings soak up more heat than does the countryside.

One analysis of temperature data found an "alarming" trend in heat wave temperatures in large cities since 1966.[412] Analyzing temperature data from about 9,000 stations globally, they found an accelerating rise during heat waves over the last three decades, with the largest rise in megacities such as Houston, Moscow, Paris, and Beijing.

Another study of temperatures in 13,115 cities found a nearly 200% increase in extreme heat exposure from 1983 to 2016. The heat conditions affected some 1.7 billion people, found the researchers, who said their results "suggest that previous research underestimates extreme heat exposure" in cities.[413] Climatologist Robert Wilby explained this underestimation:

> Temperature projections from global climate models are typically for wild or agricultural landscapes . . . . These projections are far removed from the conditions that will be encountered on city streets, inside workplaces, public spaces, and our homes. But these are the places where health, comfort, and productivity will be decided during the more intense heat waves that climate change will bring.[414]

Wilby's research on the urban impacts of a 4°c global warming found that "high indoor temperatures with high humidity could become unbearable—even deadly—for millions. . . . By 2050, 68% of humanity may live in urban areas and populations in the tropics will be most exposed to extreme humid heat."

A forecast of future us heat trends found that by mid-century cities will suffer more than double the number of days with heat index temperatures above 100°F. The number of days per year above 105 degrees will triple.[415] Another us analysis by the Union of Concerned Scientists concluded that "failing to reduce heat-trapping emissions would lead to a staggering expansion of dangerous heat."[416]

Global heating will shift cities' climates to make them resemble those in warmer regions.[417] By 2050, cities in the Northern Hemisphere will resemble those some 1,000 kilometers (600 miles) closer to the equator, the researchers found. So, London will resemble Barcelona; Portland will resemble San Antonio; Seattle will resemble San Francisco; and San Francisco will resemble Lisbon. In fact, found the study, one-fifth of the cities, mostly in the tropics, will experience climates that do not even exist on Earth today.

In the us, combined higher temperatures and increased population will produce a huge rise in the number of "person-days" of heat exposure, one study suggested.[418]

"We find that us population exposure to extreme heat increases four- to six-fold over observed levels in the late twentieth century, and that changes in population are as important as changes in climate in driving this outcome," they concluded.

Heat robs labor

Heat cripples the economy by reducing labor capacity, since outdoor work becomes difficult or even life-threatening. Losses in global labor capacity will double from 10% to 20% by 2050, predicted researchers who used occupational health and safety thresholds and climate projects to arrive at their estimate.[419] Such workers as firefighters, farmers, construction workers, and factory workers will be forced to slow their pace due to heat stress. Said co-author John Dunne:

> Most studies of the direct impact of global warming on humans have focused on mortality under either extreme weather events or theoretical physiological limits. We wanted instead to describe climate warming in practical terms that people commonly experience already.[420]

Excess heat will cause global heat-related productivity losses of $2.5 trillion by 2030, concluded a report by the UN Development Programme.[421]

In a review of research on temperature and human performance, environmental epidemiologists led by Tord Kjellstrom concluded that:

> Later this century, many among the four billion people who live in hot areas worldwide will experience significantly reduced work capacity owing to climate change. In some areas, 30–40% of annual daylight hours will become too hot for work to be carried out. The social and economic impacts will be considerable, with Gross Domestic Product product (GDP) losses greater than 20% by 2100.[422]

Researchers in another study of productivity and temperature wrote that "unmitigated warming is expected to reshape the global economy by reducing average global incomes roughly 23% by 2100 and widening global income inequality, relative to scenarios without climate change."

The poorest countries will suffer more, the researchers concluded, with their average income plummeting by 75% by 2100. The figure is likely low, because the analysis included only temperature effects, and not sources of climate-related economic loss such as hurricanes and sea-level rise.[423]

For the US, each degree Celsius of higher temperature between 1981 and 2010 cost about 1.2% of gross domestic product, found another study. And, this cost was geographically unequal, with a transfer of value northward and westward. By late in this century, the researchers calculated, the poorest third of US counties would experience economic damage between 2% and 20% of income.[424]

Heat erodes mental health

Mental stresses due to heat will also threaten survival. Extreme heat can worsen psychiatric symptoms and, according to an American Psychiatric Association statement, has been linked to:

> ... increases in irritability and symptoms of depression and with an increase in suicide. It can also affect behavior, contributing to increased aggression, incidence of domestic violence, and increased use of alcohol or other substances to cope with stress.[425]

Indeed, studies have revealed a statistical association between temperature and suicide rates.[426] [427]

Statistics also seem to bear out the theory that high temperatures make people more hostile, which can lead to violence. When sociologists analyzed the crime rate in 57 countries, they discovered that each degree Celsius of temperature increase was associated with an approximately 6% average increase in homicides.[428]

And when environmental economist Matthew Ranson analyzed 30 years of crime and temperature data from nearly 3,000 US counties, he came up with a sobering forecast of the effects of higher temperatures:

> Between 2010 and 2099, climate change will cause an additional 22,000 murders, 180,000 cases of rape, 1.2 million aggravated assaults, 2.3 million simple assaults, 260,000 robberies, 1.3 million burglaries, 2.2 million cases of larceny, and 580,000 cases of vehicle theft in the United States.[429]

So, heat not only kills. It may make us killers.

Heat begets more CO_2

In a vicious circle, rising temperatures also increase air conditioning demand, requiring more electricity, which generates more CO_2.

And in a human vicious circle, more air conditioning makes people less heat tolerant, increasing demand for air conditioning. What's more, air conditioners become less efficient as temperatures rise because they are less able to shed heat to the outdoors. Thus, hotter temperatures will feed back to increase cooling and electricity load.

The impact of such increasing demand will be stunning. Future global energy demand for air conditioning could dwarf that of the US, which now expends more energy for air conditioning than all other countries combined. Countries outside the US have the potential to use 50 times more energy for cooling than the US because of rising temperatures and incomes, calculated researcher Michael Sivak.[430]

In some countries extreme heat will require a massive increase in air conditioning, just for people to survive, found one analysis. By 2050, the electricity needed for cooling in countries such as India and Indonesia could reach 75% of the total demand, overwhelming power grids.[431]

An International Energy Agency analysis found that "without action to address energy efficiency, energy demand for space cooling will more than triple by 2050—consuming as much electricity as all of China and India today."[432]

In the US, electricity demand for air conditioning could require additional peak generating capacity costing up to $180 billion, found one analysis by environmental economists.[433]

Higher demand could increase global energy needs by up to 58% by 2050, found one computer modeling study. Decreased heating energy demand would be far more than offset by increased cooling energy demand with predicted global temperature rise, the study found.[434]

All these impacts of rising temperatures will continue unabated, driven by the unconstrained momentum of the carbon contagion.

Megadrought Era

A parched landscape bakes under withering heat in the ongoing western US megadrought. The heat drives rampant wildfires and crop failures. Reservoirs shrivel to a small fraction of their normal size, becoming vast expanses of cracked earth. The government appeals to the public to save every possible drop of water.[435] [436] [437]

The drought is clearly driven by global heating, found researchers led by A. Park Williams. Their modeling and tree-ring data showed that the period 2000–2021 was the driest two decades in the last 12 centuries.[438]

"We now have enough observations of current drought and tree-ring records of past drought to say that we're on the same trajectory as the worst prehistoric droughts," Williams told *Science* magazine.[439]

Similarly, European summer droughts that began in 2015 were the worst in more than 2,000 years, tree-ring data revealed.[440]

Hell and high water

In a seeming contradiction, global heating can cause both extreme dry and wet conditions, an analysis of California's water future suggested.[441] Global heating creates droughts by increasing heating over land and diverting rainfall. And it drives powerful flooding storms by drawing moisture and energy from warming oceans (see Superstormy Weather, Flood Warning).[442]

Such extremes mean that regions must not only cope with droughts by trying to store and conserve more water, but manage the opposite catastrophes of extreme floods. The extremes can also wreak havoc on a society dependent on stable weather—impacting agriculture, migration, and political stability.

Importantly, intense cloudbursts do not necessarily alleviate droughts because they create runoff, rather than the soaking of soils that replenishes groundwater.

Evidence of both worsening droughts and heavier rains was revealed by a computer model analysis by meteorologist Elinor Martin. She wrote "The Americas, including Central America, the Caribbean, and the

Amazon, are hot spots for worsening droughts, and northern North America and Europe are hot spots for worsening [heavy rains]."[443]

Such extremes of rainfall and drought are already occurring, found climatologists. They analyzed rainfall data from about 50,000 weather stations worldwide. The data revealed over the last three decades an increase in record rainfalls in some regions and record dry spells in others. Wetter regions included parts of the US, northern Europe, and northern Asia; record dry spells occurred in regions of Africa.[444] [445] [446]

Global drying is already shifting the geographical boundaries of deserts and drylands. The Sahara Desert has grown 10% since 1920 when defined using rainfall, found one study.[447] And in the US, the climate boundary between drier western plains and wetter eastern farmland has shifted eastward by 140 miles due to climate disruption, according to a rainfall and temperature study. The researchers said that the shift could mean that large expanses of croplands could fail, having to be converted to grazing lands.[448]

The next decades will see droughts worldwide, with aridity increasing in "most of Africa, southern Europe and the Middle East, most of the Americas, Australia, and Southeast Asia," concluded atmospheric scientist Aiguo Dai, in reviewing climate data and models. The severe droughts will arise from lower rainfalls and/or increased evaporation, he wrote.[449] [450] Already, one-quarter of the world's population faces "extremely high water stress," due to drought and overuse, according to the World Resources Institute.[451]

Even absent outright drought, a 2°C warming will cause more than a quarter of global lands to become significantly drier, predicted another modeling study. Such "aridification" will have broad impacts on agriculture, water use, and ecosystems.[452]

"Roughly half of the world's population currently experience severe water scarcity for at least some part of the year due to climatic and non-climatic drivers," concluded the landmark 2022 IPCC report on climate disruption's impacts.[453]

Currently, about 3.6 billion people live in areas that suffer water shortages at least one month a year, found another UN report. In the future, climate disruption will cause wet regions to become wetter and dry regions drier, increasing the water-scarce population from 4.8 billion to 5.7 billion by 2050, said the report.[454]

No time for ecosystem recovery

The time between future severe droughts will likely shorten, giving ecosystems less time to recover, found an analysis by climate modelers, "leading to permanently damaged ecosystems and widespread degradation of the land carbon sink."[455] Megadroughts will also exacerbate depletion of groundwater because of higher temperatures and excessive pumping for irrigation.

Many droughts will become tipping points, creating new deserts. Under a 2°C warming, large areas of southern Europe and northern Africa could become deserts, found an analysis by ecologists. They found that in about a century, climate disruption "will likely alter ecosystems in the Mediterranean in a way that is without precedent during the past 10 millennia."[456]

Even when drought-plagued regions avoid desertification, the decreasing soil moisture will produce a temperature roller-coaster, in which swings between higher and lower temperatures become greater. In modeling studies, climate scientists found that poorer areas, including the Amazon, India, the Sahel in Africa, and Southeast Asia, will be particularly hard hit.[457]

Such ecosystem devastation will increase atmospheric CO_2 levels. For example, Amazonian drought reduces tree growth, which slows carbon absorption, found an international research team. In fact, the Amazon is among those forests whose destruction will significantly increase greenhouse gas emissions (see Ghost Forests).[458] [459]

And as detailed later, megadroughts will also play a key role in future large-scale famines (see Epidemic of Hunger).

Global Wildfire Crisis

The thunderous roar of the Boeing 747 supertanker passing alarmingly low overhead brought dramatic proof of the peril from the nearby uncontrolled wildfire. It flew so slowly it seemed in danger of plummeting from the sky. The tanker disappeared over the ridge above our house to drop nearly 20,000 gallons of water on the spreading flames.

We had been in our house in the rural area north of San Diego only a year before experiencing this first wildfire season. We quickly loaded bare necessities into the car and evacuated amid the dry, gusty Santa Ana winds, as the 2017 Lilac Fire consumed more than 4,000 acres, destroying more than a hundred structures.

Since then, wildfire seasons have inflicted palls of smoke, desiccating 100-degree Fahrenheit temperatures, and howling, bone-dry Santa Anas. We have escaped danger so far. But others have not been so fortunate, as the climate-driven western US wildfires have taken many lives and destroyed massive amounts of property and forest.

US wildfires like the ones that threaten my neighborhood have tripled in frequency in the 2000s, compared to the previous two decades, found an analysis of wildfire data. The researchers called their evidence "compelling" that average fires have increased up to four times the size and are more widespread.[460]

More broadly, there is a "global wildfire crisis," concluded a report led by the UN Environment Programme. The report projected up to a 30% increase in wildfires by 2050 and a 50% increase by 2100.[461] Said the report:

> Wildfires are burning longer and hotter in places they have always occurred, and are flaring up in unexpected places too, in drying peatlands and on thawing permafrost.... The heating of the planet is turning landscapes into tinderboxes, while more extreme weather means stronger, hotter, drier winds to fan the flames.

To this infernal mix add that fires now have more fuel because of policies of suppressing fires and extinguishing them as quickly as possible. Plus, more people are intruding into wildlands and forests, and since the vast majority of wildfires are human-caused, the result will be more fires.[462]

Globally, wildfires consume about 865 million acres a year. The report *Flammable Planet* estimated that the damage from climate-disruption-induced wildfires—over and above those naturally caused—will be $50 billion to $300 billion a year by 2050. These costs include the loss of ecosystem services due to fires.[463] [464]

Wildfires trigger a climate disruption feedback, in which fires intensified by global heating in turn exacerbate it. The burning vegetation releases CO_2, which warms the planet, and the dark soot from wildfires deposits on snow and ice, speeding melting. This melting, in turn, accelerates heat absorption because bare land and open water are less reflective. One study of the atmosphere over the Arctic, for example, found that so-called "brown carbon" from wildfires produces up to 30% the warming effects of black carbon soot from burning fossil fuels.[465]

This century, wildfires are devastating forests in Australia, the western US, the northern boreal forests, and the Amazon rainforest.

Australian catastrophe

The cataclysmic Australian wildfires of 2019–2020 exemplify the causes and impacts of such wildfires. The record heat and drought, as well as dense brush, sparked fires that consumed millions of acres. Dozens of people were killed, hundreds of homes destroyed, billions of animals killed or displaced, and hundreds of millions of metric tons of CO_2 released into the atmosphere. Hazardous air quality blanketed the country and sent smoke drifting all the way to South America.[466] "Attribution" analysis of the wildfires confirmed that climate disruption did have an effect—making high-risk wildfire conditions at least 30% more likely.[467]

Western US fires increasing

The cataclysmic western US wildfires of recent years exemplify the future of the region. In 2020, records were set in at least four states. And climate disruption has clearly been implicated as a cause. Climate disruption has nearly doubled the fire area over the decades 1984 to 2015, according to calculations by climatologists John Abatzoglou and Park Williams. About 16,200 more square miles (4,200 square kilometers) of forest burned during that period because of human-caused climate disruption, they calculated.[468]

"As it gets warmer, the area burned increases exponentially as a function of temperature," said Williams. "Based on what we've seen in the last thirty years, we will see increased wildfire activity as long as fuels are available. . . . But at some point, forests will become so fragmented because of wildfires, that we will no longer see increases in the size of wildfires," he said.[469]

There has also been a substantial increase in wildfire intensity, frequency, and duration in the western US since the mid-1980s, found another study.[470] [471] And researchers have established that hotter, drier weather from global heating has been a major force driving the severity increase.[472] [473] Most notable was the devastating 2020 August Complex fire—as of this writing the largest wildfire in recorded California history—which consumed over 1 million acres.[474]

Analyzing wildfire occurrence even further back in time, researchers found that fires in the Rocky Mountains are more prevalent than any time in the last 2,000 years.[475]

The future will see at least a doubling of area burned throughout the US by mid-century, forecast a 2012 US Department of Agriculture report.[476]

Boreal forests burning

Wildfires are also consuming large swaths of the boreal forests in the northern latitudes in Canada, Alaska, Russia, and Scandinavia. Their 6 million square miles, which comprise nearly a third of Earth's forest area, hold vast amounts of carbon.[477]

Boreal wildfires can be immense. Siberian wildfires in 2021 burned more than 150,000 square kilometers (58,000 square miles) of forest and tundra, an area larger than the Netherlands, Belgium, and Denmark combined.[478]

Biologists led by Ryan Kelly found that, compared to the past 10,000 years, recent wildfire activity in the boreal forests has caused massive carbon losses to the atmosphere.[479] [480] They analyzed ancient charcoal deposits in Alaska to obtain their data because such deposits constitute the remains of past wildfires.

The researchers implicated a warmer climate's affect on tree species in the increase. Past wildfire increases have tended to be temporary because flammable coniferous forests gave way to more fire-resistant deciduous trees. However, global heating may mean "we may be out of the realm of what has happened in the past," Kelly told *Live Science.*[481]

By the end of the century, climate disruption will greatly increase the size and frequency of fires in these regions, concluded another paper by wildfire researchers. They warned that the firefighting ability may be overwhelmed, increasing the area burned "much greater than the corresponding increase in fire weather severity."[482]

Amazon aflame

In the Amazon, in 2019 and 2020 satellite sensors detected more than a million hotspots each year, marking fires both natural and human-set. The region saw a 23% increase in deforestation fires just in those two years.[483]

The Amazon is vulnerable to large-scale wildfires because of climate disruption and weather patterns such as El Niño, which diverts moisture from the region. The danger is that such fires could constitute a tipping point, creating a drier Amazon that will absorb less carbon, increasing atmospheric concentrations (see Ghost Forests).

"At risk is maintenance of the hydrological cycle and the Amazon as a system," ecologist Thomas Lovejoy told *The Washington Post.* "When the drought is combined with more people using fire . . . the opportunity for things to get out of control gets considerably larger."[484]

Lack of resilience

Forests worldwide are becoming less resilient because of climate disruption, studies have found. In one study of five Rocky Mountain states, researchers studying the aftermath of 52 wildfires found clear evidence for the decline of forest resilience.[485] To gauge resilience, they measured the viability of more than 63,000 seedlings in the aftermath of fires over the last three decades.

"In many places, forests are not coming back after fires. . . . What we've found is dramatic, even in the relatively short 23-year study period," said lead author Camille Stevens-Rumann.[486]

And in another study of conifers in western US forests, researchers found that a "critical climate threshold for tree regeneration" has already been crossed.[487] After wildfires, drier soils and higher temperatures no long favor growth of seedlings, whose shallow roots can't withstand desiccation.

So for most forests, wildfires, drought, and disease will leave a bleak, dry landscape of scrub brush and grasses. Such drastic ecological change means the extinction of forest species and the loss of ecosystem services—yet another component of the peril to human survival.

Ghost Forests

Years ago, I stood on a high mountain ridge in the Canadian Rockies, looking out over a vast, green forest expanse covered with pines and spruce under a blue sky. Beyond this forest rose jagged peaks, with a dusting of snow at their summits.

But this view was not exhilarating. It was profoundly disturbing because I saw that I stood at an ecological crossroads where two killers were causing a forest's slow death.

In the valley between two distant peaks, I could see the telltale signs of one killer—the rust color of trees infested by bark beetles invading through that gap. Nearby I could see the handiwork of the other killer: the gray skeletons of pines killed by drought. They were particularly vulnerable because they grew in gravelly soil that needed constant watering from rains, our guide told us.

Both killers were spawned by climate disruption. The bark beetles are expanding their range northward because of warmer temperatures from global heating. And the drought arose from changing weather patterns due to climate disruption. As the two killers join forces, this verdant forest will die, as will millions of acres of forests worldwide.

As is the case with forests destroyed by fire, the new landscape will be mostly scrub brush.

"Forest drought-stress by the 2050s will exceed that of the most severe droughts in the past 1,000 years," concluded bioclimatologists led by Park Williams. In their study of the effects of rising temperature on tree growth, reflecting stress, they measured tree rings laid down between 1000 A.D. and 2007. What's more, their climate models projected an increase in tree stress as temperatures rise (see Megadrought Era).[488]

Warmer temperatures also reduce forest viability, found a study of the effects of temperature increases and drought on Ponderosa pine and pinyon forests in the US West. The team reported that their results hold for many other types of forests as well.[489]

"We're saying that if the climate warms a little more, things don't get a little different, they get very different," lead author Henry Adams told *The New York Times*. "You get an acceleration in the rate of mortality. . . . Long droughts are what it takes to kill trees. As you crank up the heat though, the time it takes to kill trees is less and less."[490]

As pointed out earlier, the wildfires that burn these desiccated forests will continue until only fragments of isolated forest remain—not enough to sustain the fires (see "Global Wildfire Crisis"). These remnants may also not be enough to sustain the forests. In analyzing tree growth in isolated New England forest plots, forest ecologists have found that the edges of the plots showed reduced growth with heat stress.[491] So, the remaining trees will not only store less carbon as temperatures rise, but will decline.

Northern exposure

The northern boreal forests of Canada, Alaska, Scandinavia, and Russia are in large-scale decline. They will experience temperature increases substantially above the global average. And the climate zones are moving northward faster than many species of trees' ability to migrate. Drought, wildfires, insect pests, and thawing permafrost all threaten the ecosystem, as well as potentially emitting huge amounts of CO_2.[492]

"Boreal forests have the potential to hit a tipping point this century," said Anatoly Shvidenko, co-author of a review of boreal forest health and climate disruption.[493][494] The result may be that vast ranges of boreal forest will be transformed into shrub land.

Deforestation in the Amazon and the western US could also affect boreal forests far away, according to computer modeling that simulated the effects of a "teleconnection" among the forests.[495] The scientists found that the impact of deforestation on global circulation patterns meant that loss of Amazon or western US forests had impacts on temperature and rainfall thousands of miles distant.

"When trees die in one place, it can be good or bad for plants elsewhere because it causes changes in one place that can ricochet to shift climate in another place," said Elizabeth Garcia, lead author of the study. "The atmosphere provides the connection."[496]

Tropical forest decline and collapse

In the Amazon, drought from climate disruption kills trees and slows growth, decreasing the rainforest's ability to absorb carbon. Such drought effects were identified by an international research team that studied the effects of 2005 and 2010 droughts. They sampled trees and analyzed growth at almost a hundred sites throughout the Amazon Basin.[497]

Over previous years, the Amazon had been taking up "hundreds of millions more tonnes of carbon every year in tree growth than it loses through tree death," said co-author Oliver Phillips. "But both the 2005 and 2010 droughts eliminated those net gains."[498]

In Australian rainforests, trees are now dying from climate-related drought at twice the rate as they were over the last 35 years, found one study.[499] In the Amazon, death and decline of trees have meant that the rainforest is soaking up significantly less carbon than it did in the early 1990s, found another major study involving more than 90 scientists. In gathering their data, the researchers took samples from trees at 321 sites in eight countries over three decades.[500]

Deforestation in the Brazilian Amazon continues to increase at a high rate, amounting to more than 3.4 million acres in 2019 alone. Globally, mature rainforest loss that year was 9.4 million acres, an area nearly as large as Switzerland, according to Global Forest Watch.[501]

Major Amazon deforestation will almost certainly continue. The Brazilian government has scaled back enforcement of laws against illegal activity and opened millions of acres of rainforest to commercial exploitation.[502] [503] [504]

The Amazonian forest is now on the verge of a tipping point, in which over mere decades a lengthening dry season and drought could trigger it to transform into grassland, researchers have calculated. The result would be release of vast amounts of carbon and increased global heating.[505] [506]

This tipping point is driven by a vicious feedback cycle: The loss of Amazonian forest intensifies regional drought, leading to more tree death, according to climatologists. The feedback arises because healthy tropical forests release vast amounts of moisture into the atmosphere, which rains back onto them. Fewer trees mean less rain, which leads to fewer trees.[507]

More broadly, some 16% of humid forest has been lost just from 2002 to 2020, found the Global Forest Watch.[508] And rainforest destruction increased 12% from 2019 to 2020, found the World Resources Institute.[509]

Global forests emitting carbon

Tropical forests worldwide have become a significant atmospheric carbon source, not a sink, found researchers analyzing remote sensing data. They calculated that carbon losses from degradation or disturbance amount to 425 million metric tons of carbon each year—more than the emissions from all US cars and trucks.[510] This carbon loss has doubled during the years 2015–2019 compared to 2001–2005, found another satellite study.[511]

The Amazon in particular has become a carbon source rather than a sink, found researchers who used planes to measure emissions over large swaths of forest. Their surveys found that parts of the rainforest have been transformed by human-set fires along with hotter temperatures and droughts.[512] Another independent study using satellite data to map the forest also found that overall, the Amazon has become a net carbon emitter.[513]

Such analyses do not even take into account emissions other than CO_2, for example methane (CH_4) and nitrous oxide (N_2O). Analyzing all Amazonian greenhouse gas emissions, researchers concluded that "current warming from non-CO_2 agents . . . in the Amazon Basin largely offsets—and most likely exceeds—the climate service provided by atmospheric CO_2 uptake."[514]

While 133 countries signed a pledge to end global deforestation by 2030 at the 2021 UN Climate Change Conference, COP26, as with other such pledges it is nonbinding and contains no enforcement mechanism.[515]

"The financial announcements we've heard in Glasgow are welcome but remain small compared to the enormous private and public flows—often in the sense of subsidies—that drive deforestation," Frances Seymour of the World Resources Institute told *The New York Times*.[516]

Planting trees a phantom solution

Simply planting trees might seem a logical answer to restoring denuded forests; and numerous projects aim to plant many billions of trees worldwide. But the effects are far more complex and often very negative.[517]

Massive reforestation projects could wreck natural ecosystems, take over farmland, force people from their land, and even increase global heating. This last effect could arise because grassland and deserts are more heat-reflective than forests.

Reforestation could even dry out landscapes, because trees take up water, reducing groundwater supplies and lowering stream levels. One modeling study concluded that planting the millions of square miles of land available for reforesting could cause water loss hotspots, including some regions already facing water scarcity. Effects could be far-reaching, found the researchers, with tree-cover change in the Amazon affecting precipitation in far distant Canada, Northern Europe, and even Eastern Asia.[518]

So ghost forests—by emitting masses of CO_2 and impacting distant weather—will haunt the world.

Superstormy Weather

To grasp how global heating intensifies storms, it only takes understanding boiling water: Turn up the heat on water simmering on a stove, and it will boil more vigorously. Just like the hot stove, global heating adds energy to the atmosphere and oceans, pumping more water vapor into the air, feeding heavier rainfalls and snowfalls.

In fact, just over the last 35 years, the atmosphere has become a more efficient "heat engine," calculated a team of physicists. As the atmosphere warmed, an inordinately larger amount of heat was pumped into the air to power more-destructive storms.[519]

Scientists are certain that global heating intensifies hurricanes and typhoons (the name for Pacific hurricanes). The rainfall intensity from Hurricane Harvey (2017), for example, was linked directly to the warming of upper ocean waters from global heating.[520] Analyzing temperature profiles from a network of ocean buoys, the scientists detected the telltale signature of Harvey evaporating more water from a warmed ocean as it moved across the Gulf of Mexico, "supercharging" the storm.

For Hurricane Florence (2018), climate modelers explicitly forecast how climate disruption increased the storm's rainfall, intensity, and size. They calculated that rainfall would be increased by 50% due to climate disruption because of warmer sea-surface temperatures and greater atmospheric moisture.[521] Florence brought unprecedented, catastrophic flooding to North and South Carolina.[522]

And Hurricane Ida (2021)—besides producing catastrophic wind damage on landfall in Louisiana—caused widespread, often unprecedented, flooding along its entire track all the way to Atlantic Canada.[523] Particularly dramatic was the historic flooding in the US Northeast.[524]

Pegging the *occurrence* of a particular storm to climate disruption is "subject to substantial uncertainty, with greater levels of uncertainty for events that are not directly temperature related," according to a US National Academies of Sciences report on climate attribution.[525] So, any claim that a particular rainstorm or hurricane was *caused* by climate disruption, requires taking with a large chunk of salt.

The statistics, however, clearly show an upward trend in precipitation. According to the *Climate Science Special Report*, the US has seen an increase in extreme rainfall since 1901.[526] As cited earlier, a computer modeling study by Erich Fischer and Reto Knutti found that 18% of days with heavy rainfall can be accounted for by today's global heating (see Hellscape Earth).[527]

Climate-caused cloudbursts

Global heating is a key cause of more heavy cloudbursts, versus steady rain, across Europe and Asia. Such "convective precipitation" is defined as being "localized, short-lived, intense, and sometimes violent," found one study.[528] The study showed that increased rainfall and daily extremes "appear to be directly linearly associated with higher atmospheric water vapor accompanying a warming climate over northern Eurasia."

For the US, a modeling study by researchers led by Andreas Prein predicted that a 5°C global temperature increase would increase extreme downpours by 400% by the end of the century in almost all North American regions.[529]

"These are huge increases," said Prein. "Imagine the most intense thunderstorm you typically experience in a single season. Our study finds that, in the future, parts of the US could expect to experience five of those storms in a season, each with an intensity as strong, or stronger, than current storms."[530]

In another study, the researchers forecast that such storms' higher intensity and greater extent could cause up to an 80% increase in precipitation volume, with the continued rate of global heating.[531]

Tornado-generating thunderstorms will also increase by the end of the century. Using computer models to probe how severe eastern US thunderstorms would respond to global heating, researchers found a "robust" 40% increase in the number of days with conditions that could spawn such storms.[532]

Rivers in the sky

Global heating will also drive more "atmospheric rivers," intense, narrow flows of moisture that aim like a fire hose at regions such as the US West Coast and Western Europe. While atmospheric rivers broke the back of California's 2016–2017 drought, they also increase flooding; past such storms caused a billion dollars a year in damage.[533]

Atmospheric rivers' capacity is prodigious—able to carry as much water as the average flow of the Mississippi River at its mouth.[534] Researchers have found that atmospheric rivers are associated with up to 75% of the most extreme rain and windstorms over the world's coastlines.[535]

North Atlantic atmospheric river frequency will approximately double by the end of the century under the current rate of global heating, found studies by meteorologists.[536] [537] Globally, atmospheric river frequency will increase by about 50% by the end of the century, found one modeling study. And intensity will increase by about 25%.[538]

In California, this increase will mean a far greater risk of a megaflood-producing atmospheric river, found one analysis. It would turn lowland areas into temporary inland seas, trigger massive landslides, and erode vast sections of coastline. Overall property damage and economic costs could total nearly a $1 trillion—three times the cost of a cataclysmic southern California earthquake.[539] [540]

Flooding from such storms will become even more severe under future global heating. For example, analyzing rain and temperature records across Australia, engineers Conrad Wasko and Ashish Sharma found that with rising temperatures, storms became more concentrated in area, with more intense rainfall and flooding.[541] However, the researchers assumed that the volume of water coming down wasn't changing, which is a "very conservative" assumption, said Sharma, "because you would expect the air to hold more moisture." Factoring that in would mean even more rainfall and floods.[542]

Hurricanes more violent

The ferocity of hurricanes and typhoons, the monsters of meteorology, will increase with global heating—as exemplified by the catastrophic impacts of Hurricanes Irma in 2017 and Ian in 2022.[543] [544]

Atlantic hurricanes are fueled by higher-than-average ocean warming and a slowdown in a massive ocean circulation called the Atlantic Meridional Overturning Circulation (AMOC). It is a three-dimensional conveyor belt of ocean water that moves warm water north and cool water south (see Ruining AMOC).[545] [546]

Indeed, "it is likely that greenhouse warming will cause hurricanes in the coming century to be more intense globally and have higher rainfall rates than present-day hurricanes," concluded a research review by NOAA scientists.[547]

Statistics indicate that increased hurricane intensity is already happening and that global heating plays a role. In one study, atmospheric researchers concluded that "since 1975 there has been a substantial and observable regional and global increase in the proportion of Cat 4–5 hurricanes." The researchers correlated hurricane data with global heating over the past four decades, concluding that the intensity increase was 25–35% per degree Celsius of warming.[548] [549]

Hurricanes more devastating

The US will be struck with an even greater number of economically devastating hurricanes as global heating continues. Hurricane losses in the US will triple by the end of the century, projected researchers who specialize in economic analysis of weather events. They took into account the meteorological characteristics of the hurricanes, the increasing exposure of rising populations, and the per capita Gross Domestic Product. The finding is particularly significant because US hurricane damage accounts for more than half of all weather-related economic loss.[550] Co-author Anders Leverman said that:

> Some people hope that . . . we can outgrow climate change economically instead of mitigating it. But what if damages grow faster than our economy, what if climate impacts hit faster than we are able to adapt? . . . . We find that this is the case with hurricane damages in the United States, the hope in economic growth as an answer to climate change is ill-founded.[551]

Hurricanes and devastating winter superstorms might begin increasing within decades, asserted a far-ranging study led by climatologist James Hansen. For the study, they used data on ancient and modern ice melting, as well as computer models. "There is a possibility, a real danger, that we will hand young people and future generations a climate system that is practically out of their control," they wrote.[552]

Sea Change

We may perceive as distant and abstract climate disruption's impact on the oceans, given that we are land creatures. And the oceans' immensity—covering 140 million square miles and holding 321 million cubic miles of seawater—makes it nearly inconceivable to us that any human activity could have an impact.

However, personal experience can so very profoundly alter that perception. For me, that experience was petting the smooth skin of a baby gray whale, as I crouched in a small skiff bobbing in the waters of San Ignacio Lagoon on the Baja California coast. The gray whales migrate to the lagoon's sheltered waters each winter from Alaska—one of the longest migrations of any mammal—to mate and give birth. The friendly whale I encountered had been named Ciegito, or "Little Blind One," by the local guides because one of her eyes was malformed. She was "only" 15 feet long, weighing about a ton. Her far more gargantuan mother had brought her to our boat to allow her baby to enjoy the odd and interesting object they might have considered a diverting toy.

Ciegito would normally have a life expectancy of some 50 years. She would make the migration many times and give birth to her own offspring. But climate disruption was imperiling that life. Researchers had documented population declines and evidence of malnourishment among whales, with sunken blowholes and protruding vertebrae. And great numbers of whales were washing up dead on beaches along migration routes. The major culprit is almost certainly warming Arctic Ocean waters, which reduced the population of the shrimp-like amphipods that are their principal food source.[553]

The lagoon itself was also showing the effects of global heating. During the 2019 season when we visited, vast numbers of sardines had washed ashore, suffocated by the low oxygen content of the warming waters, our naturalist guide told us.

Such impacts arise because the world's oceans have absorbed more than 90% of the excess heat from global heating and up to 30% of human-produced CO_2 emissions. As a result, sea levels have risen, and the oceans have become warmer, more acidic, and more anoxic. Concluded a 2021 report by the UN Intergovernmental Panel on Climate Change (IPCC):

> Global mean sea level has risen faster since 1900 than over any preceding century in at least the last 3000 years. The global ocean has warmed faster over the past century than . . . around 11,000 years ago . . . and surface open ocean pH as low as recent decades is unusual in the last 2 million years.[554]

Of the environmental impacts of these ocean changes, a landmark 2022 IPCC report concluded that climate disruption:

> . . . has caused substantial damages, and increasingly irreversible losses, in terrestrial, freshwater and coastal and open ocean marine ecosystems. The extent and magnitude of climate change impacts are *larger than estimated in previous assessments* [emphasis added].[555]

The triple threats of ocean warming, acidification, and deoxygenation will "affect the ocean's biogeochemical cycles and ecosystems in ways that we are only beginning to fathom," warned environmental physicist Nicholas Gruber.[556]

Oceans under stress

Half the world's oceans will be under climate stress by 2030 if the current business-as-usual emission trajectory continues, according to an analysis by oceanographers.[557] Their modeling study predicted that by 2050, 85% of the oceans would suffer stressors: higher acidity and temperature, lower oxygen concentration, and reduced food availability for marine organisms.

This stress could have profound human impacts because the oceans are a primary protein source for one in seven of the world's population, the researchers pointed out. They warned that "climate change is essentially a one-way street, so that associated changes in the marine environment are unlikely to be reversed."

What's more, they pointed out, the environmental changes could act synergistically to increase the impact of stressors. For example, as discussed later, combined higher acidity and temperature could reduce ocean algae that provide food for other animals and oxygen to the atmosphere (see Acidified Waters).

The ocean impacts of climate disruption will be major even if countries manage to achieve a practically impossible low-emissions scenario, noted a study by ocean scientists.[558] The low-emissions scenario assumes not only that CO_2 emissions plummet to zero by 2070, but actually turn negative. That is, the world magically develops and installs machinery to extract massive amounts of CO_2 from the air (see Carbon Capture Snake Oil).

In the past, major ocean habitat destruction took many centuries to heal, as revealed by an analysis of ancient seafloor sediments by ocean ecologists. They took a 30-foot core of the seafloor sediments off the Santa Barbara coast, which represented the area's history from 3,400 to 16,000 years ago. That period was similar to today, when the climate heated abruptly after the last glacial period and the ocean became anoxic. Analyzing the fossils of organisms, including sea urchins, clams, shrimp, and marine worms, the team could trace the recovery from that heating.

"This archive reveals that global climate change disturbs seafloor ecosystems on continental margins and commits them to millennia of ecological recovery," they concluded.[559]

Said lead author Sarah Moffit, "These past events show us how sensitive ecosystems are to changes in Earth's climate—it commits us to thousands of years of recovery. It's a gritty reality we need to face as scientists and people who care about the natural world and who make decisions about the natural world."[560]

Of course, climate disruption is only one of the insults being visited upon the world's oceans. As a report from the Global Ocean Commission concluded:

> It is no exaggeration that all life on Earth, including our own survival, depends on a healthy, vibrant ocean. Containing an almost unfathomable diversity of life, billions of us rely on it for food, clean air, a stable climate, rain and fresh water, transport and energy, recreation and livelihoods. Our ocean is in decline. Habitat destruction, biodiversity loss, overfishing, pollution, climate change and ocean acidification are pushing the ocean system to the point of collapse.[561]

The report called the ocean's absorption of heat from climate disruption "perhaps the largest unseen environmental disaster of our time. . . . We can continue to lay cables and ship containers across a dead ocean, but without paying attention to sustaining the life within it, we put our own lives and those of every living thing in peril."

Heating Soup

The evidence that oceans are warming is unequivocal, according to the Environmental Protection Agency (EPA). Its report concluded that ". . . sea surface temperatures have been consistently higher during the past three decades than at any other time since reliable observations began in the late 1800s."[562]

Ocean temperature increases have set record after record, according to the American Meteorological Society (AME).[563] Researchers documented that relentless warming by analyzing data from ships, satellites, and instrument-carrying floats and ocean probes.[564][565]

"Ocean warming is the key metric and 2020 continued a long series of record-breaking years, showing the unabated continuation of global warming," co-author John Abraham told *The Guardian*. "Warmer oceans supercharge the weather, impacting the biological systems of the planet as well as human society. Climate change is literally killing people and we are not doing enough to stop it."[566]

Warming ocean waters are already reducing species richness in equatorial waters, found an analysis of the distribution of nearly 50,000 species. Many species are shifting north to cooler waters.[567] The study "found the ocean around the equator has already become too hot for many species to survive, and that global warming is responsible," wrote the authors. "When the same thing happened 252 million years ago, 90% of all marine species died," they wrote. They warned that the result could be "ecosystem collapse."[568]

What's more, like the land, the ocean also suffers regional heat waves, which can destroy organisms from coral to seagrass, found another study. The researchers predicted that the heat waves will probably intensify with continued climate disruption and are becoming "forceful agents of disturbance with the capacity to restructure entire ecosystems. . ."[569]

Major heating consequences

With the current global heating trajectory, the thermal expansion of warmer waters would add 30 centimeters of sea-level rise, in addition to that expected from ice melt, predicted another analysis.[570]

A report by the International Union for Conservation of Nature concluded that, besides rising sea levels, other heating consequences will be:

- More extreme El Niño events intensifying storms and causing fishery collapse
- Warming of land masses, including permafrost and melting glaciers, causing increased forest fires
- Melting sea ice
- Faster melting of ocean-floor methane hydrate
- Increased moisture evaporation feeding rains and floods
- Reduced CO_2 uptake because of warmer water

- Depleted oxygenation due to warmer water
- Profound changes in sea life, from microbes to whales, including reduced biological productivity of ocean life, and increased blooms of toxic algae and disease-causing bacteria such as Vibrio. [571]

The group—comprising 1,400 governmental and non-governmental organizations, with more than 17,000 experts in environmental and related fields—declared that:

> The scale of ocean warming is truly staggering with the numbers so large that it is difficult for most people to comprehend. . . . Up to now, the ocean has shielded us from the worst impacts of climate change. The costs [sic] is that its chemistry has been altered as it absorbed significant amounts of the extra CO_2 we put into the atmosphere, but it has also warmed at an alarming rate in recent decades. . . . The value of our relationship with the ocean sometimes seems difficult to cost, but is the ultimate relationship that enables life to exist on Earth.

If the atmosphere had absorbed the same heat absorbed by the top layer in the ocean between 1955 and 2010, the Earth would have been warmer by 36°C (100°F), said the report. We would be living—or rather dying—in a literal hell on Earth.

Warming oceans, besides depleting oxygen directly, could also drastically reduce phytoplankton that produce oxygen by photosynthesis, according to a model created by mathematicians who model natural systems. [572] As they float in the ocean's upper layers and absorb sunlight, such phytoplankton produce about 70% of atmospheric oxygen.

The mathematicians' model planktons' reaction to water temperature suggested that the organisms could stop oxygen production suddenly if oceans warm by 6°C. At current rates of temperature rise, such a temperature could be reached by 2100.

"Our results indicate that the depletion of atmospheric oxygen on global scale (which, if happens, obviously can kill most of life on Earth) is . . . a global ecological disaster that has been overlooked," they wrote. While the hazards of sea-level rise are well publicized, "we have shown that the danger to be stifled is probably more real than to be drowned."[573] That said, however, the mathematicians cautioned that their model has yet to be verified by field or experimental studies.[574]

Oxygen-Starved Waters

Warming oceans have caused oxygen levels to fall by more than 2% over the last half century, concluded oceanographers who compared today's global ocean oxygen concentration with historic measures. Their models predict up to a 25% reduction by 2100, due to reduced circulation and the lower ability of warmer waters to absorb oxygen. The deep ocean will experience worse anoxia because warmer ocean waters tend to layer on top, they wrote.[575]

Such stratification—which researchers have found has increased greatly over the last decades—arises from higher atmospheric temperatures and the influx of fresh water from polar melting. Besides lowering oxygenation, the increased stratification also reduces the oceans' ability to absorb heat and CO_2.[576] [577]

Even mild deoxygenation can critically affect the oceanic food chain. Oxygen-starvation drives many zooplankton at the base of the food chain to seek deeper, cooler waters with higher oxygen levels, found researchers.[578] However, the lower light in those deeper waters will not support sunlight-dependent phytoplankton, the food for zooplankton. Thus, zooplankton would have less access to sufficient food, and their attrition will reverberate up the food chain. In addition, "since large fishes in particular avoid or do not survive in areas with low oxygen content, these changes can have far-reaching biological consequences," said oceanographer Sunke Schmidtko.[579]

The volume of totally deoxygenated open ocean has risen fourfold in the last half century, found a review of ocean oxygen studies. Also, the number of anoxic sites of coastal waters and estuaries—critical nurseries for marine life—has increased by more than ten times since 1950, found the review. This anoxia is due both to global heating and to the influx of oxygen-robbing agricultural and sewage runoff.[580]

"Loss of oxygen in many ways is the destruction of an ecosystem," lead author marine biologist Denise Breitburg told *National Geographic*. "If we were creating vast areas on land that were uninhabitable by most animals, we'd notice. But we don't always see things like this when they are happening in the water."[581]

Such anoxia may increase due to feedbacks, since low oxygen tends to release oxygen-robbing phosphorus from ocean sediments, increasing anoxia.

"Models suggest that once anoxia begins to spread over continental shelves and slopes, this positive feedback may drive the ocean into prolonged deoxygenation that lasts hundreds of thousands of years," wrote ocean scientist Andrew Watson. Sewage inflow and runoff from farms since the Industrial Revolution have created anoxic coastal dead zones due to a more than doubling of phosphorus entering the oceans, he pointed out. However, he noted, even this influx is not enough to affect the entire ocean.

"Whole-ocean anoxia is thus not an immediate global concern. If sustained for long enough, the deoxygenation occurring today could nevertheless have lasting negative consequences for the global environment," Watson wrote.[582]

Acidified Waters

All the ocean's organisms—from microscopic plankton to the 20-ton whale sharks that feed on them—evolved in waters with an exquisitely delicate balance of acidity and alkalinity. That balance has been disrupted, as increasing CO_2 absorbed in ocean waters becomes carbonic acid.

The pH in the ocean has significantly decreased—meaning that the ocean has become more acidic—since the Industrial Revolution, according to the National Oceanic and Atmospheric Administration (NOAA). The decrease seems numerically trivial, in that the pH has gone down by 0.1 pH units. But the pH scale is logarithmic, so the pH decrease represents about a 30% acidity increase.[583]

The oceans' pH today averages about 8.1, with 7 being neutral. Higher pH is alkaline, and lower pH is acidic. If the current trajectory of increasing CO_2 continues, the average ocean pH would drop to less than 7.8 by 2100, one study showed. This is a level not seen in about 14 million years—a manyfold increase in acidity over current levels.[584]

Laboratory experiments have indicated that acidification will produce profound effects on all ocean life. One analysis led by marine scientist Stephanie Dutkiewicz found that, like a deoxygenated ocean, an acidified ocean would alter phytoplankton populations at the base of the food chain, causing the balance of species to change, with some dying out and others flourishing.[585]

"I try not to be an alarmist," said Dutkiewicz. "But I was actually quite shocked by the results. The fact that there are so many different possible changes, that different phytoplankton respond differently, means there might be some quite traumatic changes in the communities over the course of the 21st century. A whole rearrangement of the communities means something to both the food web further up, but also for things like cycling of carbon."[586]

Dissolving shells

Acidification's corrosive effect on the shells of marine animals is particularly dramatic. Such animals as crabs and snails need a slightly alkaline environment to absorb dissolved carbonate in water to form their shells. As waters grow more acidic, that absorption is compromised.

Researchers have already detected evidence of acidity-related dissolution in the shells of Dungeness crabs, oysters, and snails along the US West Coast. Coastal waters with the highest acidity showed the greatest damage to larval crabs' shells, found researchers.[587] And a study of oysters in an Oregon hatchery revealed that water acidity increased damage to young oysters and larvae.[588]

A study of tiny snails called sea butterflies from West Coast Pacific Ocean sites revealed that more than half of the snails showed damaged shells, with surfaces resembling cauliflower or sandpaper. Such damage threatens a snail's survival and could reverberate up the food chain because fish such as pink salmon feed on them. The researchers estimated that the incidence of shell dissolution in snails has doubled near shore due to acidification and is "on track to triple by 2050."[589]

"I was surprised by the sheer spatial extent of the dissolution," lead researcher Nina Bednaršek told *Science* magazine. "This is something we have not predicted before—the extent of the population that's already affected."[590]

Damaged shells might seem a trivial effect of acidification, but they could be the equivalent of the miner's canary. They could foreshadow future profound impacts on overall ocean biochemistry because the coastal region that is the crabs' and snails' habitat is more acidic than the broader ocean. Near the shore, there is an upwelling of deep, more acidic waters to the surface, where those waters become even more acidic because of dissolved atmospheric CO_2.

Acidity can also affect shellfish survival by harming their ability to anchor themselves. One study showed that the tough threads that attach mussels to rocks and other surfaces are weakened under an acidic ocean environment. Such attachment is critical for the creatures to survive, keeping them out of the reach of predators. In laboratory experiments, the researchers tested the animals' attachment under different conditions of acidity. When they dropped the seawater pH to that expected in the future, the mussels' attachments were weaker.[591]

Ocean acidification can also affect behavior of marine life. In laboratory experiments, biologists observed how black turban snails under different acidities escaped their predators, sea stars. They found that at pH levels expected by 2100, the snails' escape response was impaired. While such behavioral effects might seem trivial, and the effects subtle, they could portend profound consequences for life in a future acidified ocean.[592]

Acidity + anoxia = death

The combination of acidification and anoxia will profoundly affect ocean life—a phenomenon that paleontologists observed when they studied rock strata from the Triassic era some 200 million years ago. It was a period of one of the Earth's great mass extinctions.

Their analysis found evidence of a "two-pronged kill mechanism" underlying the extinction. During that era, massive volcanism spewed enormous amounts of CO_2 into the atmosphere, warming it and the oceans. Absorbed by the oceans, that CO_2 caused acidification that dissolved animals' shells. Together with the anoxia caused by ocean warming, the result was death for all but the hardiest species.[593]

The two killers may also act synergistically, with their combined effects worse than the sum of individual ones. Such a synergy was revealed in laboratory experiments in which researchers subjected fish to low oxygen alone, or both low oxygen and low pH. Then they recorded their respiration and death rates. Fish exposed to low oxygen alone could cope by beating their gill flaps to take in more oxygen, the researchers observed. But those exposed to a both insults died at oxygen levels that would otherwise be survivable.[594]

Ocean acidification might even indirectly speed global warming, other studies have hinted. Modeling the increased acidity in global ocean waters, researchers found that the acidified waters showed reduced emissions of a sulfur-containing compound that helps form clouds that cool the atmosphere by reflecting sunlight. The researchers concluded that "our results indicate that ocean acidification has the potential to exacerbate [human-caused] warming through a mechanism that is not considered at present in projections of future climate change."[595]

Flood Warning

It was 2013. The terrifying wall of dark water exploded over the hood of our car, as we plunged into the rising waters of a stream that had overflowed its banks, inundating the bridge we were crossing. We were shocked at the deluge because we had seen no rain at all as we drove up the mountain road to our North Carolina cabin. But intense cloudbursts at the peaks had launched a flash flood tearing down the mountain slopes.

Fortunately, we were in a heavy, all-wheel-drive SUV, or my family and I might well have been swept away that night. That same flash flood did uproot trees, carry away cars, and even collapse an entire mountainside, sending a road and tons of rock plummeting into a valley.[596]

To experience such a traumatic event is to understand viscerally the immense power of water and how that power will impact society under future temperature rise. In my years in the mountains, I came to respect water as an insidious, powerful, often irresistible substance. As it flows, its energy increases with the square of its velocity. It penetrates any breach, going wherever gravity takes it.

Global heating is already bringing unprecedented coastal and inland flooding. The US has seen such devastating storms as Hurricane Harvey in 2017, which inundated the Gulf Coast, dropping almost five feet of rain in some areas—an amount likely increased by climate disruption.[597] That year, extreme monsoons flooded regions of India, Bangladesh, and Nepal, killing nearly a thousand people.[598] Those floods also exposed millions of people to waters carrying toxic wastes.[599] In 2018, Hurricane Florence brought catastrophic flooding to North and South Carolina in the US.

The relentless rise in sea level has been clearly revealed by decades of studies using satellites and radar altimeters.

"The rise of sea level caused by human interference with the climate now dwarfs the natural cycles," said Michael Freilich, NASA project scientist for the Sentinel-6 satellite that maps ocean topography. "And it is happening faster and faster every decade," he told the NASA Earth Observatory blog. "What stands out from the satellite altimetry record is that the rise over 30 years is about ten times bigger than the natural exchange of water between ocean and land in a year."[600]

Future hell of high water

Past hurricane deluges and rising sea levels are but harbingers of the fate of coastal regions worldwide. Extreme sea level events—triggered by storm surges, tides, and waves—will increase drastically over the next decades found one study. Analyzing more than 7,000 coastal areas, the researchers concluded that by 2100, even under 1.5°C of heating, about half will experience the current 100-year event at least once a year—"and often well before the end of the century," they wrote.[601]

In fact, actual expected temperature increases by 2100 are much larger (see Six Degrees to Termination).

The flooding that inundates the world's cities will come not only from sudden storms, but also insidiously invading seas. The creeping catastrophe will consist of a steady increase in sunny-day flooding from waves and high tides, punctuated by disastrous inundation from hurricanes and other storms. Coastal cities will fight back with seawalls and other futile mitigation measures, ultimately to their social and economic exhaustion.

Although estimates of future sea-level rise vary, all predict major impacts. Independent analyses have predicted that by 2100 sea levels will have risen from about half a meter to more than two meters.[602] [603] [604] [605] [606] [607] [608] [609]

The cost of sea-level rise will be immense. A nearly one-meter sea-level rise could cost some $14 trillion a year by 2100 in global flood damage, one study found. And an approximate two-meter rise could cost $27 trillion a year by 2100.[610]

The biggest source of uncertainty in sea-level rise is how fast the huge Antarctic ice sheet will melt (see The Inexorable Melt).

"In the beginning people thought, 'let's just assume that those things are stable,'" climatologist Gavin Schmidt told Reuters. "There are very few climate models that have a credible simulation of any kind of dynamic ice sheet behavior at all."[611]

Climatologists have attempted to predict sea-level rise using models of Antarctic ice sheet loss. One study projects a sea-level rise of up to 1.5 meters by 2100 from Antarctic melting under a high-emission future—which doesn't even take into account sea-level rise from other sources. Such a sea-level rise would submerge land currently home to more than 150 million people, the team projected.[612]

Sea-level rise is accelerating, studies have found. From 1880 to 2013, the rate of sea-level rise was 1.5 millimeters (0.06 inches) a year. But since 1993, it doubled to as much as 3.5 millimeters (0.14 inches) a year, noted an Environmental Protection Agency (EPA) report.[613] That rate is continuing to accelerate, found an analysis of satellite data on sea levels, such that 2100 would see a 0.6-meter (2-foot) sea-level rise.[614]

The most extreme predictions have come from data on ancient sea-level rises. During the last interglacial period about 125,000 years ago, sea levels were 6–10 meters higher than today.[615] Global air temperatures were only about 1°c higher than today and average sea-surface temperatures were about the same as now. During that time, Antarctic ice melting caused most sea-level rise, followed by melting in Greenland, according to one study.[616]

"This research shows that Antarctica, long thought to be the 'sleeping giant' of sea-level rise, is actually a key player," the team wrote in *The Conversation*. "Its ice sheets can change quickly, and in ways that could have huge implications for coastal communities and infrastructure in future."[617]

What's more, once sea level rises, it will not come down—and in fact will continue going up. Sea-level rise will persist for centuries to millennia, with one study calculating a rise of about 2.3 meters for every degree Celsius of temperature increase.[618] And when paleoclimatologists compared ancient global heating events to today, they predicted a continual rise over centuries to millennia, reaching at least several meters higher.[619]

Coastal catastrophe

Measuring only sea-level rise does not capture the full impact of future coastal flooding. Adding to the hazard will be sinking landmasses, storm and tidal surges, and the inundating action of ocean currents and waves.

For example, wave-driven flooding exacerbated by sea-level rise will render thousands of low-lying tropical atolls uninhabitable by mid-century. The waves will destroy island infrastructure and render freshwater aquifers undrinkable.[620]

The coastal impacts of sea-level rise will be catastrophic because about two-thirds of the global population lives within about 40 miles of the ocean, and almost half of the cities with populations over one million sit in or near flood-prone estuaries.

One analysis estimates that 190 million people occupy land that will be below high tide lines for 2100—even under a low-emission scenario. The researchers forecast that vast low-lying regions will be inundated, including parts of China, India, Bangladesh, Indonesia, and Thailand.[621]

Sea-level rise will hit some areas harder than others because it will not be uniform. While water in a small body stays the same level throughout, masses of water in oceans can bulge or dip, and gravity can cause uneven distribution. Coastal land can sink from groundwater pumping, worsening sea-level rise.

In fact, sea level already appears to be rising three to four times faster than average in a thousand-kilometer-long hotspot along the US Atlantic Coast north of Cape Hatteras, North Carolina, according to an analysis of data from tide gauges throughout North America.[622]

For a 2°C global heating above preindustrial levels, more than 90% of coastal areas would experience greater-than-average sea-level increases, calculated oceanographers in one study. And the US Atlantic Coast and Norway would experience about double the average.[623]

A 3°C temperature increase would drown such cities as Alexandria in Egypt, Miami, Osaka, and Shanghai, found another study.[624]

A 4°C warming could inundate areas that are home to 470 to 760 million people worldwide, found a study by Climate Central.[625]

An analysis of 136 cities worldwide ranked the most economically vulnerable cities.[626] It took into account the potential cost of damage and level of flood protection. The ten most vulnerable cities, in descending order: Guangzhou, Miami, New York, New Orleans, Mumbai, Nagoya, Tampa, Boston, Shenzhen, and Osaka. Such cities are economic centers, so their inundation would damage their countries' entire economies.

The study calculated that the $6 billion average annual global loss in 2005 from floods will increase to more than $60 billion a year in 2050, even if coastal cities invest in major flood protection. With no adaptation, damage costs could rise to over $1 trillion a year by 2050, found the study.

US flooding now

In the US, unchecked global heating would inundate land that is home to more than 20 million people by 2100, found one study. The researchers used data on topography, population, tide levels, and sea-level rise scenarios to make their calculation.[627]

However, US flooding from sea-level rise is already happening, according to an EPA report.[628] Nearly every site measured had experienced an increase in coastal flooding since the 1950s, found the report, and that the rate is accelerating along the East and Gulf coasts. Already, the Mid-Atlantic region has experienced the largest increases in flooding and now suffers the highest number of coastal flood days in the US.

By 2045, chronic flooding in the US will inundate homes and business valued at about $136 billion, found a report by the Union of Concerned Scientists (UCS).[629] And by 2100, nearly 2.5 million homes and businesses, valued at more than $1 trillion, will be at risk of chronic flooding.

Another UCS study found that—with a moderate or high rate of sea level rise—without major preventative measures:

- By 2035 nearly 170 coastal US communities—roughly twice as many as today—will face chronic inundation
- By 2060, more than 270 coastal US communities will be chronically inundated
- By 2100, nearly 490 communities will be chronically inundated.

The report concluded that by 2100, with a rapider 2-meter rise, more than 50 heavily populated areas, including Oakland, Miami, St. Petersburg, and four of the five New York City boroughs will face chronic inundation.[630]

By 2100, almost 1.9 million US homes would be underwater, concluded a report by the real estate website Zillow. As many as 300 cities would lose at least half their homes, and 36 cities would be completely lost.[631]

Hurricane surges and king tides add to rise

Even the smaller sea-level rises expected over the next decades will be made destructive by storm surges and "king tides"—the highest tides caused by the alignment of the Earth, moon, and sun.

Rising temperatures will bring an estimated doubling of Hurricane Katrina-magnitude hurricane surges in this century, concluded one study by climatologists. They correlated past storm surges with temperature records.[632] Hurricane Katrina devastated the US Gulf Coast with the highest storm surge ever recorded there: 27.8 feet at Pass Christian, Mississippi.

The researchers warned that "we have probably crossed the threshold where Katrina-magnitude hurricane surges are more likely caused by global warming than not." By comparison, Hurricane Harvey's still-devastating highest storm surge was 8.4 feet.[633]

King tides are more common than hurricanes, but also damaging. When they strike low-lying areas like Florida, they flood streets, kill forests and farmland, and foul wells with salt water.

Such non-storm-related tidal flooding inundates streets and bubbles up from storm drains. It has doubled since 2000, according to the National Oceanic and Atmospheric Administration (NOAA).[634]

Such "nuisance" flooding will soon reach a tipping point on US coasts, calculated William Sweet and Joseph Park.[635] Relatively rare flooding events will abruptly become the norm, with flooding more than 30 days a year. Analyzing sea-level rise using tidal records, they found that by 2030 some US cities—such as Boston, New York City, St. Petersburg, Galveston, and Seattle—will have more than 30 days of nuisance flooding. By 2050 most locations studied will surpass 30 days a year of tidal flooding.

By 2050, *solely* from tides, flooding in the US Atlantic and Gulf, plus Pacific Islands, will occur up to 60% of the time, in a scenario of intermediate sea-level rise—a 1-meter global rise by 2100—concluded a NOAA report. And by 2100, in most global regions, high tide flooding will occur 365 days a year under the intermediate scenario.

The scientists wrote that the high tide flooding every other day "would bring to fruition the saying championed by NOAA's (late) Margaret Davidson: 'Today's flood will become tomorrow's high tide.'"[636]

Such flooding will spur massive adaptation efforts, including constructing barriers and "managed retreat," in which communities are rebuilt above flood levels. Even with such efforts, there will be mass global migrations away from coasts, triggering potential conflict and even political collapse (see Environmental Exodus).

Rivers rise

Although sea-level flooding receives the most attention, river floods are "among the most common and devastating natural disasters worldwide," pointed out researchers who modeled their future.[637] They forecast that global river flooding will drastically increase over the next decades even with major emissions reductions. More than half of the US will need to double river flood protection within the next two decades, they concluded.

A prime example of such flooding is the catastrophic inundation in dozens of US states during 2019. In that flooding, which broke many records, nearly two-thirds of the lower 48 states faced higher flooding risk.[638]

The human and economic impacts of global river flooding will be profound, found another analysis. The researchers predicted that a 1.5°C warming would cause a loss of life up to 83% greater than the current average. A 2°C warming would cause a 134% increase; and a 3°C warming a 265% increase. They calculated that a 1.5°C warming would cause river flooding damage to rise 240% above the current estimated $130 billion a year; 2°C warming would trigger a 520% rise; and 3°C warming a 1,000% rise.[639]

Ravaged Shores

Decades ago, I had the transcendent experience of snorkeling on a Polynesian tropical reef near Tahiti. Floating in the warm, crystal-clear water, I marveled at the swirling kaleidoscope of yellow, green, red, and blue fish gliding and darting through the forest of delicately hued corals.

More recently, I dove on the Australian Great Barrier Reef. The contrast was stunning. It was like swimming in a sea littered with bones. The bleached white coral and brownish, algae-covered dead coral offered a bleak testament to the damage from global heating.

Coastal regions—coral reefs, estuaries, salt marshes, and mangrove swamps—are being devastated by the multiple impacts of climate disruption. Rising sea levels and waters that are heated, oxygen-starved, and acidified will disrupt ecosystems critical to protecting coasts from storms, and to spawning and harboring marine life.

Of course, coastal zones are also being damaged by other human-caused insults—including farm, factory, and sewage plant toxic runoff; and habitat destruction from aquaculture and coastal development.

Loss of coral reefs and other coastal ecosystems produces immense economic impact. Coral reefs are worth nearly a trillion dollars a year in such areas as fishing, recreation, and tourism, concluded an economic analysis by biologists. Their report valued mangrove swamps at $1 trillion a year and seagrass at $2.1 trillion.[640]

Coral researchers have projected that 70% to 90% of coral reefs will disappear by about mid-century, with almost all gone by 2100.[641]

As of this writing, the Great Barrier Reef, which stretches for 2,300 kilometers (1,400 miles), has lost more than 50% of its coral since 1995, according to a study by marine biologists.[642] US reefs in Hawaii and Florida have been struck with regular bleaching, according to NOAA's Coral Reef Watch.[643]

Chronic assault on coral

Warmer waters don't kill coral directly but starve them to death. Coral constitutes a delicate symbiosis, in which the coral polyps harbor algae that produce nutrients for the coral. When exposed to warmer water, coral expel the algae, losing the vast majority of their nutrition.[644]

While coral researchers are unclear on the ultimate fate of coral reefs, their modeling has revealed that continued rising emissions and global temperatures will cause major, if not catastrophic, bleaching.[645 646 647 648]

While reef polyps can rebound from pulses of warming, chronic global heating does not allow recovery. Tropical reefs are already entering "a new era in which the interval between recurrent bouts of coral bleaching is too short for a full recovery," noted a study of coral bleaching events at 100 locations between 1980 and 2016.[649] The research team found a fivefold decrease in the time between events.

They also surveyed the effects of 2016 and 2017 marine heat waves on the Great Barrier Reef, concluding that the reef is permanently changed. They dubbed the alterations a "radical shift in the disturbance regimes of tropical reefs."[650]

In another coral study, marine biologists found that separate bleaching events in past decades afforded the reefs a "protective, sub-bleaching stress, before reaching temperatures that cause bleaching." This pre-stress made the coral more heat tolerant. But that heat tolerance was lost under chronic temperature stress from global heating, they found.[651]

Ocean acidification also damages reefs, dissolving their structure. In one study, when researchers measured the calcification rates of Florida reefs over two years, they found that parts of the reefs had already crossed the tipping point where erosion was greater than deposition.[652]

To add to reefs' misery, projected sea-level rise will submerge reefs faster than their growth can keep up with, found an analysis. So, coral reefs will be submerged beyond the depth that at which their algae can obtain the necessary energy from sunlight. In a calculation of the growth potential of more than 200 tropical reefs, researchers found that few reefs will be able to grow to surmount sea-level rise.[653]

Estuary decline

Estuaries are being damaged by sea-level rise, warming temperatures, drought, toxic stormwater runoff, flooding, and storm damage.[654] Yet estuaries, like coral reefs, are the nurseries for ocean life, harboring a rich diversity of plant and animal species. Most fish and shellfish spend some or all of their lifetimes in estuaries. And the many people who live near estuary shorelines depend on the jobs, food, and storm protection that estuaries provide.

Invaluable marshes

Mangrove forests and salt marshes offer breeding grounds, as well as storm surge buffers, and carbon storage as organic matter in roots and soil.[655]

Flood-protection benefits from mangroves alone exceed $65 billion a year, according to one analysis. The researchers calculated that if mangroves were lost, 15 million more people would be flooded annually across the world.[656]

Another study calculated the amount of coastal protection afforded by mangroves in 42 developing countries. It forecast the effect of a future one-meter sea-level rise and 10% storm intensity increase. Today's climate disruption puts about 3.5 million people and $400 million in

Gross Domestic Product (GDP) at risk, the researchers calculated. The future scenario would increase the vulnerable population by 103% and the GDP at risk by 233%.[657]

In terms of carbon storage, mangroves account for about 14% of the carbon sequestration by the global ocean.[658] One calculation is that the Everglades mangrove forests have a carbon storage capacity worth billions of dollars.[659]

In fact, one study suggested that salt marsh carbon storage could increase over the next decades with global warming. Sea-level rise would trigger the marshes to grow higher and bury more carbon. However, fast-rising seas could also inundate the marshes.[660] [661] [662]

Dying Ocean

Sitting in the lab of Australian marine biologist Rob King is an apparatus that could foretell the future of the entire Antarctic food chain. The apparatus comprises a row of white plastic tanks fed by plastic tubes. Inside each tank, immersed in seawater, are black cylinders containing the eggs of the tiny shrimplike Antarctic krill. In their experiments, the lab's researchers expose the eggs to varying concentrations of ocean-acidifying CO_2, as well as the higher temperatures expected in a future ocean. The experiments combine CO_2 and temperature effects because there may be a synergy between the two components, rather than merely an additive effect.[663]

Krill are the foundation for the entire Antarctic food chain. Schools of krill totaling hundreds of millions of tons swarm beneath the Antarctic waters, providing food for fish, seals, penguins, and whales.

Research in King's laboratory has revealed that krill eggs cease to hatch at atmospheric CO_2 levels around 2,000 parts per million. Current *average* atmospheric levels have surpassed 400 parts per million, expected to rise to 1,500 by 2100, according to King. However, krill eggs are exposed to even *greater* CO_2 levels because before hatching they sink as much as a kilometer below sea level, where concentrations of CO_2 are higher.[664]

Other pressures may also threaten the krill population. They may run out of food because melting sea ice will deprive larvae of an attachment point beneath the ice that they need to feed on phytoplankton that grow there. And, as indicated earlier, phytoplankton themselves could suffer due to warmer waters (see Heating Soup).

One study showed that business-as-usual projections of warmer temperatures and loss of sea ice could reduce the habitat for newly hatched krill by 80% by 2100.[665]

Oceans deforested

The denuding of undersea forests is just as environmentally damaging as terrestrial deforestation, although it is invisible to all but scuba divers. Like terrestrial forests, the vast seagrass meadows and kelp forests in shallow continental waters provide critical habitat for both young and adult creatures.

Seagrass stores massive amounts of carbon and can even remove dangerous pathogens from seawater, found a field study. In waters off Indonesia, ecologists did bacterial analyses on seawater samples in seagrass meadows, as well as sites without the plant. The seagrass meadows showed half the bacterial population of the other sites.[666]

Seagrass habitat is declining worldwide, and an analysis by dozens of marine researchers found that about 14% of species are at risk of extinction.[667] When seagrass dies, that carbon will be released.[668]

The status of kelp forests is more complex. A global study found decreases in some areas and increases in others. Some areas were being damaged by warmer waters—as well as pollution, invasive fish species, and kelp harvesting. In contrast, other areas were thriving due to beneficial local conditions.[669]

Fisheries unsustainable

Compromised by an array of threats including climate disruption, sustainable fish stocks have decreased from 90% in 1974 to 65.8% in 2017, according to a UN report.[670] A drop of more than 3 million metric tons of fish caught per year per degree of warming was projected by another study.[671]

Fisheries are already feeling the effects of warmer oceans. Between 1930 and 2010, ocean warming produced a 4.1% reduction in yield of a broad array of species of fish and shellfish, calculated another analysis.[672]

Said study co-author Malin Pinsky: "We were stunned to find that fisheries around the world have already responded to ocean warming.... These aren't hypothetical changes sometime in the future."[673] Indeed, another study projected an annual fisheries revenue loss of billions of dollars by 2050 in high CO_2 emission scenarios.[674]

Marine fishery declines will last for a millennium because the marine algae phytoplankton at the base of the ocean food chain will be starved of nutrients, found oceanographers. Their models projected that climate-driven changes in ocean circulation will tend to drive nutrients to the deep ocean, reducing the levels at the surface, where phytoplankton live.[675] [676]

Freshwater fish will also suffer precipitous declines from global heating, with 30% at risk of extinction, found a large-scale study by an environmental consortium. Populations of migratory fishes such as salmon and sturgeon have already fallen by 76% since 1970. And populations of larger fish such as beluga sturgeon and the Mekong giant catfish have declined by 94% since 1970, the study found.[677]

Up to 60% of marine and freshwater fish species will fail to cope with a 5°C atmospheric global warming, projected one study. The analysis of data on nearly 700 species found that embryos and spawning adults were more sensitive to temperature extremes than larvae and nonspawning adults.[678]

Migration to cooler waters might enable some species to survive. But such movement presents many obstacles and hazards. For example, temperature-sensitive fish might have to shift their range beyond their food source of nonsensitive species, which don't have to move.[679]

Also, dozens of species of commercial fish will be driven to extinction because of their inability to adapt to warming waters, predicted other studies. Some fish that migrate will find themselves in different ecosystems, with different food sources and predators. About 50 species that live at or near the poles will go extinct. And other species in enclosed waters such as Mexico's Sea of Cortez and the Mediterranean will have nowhere to go.[680]

Warmer waters will cause hundreds of species that do survive to become smaller, found a study of fish physiology. Fish growth is stunted because the warmer water speeds the fishes' metabolism, but the lower oxygen concentrations prevent them from getting enough oxygen.[681]

Such anoxia—caused by warmer waters' lowered ability to dissolve oxygen—has likely already begun to affect fisheries. And one modeling analysis predicted by 2080 widespread and severe ocean deoxygenation in the ocean layer important for commercial fish species to survive.[682]

The future will likely see tragic miscalculations of fisheries' productivity, given the uncertainties in the understanding of ocean processes. The result will be major economic loss and loss of a food source. The New England cod fishery has virtually collapsed because fishing quotas didn't anticipate that the Gulf of Maine fishing ground would warm faster than 99% of the rest of the world's oceans, found a study by marine scientists.[683]

Factors other than climate disruption are also driving major ocean species loss, according to a World Wildlife Fund report (see Mass Extinction).[684] Overexploitation is the major current threat, along with habitat loss and degradation.

However, as climate disruption renders the seas ever more uninhabitable, it will become a major cause of the ultimate unraveling of the ocean's ecological web.

Ruining AMOC

It seems far-fetched to propose that an Atlantic Ocean current drives effects as disparate as a warmer climate on the US East Coast and Northern Europe, and monsoons in Africa and India. But it does.[685]

These effects are the global gifts of a colossal oceanic conveyor belt called the Atlantic Meridional Overturning Circulation (AMOC). The current is powered by "thermohaline" circulation due to density differences in ocean salinity, as well as winds. The current propels warmer water northward from the tropics to the waters off North America and Northern Europe. By the time the AMOC waters reach the north, the waters have become cooler, saltier, and denser. They sink deep into the Atlantic abyss to flow southward, where the heat-transport cycle begins anew.

The AMOC warms the land along the North American Eastern Seaboard and Northern Europe significantly above the temperatures that might otherwise exist at those latitudes. And the moisture that the warm Atlantic waters pump into the atmosphere nourishes the life-giving monsoons in Africa and India. The AMOC also influences the number and strength of Atlantic hurricanes, governing the amount of heat and moisture that powers them.[686]

This current is now the weakest it has been in the last thousand years, showing a rapid decline since the mid-twentieth century, researchers have found.[687] If it stalls, the northern Atlantic coasts will experience cooling and greater sea-level rise because of shifting currents; Africa and India could suffer catastrophic droughts; and Atlantic hurricanes could intensify into superstorms.[688] [689] Also, the upwelling of nutrients that feed marine life and support fish stocks could dwindle.

In modeling studies, researchers found clues to the weakening. The models revealed that melting Arctic ice is sending cascades of freshwater into the system. This less-dense freshwater is disrupting the descent of the warmer surface ocean saltwaters that had flowed from the south. The studies forecast a weakening of the AMOC over the next century.[690]

In fact, there is foreboding evidence that the AMOC may well be reaching a tipping point at which it will collapse. Researcher Niklas Boers—analyzing data on sea-surface temperatures and salinity—concluded that "in the course of the last century, the AMOC may have evolved from relatively stable conditions to a point close to a critical transition."[691]

"The signs of destabilisation being visible already is something that I wouldn't have expected and that I find scary," Boers told *The Guardian*.[692]

IV
Viral Human Consequences

Alien Earth

Over the millennia, human civilization has developed in a reasonably stable environment. Certainly, there were short-term disruptions—storms, droughts, floods, climate-changing volcanic eruptions, wildfires, and pandemics. But over the longer term, the seasons came and went dependably, and the forests, fields, and oceans yielded their expected bounty.

The temporary disruptions of the past are nothing like those to come from the slow-motion catastrophes described in the previous chapters. We will find ourselves occupying an alien planet, where the environmental stability on which we depended is no more. As the landmark 2022 report by the UN Intergovernmental Panel on Climate Change (IPCC) on climate disruption's effects asserted:

> Widespread, pervasive impacts to ecosystems, people, settlements, and infrastructure have resulted from observed increases in the frequency and intensity of climate and weather extremes, including hot extremes on land and in the ocean, heavy precipitation events, drought and fire weather.[693]

What's more, these separate environmental disasters can interact in tragic, unpredictable synergies. As the *National Climate Assessment* report put it, the impact of "compound extreme events" such as combined heat and drought, or flooding from heavy rainfall on waterlogged ground, "can be greater than the sum of the parts . . . Few analyses consider the spatial or temporal correlation between extreme events."[694]

We most cope with more than individual climate disasters, habitat destruction, and resource depletion. There will be profoundly damaging synergies. For example, migrations by plant and animal species are likely to trigger ecological turmoil that impacts humans, assert marine ecologists led by Gretta Pecl. They state that:

"Even if greenhouse gas emissions stopped today, the responses required in human systems to adapt to the most serious effects of climate-driven species redistribution would be massive."[695]

The health impact of Alien Earth will also be profound, far beyond the disaster of the COVID-19 pandemic. A report by scores of US medical organizations said:

Climate change is one of the greatest threats to health America has ever faced—it is a true public health emergency. . . . Without transformational action, climate change will be increasingly severe, leading to more illness, injury, and death; mass migration and violent conflict; and worsening health inequities.[696]

Reports in the journal *Lancet* in 2020 called climate disruption "the greatest global health threat facing the world in the 21st century."[697] The 2021 *Lancet* report "finds a world overwhelmed by an ongoing global health crisis, which has made little progress to protect its population from the simultaneously aggravated health impacts of climate change."[698]

Climate disruption is already causing major loss of life globally from disease and hunger, according to the 2012 report *Climate Vulnerability Monitor: A Guide to the Cold Calculus of a Hot Planet.*

The report was commissioned by 20 governments and reviewed by some 50 scientists, economists, and policy experts. It calculated impact for 184 countries. The report estimated that climate disruption was responsible for 400,000 deaths annually due to hunger and communicable disease exacerbated by climate disruption. Burning of fossil fuels caused some 4.5 million deaths annually due to air pollution, hazardous occupations, and cancer, said the report.[699]

The World Health Organization says that climate change is expected to cause about 250,000 *additional* deaths a year from malnutrition, malaria, diarrhea, and heat stress.[700] A World Bank Group analysis found that climate change could force an *additional* 100 million people into extreme poverty, compared with 736 million today.[701] [702]

The sections that follow explore how Alien Earth will become irreversibly more toxic and disease-plagued, its people more malnourished, and its political institutions more unstable.

Toxic Earth

The choking smog in cities across China dooms millions of its residents to lung disease and early death. During the smothering "airpocalypse" of 2013, schools were closed, traffic restricted, flights canceled, and people warned to stay indoors.[703] [704] Some 400 million people live in the 23 affected cities, from which "smog refugees" fled to seek breathable air.[705]

Seventy percent of China's 74 largest cities recorded air pollution levels above the nation's standards. About 90,000 deaths were attributed to the smog, and hundreds of thousands more were sickened.[706]

While the obvious major culprit was coal burning in power plants and factories, the not-so-obvious culprit was climate disruption.

Surprisingly, China's smog-trapping air stagnation was exacerbated by loss of Arctic sea ice and heavy snows in Eurasian boreal forests, which damped air circulation to China, found atmospheric scientists.[707]

What's more, China's smog will get worse, predicted researchers who used climate models to analyze past climates and predict future scenarios. They projected a 50% increase in the frequency and an 80% increase in the persistence of weather patterns conducive to the 2013 smog.[708]

US air quality is decreasing because of climate disruption, found an American Lung Association report. The report found that "... worsening air quality threatened the health of more people, despite other protective measures being in place. Climate change clearly drives the conditions that increase these pollutants."[709]

Persistent toxic pollutants

A witch's brew of chemicals and toxic organisms—including methylmercury, toxic algae, and mold—could spread more widely and become more toxic due to global heating.

Particularly noxious are the chemicals called Persistent Organic Pollutants, or POPs.[710] These include DDT, polychlorinated biphenyls (PCBs), and dioxins. They can last up to a decade in the environment. These pesticides, solvents, and other industrial chemicals affect human health, and they can all be transported by wind, water and wildfires far from where they are released.

Scientists are still uncertain about the effects of global heating on POP toxicity. However, initial studies have revealed how heating could make the chemicals more hazardous. For example, rising temperatures could make the chemicals more volatile and drive more of them from warming soils. Melting glaciers and permafrost can release them into waters, as can soil erosion from droughts and floods. On the other hand, it's possible that warmer temperatures could hasten breakdown to less-toxic components.[711]

Flooding will also increase exposure to toxic chemicals. Just in the US, some 2,500 industrial plants that handle toxic chemicals lie in flood-prone areas, found a survey by *The New York Times*. Chemical companies are continuing to build in such areas as the Gulf of Mexico region, found the report.[712]

A review by toxicologists detailed how climate disruption could not only increase the toxic chemical exposures—for example, by increasing pesticide concentrations in surface waters and groundwaters—but it could also make medical effects of toxic chemicals worse.[713]

"Dietary changes, psychosocial stress, and coexposure to stressors such as high temperatures are likely to increase the vulnerability of humans to chemicals," the report noted. Higher chemical exposures and vulnerabilities could trigger more heart and lung disease and increase risk of cancer and endocrine, neurological, and reproductive disorders.

Mercury from melting and fires

Thawing Arctic permafrost from warmer temperatures could release huge amounts of accumulated mercury. Environmental chemists have found up to five times the level of mercury in Arctic tundra as in temperate regions.[714] Global permafrost soils hold some 1.7 million metric tons of mercury, "nearly twice as much [mercury] as all other soils, the ocean, and the atmosphere combined," estimated hydrologists who measured mercury in cores from Alaskan permafrost sites.[715]

The mercury originally spread through the atmosphere from volcanoes, forest fires, coal burning, and industrial processes. It accumulated in the Arctic over centuries as plants absorbed it, died, and were deposited in the soil. A warming Arctic would release this mercury into rivers and streams that flow into the oceans.[716]

Such released mercury enters the food chain when microbes in soil and water convert it into methylmercury and are consumed by zooplankton.[717] These plankton are, in turn, consumed by higher organisms that are in turn consumed by fish. Methylmercury is "biomagnified" in the food chain because it is not eliminated readily by the consuming organisms, including humans. Eaten in fish and shellfish, it can reach the brain and cross the placenta, absorbed by fetuses.[718] It acts as a neurotoxin and has been linked to increased risk of cardiovascular disease and heart attack.[719]

Methylmercury concentrations in fish and shellfish will also increase due to greater runoff from heavier rains caused by climate disruption. Environmental chemists have estimated that such coastal-region runoff has already increased by 10–50% worldwide.[720]

The scientists explored how such runoff might affect methylmercury levels in organisms by using mercury isotopes to track mercury movement in scale models of coastal estuaries. The experiments revealed that the increased organic matter flushed into water enhanced by two to seven times accumulation of mercury in zooplankton.

For forest fires, researchers still do not understand how mercury release impacts human health and the environment. They do know that the fires volatilize the considerable amount of mercury sequestered in soils, leaf litter, and debris. They also know that gaseous mercury can remain in the atmosphere for long periods, and that mercury-bearing particulates can fall to earth where they can enter watersheds and be transformed to methylmercury. But they have little data on what happens to that mercury.[721]

Toxic microbe upsurge

Global heating will increase toxic algal blooms and bacterial growth because of warmer waters and greater nutrient runoff from farmland. Toxic algae renders crabs and shellfish poisonous, and poisons waters used for drinking, irrigation, and recreation. The cost of toxic algal blooms is already immense—more than $5 billion annually in the US, and well over $13 billion worldwide.[722]

Marine biologists have found that higher ocean temperatures have already expanded the conditions that encourage such blooms in the North Atlantic and North Pacific. The researchers used ocean temperature records to calculate growth rates and blooms for two toxic algae species that cause shellfish poisoning. They found a significant temperature-linked rise in blooms since 1982.[723] [724]

In a kind of climatic smoking gun, other environmental scientists linked the 2015 large-scale bloom of the toxin domoic acid off the West Coast to then-anomalously warm ocean temperatures. The bloom closed fisheries and killed more than 30 whales, along with other marine life, in California, Oregon, and Washington. In humans, domoic acid can produce nausea and vomiting, and memory loss when consumed in seafood.

"Our findings have implications in coastal zones worldwide that are affected by this toxin and are particularly relevant given the increased frequency of anomalously warm ocean conditions," the researchers concluded.[725]

Mold-infected crops

Global heating will increase growth of molds that produce mycotoxins—the most widely known being aflatoxins—for coffee, corn, peanuts, sorghum, and wheat, according to a report by the UN Environment Programme. In children, aflatoxins can stunt growth and delay development, and in adults can cause liver damage and liver cancer. The warmer and more humid weather will also spread molds' range beyond the tropics northward, where they have not been a problem before.[726]

Diseased Earth

Climate disruption will cause a myriad of diseases to spread more widely. One analysis concluded that over half of human infectious diseases have been aggravated by climate disruption.[727] The researchers' analysis of some 77,000 scientific papers on the diseases revealed more than a thousand transmission pathways by which climate disruption led to more disease. For example:

- Climate migration will bring people closer to pathogens
- Disease-carriers will increase their range; and
- Global heating will increase some organisms' virulence

The researchers warned that "The sheer number of pathogenic diseases and transmission pathways aggravated by climatic hazards reveals the magnitude of the human health threat posed by climate change. . ."

Insect-borne diseases will be particularly dangerous. In the US, the geographical range of ticks carrying Lyme disease is already expanding, and the tick season is lengthening. Rising temperatures are also fostering the growth of mosquitoes that harbor West Nile and Zika. And a greater number of people will be exposed to water-related illnesses from bacteria, viruses, and protozoa, according to the report, *The Impacts of Climate Change on Human Health in the United States.*[728]

Between 2004 and 2016, disease cases from mosquito, flea, and tick bites have more than doubled in the US, according to the Centers for Disease Control and Prevention.[729]

Climate disruption will also increase "zoonotic spillover"—the spread of mammalian animal diseases to humans. Such diseases will spread because of the climate-caused destruction of wild animals' habitats and the migration of animals to new areas.

One study identified at least 10,000 viruses that could infect humans, but currently circulate silently in wild mammals. [730]

"We predict that species will aggregate in new combinations at high elevations, in biodiversity hotspots, and in areas of high human population density in Asia and Africa, driving the novel cross-species transmission of their viruses an estimated 4,000 times," wrote the researchers.

Water-related illness such as E. coli, salmonella, and cholera will rise, as increased flooding inundates wastewater treatment plants (see Flood Warning). Such treatment plants are vulnerable to sea-level rise because they are sited in coastal lowlands to enable gravity feed and effluent outfall. In the US, researchers have calculated that a three-foot sea-level rise would cause the release of untreated sewage that would affect two million people, and disrupt water and water treatment for more than eight million.[731]

Globally, by 2030, climate disruption will cause about 48,000 more deaths annually due to diarrheal disease and 60,000 due to malaria, according to the World Health Organization (WHO). Overall, WHO estimates that climate disruption will be responsible for about 250,000 additional health-related deaths a year between 2030 and 2050. Besides disease, the deaths will be due to such causes as heat and malnutrition.[732]

Mosquitoes swarming

With warmer temperatures, the range of the *Aedes aegypti* mosquito—which carries dengue, chikungunya, Zika, and yellow fever—could expand considerably, tropical biologists have projected.[733] Dengue viruses already infect up to 400 million people a year.[734] The future will be even more grim, forecast a landmark report of the UN Intergovernmental Panel on Climate Change (IPCC):

> In particular, dengue risk will increase with longer seasons and a wider geographic distribution in Asia, Europe, Central and South America and sub-Saharan Africa, potentially putting additional billions of people at risk by the end of the century.[735]

Climate disruption aids the spread of virus-carrying mosquitoes by providing more breeding grounds due to increased rainfall. And warmer temperatures and higher humidity enable the mosquito to invade northward, to feed more actively, and to have a longer season.[736] [737]

The Asian Tiger mosquito *Aedes albopictus*—which carries dengue, chikungunya, and West Nile virus—will also increase its range in the US, predicted entomologists. The mosquito originated in Southeast Asia and has spread to all the continents except Antarctica. The researchers predicted that the mosquito will expand its range in the northeastern US up to 16% in the next two decades and up to 49% by the end of the century.[738]

The number of "disease danger days" has increased in the US over the last decades according to an analysis by Climate Central. Those are days when higher temperatures foster mosquito breeding. The analysis found, of 244 cities analyzed, 94% are seeing an increase in the number of days at heightened risk for disease.[739]

Mosquitoes and disease-causing parasites will rapidly evolve to take advantage of the cauldron of unstable, changing ecosystems created by climate disruption. Carriers will not only spread to new regions because of warmer temperatures. Parasites will also readily switch hosts, surviving even if their natural host goes extinct, wrote Eric Hoberg and Daniel Brooks.[740]

"The planet is thus an evolutionary and ecological minefield of [emerging infectious diseases] through which millions of people, their crops and their livestock wander daily," they wrote. (Their article is part of a special issue of the journal *Philosophical Transactions of the Royal Society B* on "Climate Change and Vector-Borne Diseases of Humans.")[741]

Thawing permafrost may also revive dormant disease, such as the 2016 anthrax outbreak in Siberia. The disease came from the buried carcass of an infected reindeer, and epidemiologists warn that buried people, animals, and plants could be the source of other bacterial and viral diseases from previous centuries. Thawing permafrost in regions such as Siberia could disturb cattle burying grounds that could harbor anthrax.[742]

"We really don't know what's buried up there," microbiologist Birgitta Evengard told NPR. "This is Pandora's box."[743]

Fungal evolution

Fungi may also evolve to thrive in a warmer world, with sometimes deadly results. The fungus *Candida auris* represents such an ominous future of fungal infections in humans.[744] It is often drug resistant and causes major outbreaks in healthcare facilities.

Different genetically distinct fungal strains have emerged seemingly independently on three continents. In one study, about a third of patients with delayed diagnosis with the drug-resistant fungal strain died.[745]

Researchers suspect that one culprit may be global heating. Normally fungi cannot live in the higher temperature of the human body. But new fungal strains that evolve as a result of global heating could breach this "thermal restriction zone," found a study that compared the temperature susceptibility of the *Candida auris* fungus with its close relatives.[746]

"Global warming may lead to new fungal diseases that we don't even know about right now," said Arturo Casadevall, the study's leader. "What this study suggests is this is the beginning of fungi adapting to higher temperatures, and we are going to have more and more problems as the century goes on.[747]

Ocean-borne disease

Oceans will become more biologically hazardous with global heating, given that they are basically vast petri dishes.

Warmer oceans could harbor greater concentrations of the *Vibrio* bacterium that causes cholera and vibriosis—a skin infection from contact with ocean water, or a gastroenteritis-like disease from eating raw shellfish or ingesting ocean water.[748] One team of microbiologists discovered a correlation between cholera incidents and increasing temperatures when they analyzed preserved ocean samples collected between 1958 and 2011. They noted that the increases were associated with unprecedented occurrence of *Vibrio* infections in Northern Europe and the US Atlantic Coast in recent years.

"The evidence is strong that ongoing climate change is influencing outbreaks of *Vibrio* infections on a worldwide scale," they wrote. They predicted that ocean temperature rise will exacerbate the pathogen's spread.[749]

Even slightly warmer oceans foster the northward spread of *Vibrio* strains that cause vibriosis. One study found that warmer sea-surface temperatures correlated with unexpected vibriosis outbreaks in the Baltic Sea area of Northern Europe.[750] The study found that even a 1°C increase in sea-surface temperature nearly doubled the number of vibriosis cases. The study is particularly significant because the Baltic Sea is "to our knowledge, the fastest-warming marine ecosystem examined so far anywhere on Earth."

"The big apparent increases that we've seen in cases during heat wave years . . . tend to indicate that climate change is indeed driving infections," the study's lead author, Craig Baker-Austin, told Reuters.[751]

Destruction of the ocean environment also increases the seas' disease-causing potential. For example, seagrass reduces disease-causing bacteria, but seagrass meadows are declining. Joleah Lamb and colleagues experienced the health impact of seagrass loss firsthand, when they took a scuba diving expedition on areas that lacked nearby seagrass meadows.[752]

"By the end of the four-day workshop, we all came down with amoebic dysentery," study co-author, C. Drew Harvell, told *The New York Times*. "One scientist developed typhoid, and we had to ship her out."[753]

Climate disruption diabetes

Global heating could increase cases of diabetes—an odd prospect, given that diabetes is not a communicable disease. Type 2 diabetes can occur when people gain weight, and their increase in body fat and lack of exercise render their bodies less sensitive to insulin. The connection between outdoor temperature and diabetes arises because temperature affects the type of fat that people accumulate. Higher temperatures could reduce the formation of "brown fat," which tends to combat obesity.[754]

Researchers found a statistical correlation between outdoor temperature and diabetes when they analyzed US temperature and diabetes incidence between 1996 and 2009. "On the basis of our results, a 1°C rise in environmental temperature would account for over 100,000 new diabetes cases per year in the US alone, given a population of nearly 322 million people in 2015," they concluded.

The global health impact of such an increase could be profound. The researchers noted that "the prevalence of type 2 diabetes is increasing rapidly worldwide. In 2015, 415 million adults globally suffered from diabetes, and expectations are that the prevalence will rise by almost 55%, up to 642 million cases by 2040."

Children vulnerable

Children are especially affected by the effects of compound stressors from climate disruption, noted the American Psychological Association (APA) report *Mental Health and Our Changing Climate: Impacts, Implications, and Guidance.*[755]

"Children are more vulnerable to many of the effects [of climate disruption] due to their small size, developing organs and nervous systems, and rapid metabolisms," said the report. They are more sensitive to heat stress because their physiology makes them less able to regulate temperature. "Climate impacts may have long-term and even permanent effects, such as changing the developmental potential and trajectory of a child."

Fetuses are vulnerable to heat waves and children to malnourishment, which severely threatens health and development, noted the APA report. Also, "early exposure to disease provoked by climate change can have a major and permanent impact on neurological development."

Children are also not immune to dealing with mental health issues from climate disruption, the report noted. "Children can experience PTSD and depression following traumatic or stressful experiences with more severity and prevalence than adults."

Compound climate mental stress

The accumulated effects of compound stresses from climate disruption "can tip a person from mentally healthy to mentally ill," noted the APA report. Such effects can be both direct and indirect. Direct effects can arise from natural disasters, and indirect effects from weakened infrastructure and food shortages.

Chronic stress can also translate into physical health problems, including cardiovascular disease and pathogenic diseases because the resulting lowered immune response leaves people more vulnerable to pathogens, stated the APA report. Citing estimates that 200 million people will be displaced by climate disruption by 2050, the report said:

"Migration in and of itself constitutes a health risk. Immigrants are vulnerable to mental health problems, probably due to the accumulated stressors associated with the move, as well as with the condition of being in exile." Migration will also erode supportive social networks, as communities are disrupted; "the loss of such networks places people's sense of continuity and belonging at risk" (see Environmental Exodus).

Not all impacts will be obvious and immediate. "Gradual, long-term changes in climate can also surface a number of different emotions, including fear, anger, feelings of powerlessness, or exhaustion," said the APA report. Climate disasters on Alien Earth can have insidious psychological impacts. The report said that:

> As climate change irrevocably changes people's lived landscapes, large numbers are likely to experience a feeling that they are losing a place that is important to them—a phenomenon called *solastalgia* . . . Loss of place is not a trivial experience. Many people form a strong attachment to the place where they live, finding it to provide a sense of stability, security, and personal identity.

Climate disruption will threaten both children's and adults' mental health in myriad ways, according to the Climate Psychiatry Alliance, a group of mental health professionals.[756]

Besides the direct effects on physical and mental health, climate disruption will have indirect effects, pointed out a review by public policy researchers.[757] They predicted that forced migration will expose migrants to diseases for which they have limited resistance and will aid disease spread. The report concluded:

> Climate change migration, in response to deteriorating conditions, will stress health systems in receiving countries and cause immense psychological pain, as millions of people are forced to try to find a new home. Increased conflict in part caused by climate change will worsen health and further burden health systems, and may already be occurring.

Climate disruption violence

Increased temperatures heighten aggression and violence, according to the APA report. Heat may increase the body's "arousal" in a way that decreases self-regulation and increases hostile thoughts, said the report.

Statistical evidence does link heat and violence. In one study of weather and shootings in Chicago, researchers found that a 10°C higher temperature was "significantly associated" with 34% more shootings on weekdays and 43% more shootings on weekends or holidays.[758]

More broadly, when public policy researcher Matthew Ranson analyzed thirty years of statistics on crime and weather, he found that "temperature has a strong positive effect on criminal behavior." He extrapolated his findings to expected future temperatures, projecting that the period to the end of the century would see tens of thousands more murders and rapes and millions more assaults.[759]

In a blunt assessment of climate disruption's future health effects, more than two dozen climatologists, lawyers, and philosophers asserted:

> Climate change is the biggest global health threat of the 21st century. . . . Effects of climate change on health will affect most populations in the next decades and put the lives and well-being of billions of people at increased risk.[760]

What's more, wrote authors Alice C. Hill and Leonardo Martinez-Diaz in their book *Building a Resilient Tomorrow*:

> Despite the clear and present danger climate change poses to public health, the efforts of the medical profession and public health authorities to date have not matched the urgency of the problem. Medical facilities are not being designed, built, and retrofitted to withstand climate impacts. Because we lacked sufficient capacity to track, monitor, and warn the public about the spread of disease in a warming world, we find ourselves in a reactive mode, struggling to keep up. Nurses, doctors, and public health officials are often unaware how climate change upends their understanding of public health threats and what to do about the growing risks.[761]

Epidemic of Hunger

Current statistics on world hunger are sobering, but the upward trend is shocking. In 2019, about 8% of the world population was undernourished, which increased to 9.8% in 2021, according to the UN Food and Agriculture Organization (FAO).[762]

Up to 828 million people were affected by hunger in 2021, said the FAO report. Such global hunger has multiple causes besides climate variability and extremes, including the COVID-19 pandemic and economic downturns, said the report. More recently, the war in Ukraine profoundly exacerbated world hunger by disrupting grain supplies.

Other reports have also documented relentless increases in hunger—for example that 135 million people were "food insecure" in 2019, rising to 193 million in 2021.[763] [764]

Climate disruption is already reducing global yields of key crops such as rice and wheat, found an analysis led by food security analyst Deepak Ray. And those reduced yields are translating into a reduction in consumable calories of about 1% a year for the top ten global crops.[765] Wrote Ray:

> This may sound small, but it represents some 35 trillion calories each year. That's enough to provide more

than 50 million people with a daily diet of over 1,800 calories—the level that the [FAO] identifies as essential to avoid food deprivation or undernourishment.[766]

Future population increases will create a major food gap between production and demand, concluded a World Resources Institute report. The report projected a gap of 56% of crop calories between the amount of food produced in 2010 and that required in 2050. The report also projected a "land gap" twice the size of India between existing farmland area in 2010 and that required by 2050. Closing the gaps will require "action by many millions of farmers, businesses, consumers, and all governments," noted the report.[767]

Projected crop yields must rise faster to meet the required demand for doubling of food production, according to another study led by Ray. He and his colleagues drew on 2.5 million crop statistics from 13,500 governmental agencies and other groups. Crop doubling by 2050 would require an annual 2.4% a year increase, they calculated. However, the statistics revealed far lower annual increases in the four most important crops: corn (1.6%), rice (1.0%), wheat (0.9%), and soybeans (1.3%).

"Clearly, the world faces a looming and growing agricultural crisis. Yields are not improving fast enough to keep up with projected demands in 2050," Ray and colleagues concluded.[768]

While projected reductions in crop yields vary among studies, they agree that losses will be major—with significant drops as early as the 2030s, if not sooner, and reductions by up to half beginning mid-century. The studies covered all the major crops: corn, wheat, rice, and soybeans.[769 770 771 772 773 774]

"As more data have become available, we've seen a shift in consensus, telling us that the impacts of climate change in temperate regions will happen sooner rather than later," noted Andy Challinor in a press release.[775]

Farming cannot adapt to a climate-disrupted future because of its narrow range of crops and its heavy dependence on fossil fuels (see Carbonized Farming). As the FAO pointed out, "75% of the world's food is generated from only 12 plants and 5 animal species, making the global food system highly vulnerable."[776]

How heat reduces yields

Higher temperatures reduce crop yields by stressing plants, mainly through increased soil evaporation. On hot days, plants wilt because they open their leaf pores, losing water.[777] Higher temperatures also enhance the growth of pests, including mold and insects (see Diseased Earth).

In the future, an intensifying of heat-caused evaporation from soils will overcome the moisture contribution from rainfall, found a modeling study. The resulting soil drying will drive areas into drought that would otherwise receive sufficient rainfall.[778]

Drought and extreme heat have already reduced crop yield, according to a study by Earth system scientists. Analyzing records of crop yields, and disasters of drought and heat, they estimated that between 1964 and 2007, the disasters reduced by up to 10% global yields of crops such as corn, rice, and wheat.[779]

Each 1°C in global temperature increase will reduce global yields of wheat (6%), rice (3.2%), and corn (7.4%), found an analysis by more than two dozen agricultural researchers. They said their study—combining models, statistical data, and field-warming experiments—"shows substantial risks for agricultural production, [which is] already stagnating in some parts of the world."[780]

And when researchers modeled effects of higher temperatures on corn and soybeans, they projected that corn and soybeans would lose up to 6% of yield for each day above 30°C (86°F).[781]

Another study of heat and harvests predicted that, by the end of the century, the tropics and subtropics will be blasted by temperatures exceeding even the most extreme temperatures of the past decades.[782] In that study, the researchers applied 23 global climate models to estimate future temperatures. For temperate regions, they projected normal future temperatures that match the hottest on record.

As an example of the harvest impact of such temperatures, they cited the 2003 heat wave in Western Europe, when corn harvests fell by one-quarter in France. That summer, mean temperatures rose 3.6°C (6.5°F) above normal. An estimated 52,000 people died between June and August from heat stress, making it one of the deadliest climate-related disasters in Western history. They warned in another paper that future warming could increase "globally synchronized maize production shocks."[783]

Other crop-specific studies have also concluded that corn, wheat, and rice will all suffer severe declines due to future global heating.[784] [785] [786]

New northern breadbaskets?

As global temperatures rise, Canada, Russia, and other northern countries will evolve into regions more amenable to crop production.[787] One modeling study found that continued global warming will render vast new regions of Siberia amenable to farming by 2080.[788]

However, there are major caveats to the prospect that these regions could become breadbaskets that could head off world famine. For one thing, the countries would have to create the infrastructures for large-scale agricultural industries—including providing fertilizer, machinery, and shipping to global markets. Given their low populations, the countries would also have to welcome large numbers of immigrants to do the farming—perhaps amid resistance from native peoples.

But most important, this agricultural revolution would have to proceed against the ecological, social, and political upheaval that climate disruption will bring by later this century.

Climate malnutrition

Beside a decrease in crop yield, crop nutritional quality will also suffer. Rising CO_2 levels cause crop plants to produce more carbohydrates at the expense of such nutrients as proteins and minerals.[789]

Mathematical biologist Irakli Loladze analyzed data from studies of 130 plant varieties collected worldwide over three decades to determine how CO_2 will affect crop plants. He found significant depletion of 25 important minerals—including calcium, magnesium, potassium, zinc, and iron—with higher CO_2 levels. His analysis indicated that higher CO_2 levels were connected to an average 8% decrease in the minerals.[790]

Crop researchers have conducted many experiments in which they grew plants at higher CO_2 concentrations meant to mimic future levels— comparing them with a control group grown under ambient conditions.

In one such study, researchers grew rice, wheat, corn, soybeans, field peas, and sorghum under higher CO_2 for twelve years. They found that in many cases, the higher CO_2 levels decreased zinc, iron, and protein concentrations.[791] In another study, researchers found a decrease in protein of about 6–14% in rice, wheat, barley, and potatoes grown under high CO_2 concentrations.[792]

They concluded that "by 2050, assuming today's diets and levels of income inequality, an additional 1.6% or 148.4 million of the world's population may be placed at risk of protein deficiency" because of elevated CO_2.

Rice is the world's most important human food crop, feeding billions. Crop scientists estimate that 600 million people will face nutritional deficiency because of the impact of higher CO_2 levels on rice. When scientists exposed 18 rice lines grown in Asia to higher CO_2 levels, they found significant declines in proteins, B vitamins, and essential minerals.[793]

Yet another study combined an agricultural model with risk assessments of the effects of changes in food consumption on the likelihood of deaths from such disorders as coronary heart disease, stroke, and cancer. That study found that poor nutrition could lead to some half a million total deaths by 2050.[794]

One telling biochemical plant study clearly revealed a drop in protein as CO_2 increased. In that study, plant physiologists analyzed goldenrod pollen grain samples dating back to 1842. They found a decline in the pollen's protein content by a third. This study overcame a problem with analyzing nutrition in crop plants, in that the plants have been genetically altered by breeding. So, different crop strains might show different nutritional changes. However, goldenrod is wild, and changes in its protein content over decades would more accurately reflect the effects of rising CO_2.[795]

De-nihilist CO_2 deception

One erroneous assertion of climate de-nihilists is that higher CO_2 levels will increase crop yields by enhancing crop growth and decreasing water requirements.

True, one study has shown that "CO_2 fertilization" does increase global plant growth.[796] However, the argument is fallacious, researchers have noted. For one thing, the fertilization effect is limited by limitations on soil nitrogen. Also, the effect saturates as CO_2 levels rise; higher levels also benefit weeds; and higher CO_2 levels cause nutrient loss (see Epidemic of Hunger).[797]

In fact, CO_2 fertilization is decreasing worldwide, due to limitations on water and fertilizer, found another study using modeling and ground-based and satellite data.[798]

21st-century Dust Bowl

In the US, this century could see a repeat of the devastating Dust Bowl that struck the American Great Plains in the 1930s, researchers have predicted. At current greenhouse gas levels, the heat waves that cause the region's Dust Bowl could recur once every four decades, versus the once-in-a-century frequency of 1936, one analysis revealed.[799]

Besides wreaking havoc on agriculture, such conditions create dust storms whose ultrafine particles penetrate lungs and can cause lung and heart disease.[800] Such dust can also carry pathogenic bacteria.[801]

Increases in windblown dust are already occurring, found one study using remote-sensing satellite data. The data showed a doubling of dust storms over the past 20 years, due to more frequent droughts and cropland expansion.[802]

"Our results suggest a tipping point is approaching, where the conditions of the 1930s could return," study leader Gannet Hallar told *Science*.[803]

A 21st-century Dust Bowl would be too severe for even 21st-century agricultural technology to overcome, predicted climatologists Michael Glotter and Joshua Elliot. They simulated the effects of future temperatures and consecutive droughts on wheat, corn, and soybeans. An increase of 4°c above today's average temperatures would reduce crop yields by up to 80%, they found.[804]

"By mid-century, even a normal year in precipitation could be as bad as what we saw in 1936," said Elliot. "And a year with even a 10–20% loss of precipitation becomes extraordinarily damaging."[805]

A us Dust Bowl would have global impacts. A four-year decline in wheat production of the same magnitude as the 1930s event would almost entirely exhaust us reserves and slash global reserves by almost one-third, according to one study.[806]

Depleted groundwater and "water wars"

As droughts increase, groundwater will be depleted, researchers predict. Most of the largest aquifers in the world are already being depleted faster than they are refilling, found an analysis of satellite data and groundwater use.[807]

Many aquifers could run out of water as early as the 2030s, found a more detailed study by hydrologist Inge deGraaf. She used data on the structure of groundwater-containing aquifers, on water withdrawals, and on interactions between aquifers and their water sources. She found that aquifers in India, Spain, and Italy could be depleted between 2040 and 2060. In the us, California aquifers could be depleted in the 2030s. And aquifers supplying Texas, Oklahoma, and New Mexico could be dry between the 2050s and 2070s. She concluded that by 2050, up to 1.8 billion people could live in areas where groundwater had been pumped dry, or nearly so.[808] [809]

A quarter of the world's population will face "extremely high water stress" due to drought and overuse, according to the World Resources Institute.[810]

That desperate future is dramatically evident in Mexico City, Mexico, and in Chennai, India, where the quest for water is a daily challenge due to persistent drought, drying wells, and rising demand. Both cities depend on a hodge-podge of water trucks to deliver water, amid growing scarcity and failed municipal systems. Michael Kimmelman of *The New York Times* wrote about Mexico City:

> Always short of water, Mexico City keeps drilling deeper for more . . . It is a cycle made worse by climate change. More heat and drought mean more evaporation and yet more demand for water, adding pressure to tap distant reservoirs at staggering costs or further drain underground aquifers and hasten the city's collapse.[811]

In Chennai in 2019, lines of people waiting for water stretched for blocks as the main reservoir became a dry, cracked lake bed.[812] A government report warned that 20 additional major cities in India could soon run out of water, affecting about 100 million people.[813]

Historically, water shortages have caused unrest and wars. The future could see such conflicts in critical river basins, including the Nile, Ganges-Brahmaputra, Indus, Tigris-Euphrates and Colorado rivers, according to a model created by environmental economists. Their model combined factors that would lead to unrest—including water scarcity, high population, and power imbalances.[814]

Salt-poisoned farmland, chokepoints, and synchronized shocks

As higher temperatures and drought kill crops, saltwater intrusion from sea-level rise will render barren vast areas of low-lying farmland. Higher temperatures will increase inland salinization due to increased evaporation. The result of such salinization will be not only catastrophic crop failures but a major trigger for climate migration.[815]

Prominent salinization hotspots include southern and western Australia, Mexico, South Africa, the US Southwest, and Brazil, found one study. Other hotspots include central India, and dry areas of Mongolia, northern China, Spain, Morocco, and Algeria.[816]

Increasing floods and storms will create transportation chokepoints in areas that see high trade volumes, preventing food from reaching its destination, pointed out another analysis.[817] The researchers wrote:

As extreme weather events become more common, the chances of coincidental disruptions occurring at different locations are likely to increase. Examples might include distant chokepoints being simultaneously disrupted by different weather systems, or a major chokepoint in one part of the world being closed during a harvest failure in a crop-growing region elsewhere. In such circumstances, market impacts are compounded.

They cited as an example a hurricane the size of Katrina (2005) shutting down US Gulf of Mexico exports, just as extreme rainfall rendered Brazil's roads impassable (which happened in 2013). The result would delay up 50% of global soybean exports.

The likelihood of simultaneous crop failures worldwide producing "synchronized production shocks" will greatly increase with higher temperatures, found climatologists studying global corn production.[818] Today, the likelihood is near zero of significant simultaneous production losses, they found. But in a 4°C-warmer world, this likelihood skyrockets to 86%.

"Our results portend rising instability in global grain trade and international grain prices, affecting especially the ~800 million people living in extreme poverty who are most vulnerable to food price spikes," they wrote.

Staggering burden of hunger

The perilous future of agriculture under climate disruption was succinctly summarized in an FAO report:

Climate change will affect agriculture and forestry systems through higher temperatures, elevated carbon dioxide (CO_2) concentration, precipitation changes, increased weeds, pests and disease pressure. Global mean surface temperature is projected to rise in a range from 1.8°C to 4.0°C by 2100. Such changes will have more or less severe impacts on all components of food security: food production and availability, stability of food supplies, access to food and food utilization . . . . In particular, the effect of increased demand for irrigation water could be enormous.[819]

Wrote one group of researchers specializing in studying the effects of climate on crops: "The global burden of undernutrition and micronutrient deficiencies remains staggering." They pointed out that more than two billion people are deficient in one or more nutrients, and 790 million people are deficient in caloric intake. They called keeping up with increasing global nutritional needs constitutes "one of the great humanitarian challenges of the twenty-first century."[820]

Population Metastasis

The ominous reality of global population growth over the next century is revealed in projections by the UN *World Population Prospects 2022* report.[821] It forecasts population rising from around 8 billion in 2020, to almost 10 billion in 2050, and around 11 billion in 2100. Some developed countries are expected to lose population, including China, Japan, and European countries. However, others such as those in Africa, will grow fast enough to more than offset those losses.

Such population pressure portends future famines, given the projected drop in crop production (see Epidemic of Hunger). And population growth will produce even greater climate disruption, given that more people unavoidably means more carbon emissions.

Ecological overshoot

Population growth raises the specter of what population biologists call "ecological overshoot." In such overshoot, when a population expands beyond the capacity of the environment to support it, its numbers continue to grow for a limited time. Then the population suffers a catastrophic decline. Researchers have demonstrated such overshoot in organisms from yeast to reindeer, and there is compelling reason to believe it will happen in the human population.[822]

One measure of humans' demand on the environment is our "ecological footprint"—a concept originated by Mathis Wackernagel and William Rees.[823] Our ecological footprint has exceeded the regenerative capacity of the biosphere since the 1980s, calculated Wackernagel and colleagues.[824] The global population now uses the equivalent resource and waste absorption capacity of 1.6 Earths, concluded another calculation by the Global Footprint Network.[825]

Population collapses occur when ecosystems "shift abruptly and irreversibly from one state to another when they are forced across critical thresholds," concluded a review of past collapses by paleoecologists.[826] They found "evidence that the global ecosystem as a whole can react in the same way and *is approaching a planetary-scale critical transition as a result of human influence* [emphasis added]."

Comparing today's climate disruption with that caused by the last ice age, lead author Anthony Barnosky said in an article in *Wired*: "Everything that happened the last time around is happening now, only more of it. . . . I think the evidence makes it pretty clear that another critical transition or tipping point is very plausible within the next century."[827]

The evidence presented so far in this book constitutes a compelling case for looming ecological collapse. That collapse would spawn a future in which the human species finds itself driven toward extinction.

Environmental Exodus

"Climate change is a new driver of human migration that many people expect will dwarf all others in its impact," said the chillingly matter-of-fact opening statement of the report *Climate Change and Migration Dynamics*.[828] The report concluded that global society's ability to keep up with the need "is even more unpredictable than the precise course of climate change itself." Driving these mass migrations, said the report, are sea-level rise, higher temperatures, drought, flooding, and severe storms.

Just as unpredictable is the number of people who would be displaced by climate disruption. Reports published over the last decades have projected a huge range, from 25 million to one billion by 2050.[829] [830] [831] [832] The problem is that attributing migration to climate change is incredibly complex. A myriad of interacting factors—political, demographic, economic, social, and environmental—influence decisions to migrate.[833] [834] However, studies have revealed some specific estimates:

- By 2050, 50–700 million people would be forced to migrate globally due to land degradation and related problems, found a land degradation assessment, cited earlier.[835]
- By 2050, 200 million people would become refugees *within* countries' borders, according to the World Bank. The migration will produce climate-vulnerable "hotspots" where tens of millions of people will either leave or seek to move into.[836]
- By 2100, up to 187 million people globally from coastal areas would be displaced by a two-meter sea-level rise, calculated coastal engineers using a computer model.[837]
- For US coastal areas, some 13 million people would flee inland due to a 1.8 meter sea-level rise, concluded an analysis by demographers. The refugees from such states as Florida, Louisiana, New Jersey, and Virginia would go to inland areas that would try to absorb the influx, even though they might be suffering from their own climate disruption impacts, such as groundwater depletion, drought, and heat waves.[838]

Fleeing the heat

Unlivable temperatures will in particular drive migration. By mid-century, even a 2°C global temperature increase will trigger a mass climate exodus in the Middle East and North Africa, according to a forecast by atmospheric scientists.[839] While 2°C seems minimal, the rise in temperature over land is far higher. The hottest temperatures in the regions could reach 45°C (113°F) by mid-century, and 50°C (122°F) by the end of the century, the researchers predicted. What's more, during the hottest periods, nights will not cool down, and heat waves will be more prolonged, they concluded.

Even a moderate global temperature increase will produce "potentially extreme population displacement" in the tropics, predicted environmental economists.[840] They modeled how many and how far people in tropical countries would have to travel to flee to tolerable temperatures in a 2°C warmer world. They found that almost 34% of the world population would have to migrate more than 500 kilometers and almost 14% would have to migrate double that distance. They concluded that ". . . the large displacements in the tropics lead to an almost complete evacuation of the equatorial band, with the displaced populations accumulating in tropical margins." This migration could mean a fourfold population increase in those areas, their model showed.

Beyond computer models, environmental economists have found a direct statistical correlation between temperature change and migration.[841] [842] They analyzed how temperatures in 103 source countries translated into asylum applications to the European Union. They found that temperature anomalies brought an increase in applications, and ominously, the increase was nonlinear with temperature. The researchers wrote that "Our findings support the assessment that climate change, especially continued warming, will add another 'threat multiplier' that induces people to seek refuge abroad."

Migration triggering conflict

Environmental refugees will constitute a major global security challenge, concluded a report by the National Intelligence Council (NIC).[843] The report asserted that:

> When climate-related effects overwhelm a state's capacity to respond or recover, its authority can be so undermined as to lead to large-scale political instability. . . . In the most dramatic cases, state authority may collapse partially or entirely.

Environmental migration may, in fact, be misperceived as arising from other factors. For example, the popular perception has been that the wave of immigrants from El Salvador, Guatemala, and Honduras seeking US asylum are fleeing gang violence and lack of jobs.[844] However, as the UN Food and Agricultural Organization concluded, those countries have suffered severe drought for over a decade, devastating their economies.[845] Indeed, media reports have unequivocally documented climate impacts on the migration to the US southern border.[846] [847] [848] [849] [850] And, while escape from violence may be a significant driver of migration, drought plays an indirect role in helping spawn that violence.[851]

Given the certainty of such droughts and other climate shocks globally over the next decades, such migrations can be seen as harbingers. As the next section reveals, environmental exodus is only one of many security threats from climate disruption.

Global UnSecurity

Besides the Central American migration, political turmoil from climate disruption is occurring across the globe. Among the flashpoints cited by environmental journalist Joseph A. Davis:

- The African Sahel region and the Horn of Africa, where droughts have exacerbated terrorism and conflict
- The Mekong region, Southeast Asia, and the Middle East, where conflicts have arisen between nations that have constructed dams and those downstream that depend on the rivers' water
- Arctic Ocean waters, where conflicts will arise among nations seeking to use the newly opened waters for shipping, fishing, oil, mining, and military uses.[852]

However, warned political scientist Jan Selby, climate disruption may be misleadingly used as a political and economic smokescreen:

Indeed, climate change is already regularly invoked to questionable ends across the Middle East and North Africa. It is used to explain away ecological catastrophes actually caused by unsustainable agricultural expansion, to make the case for investment in new and often unnecessary mega-projects, to obscure state mismanagement of local environmental resources and to argue against the redistribution of such resources to oppressed and minority groups. Climate change is also invoked to attract donor or research funding, to call for increased military spending, to construct new fictitious financial commodities or simply as a performative display of global citizenship and moral virtue.[853]

Clearly, though, climate-caused deterioration of world order—which might be dubbed "UnSecurity"—will intensify and grow with worsening climate disruption.

UnSecurity is much broader than social and political turmoil. It includes rising food prices, health risks, economic shocks, and more frequent weather disasters. These shocks can synergize with one another to create a general deterioration in security.

"Extreme weather events, such as heavy rainfalls, floods, droughts, cyclones, and heat waves, will disrupt critical human and natural systems," noted a National Intelligence Council report.[854] Such events "could trigger crop failures, wildfires, energy blackouts, infrastructure breakdown, or infectious disease outbreaks."

Even seemingly purely environmental events could have an impact, the report noted. For example, thawing of Arctic permafrost could rupture Russian oil pipelines, with both economic and political impacts—for example, threatening the stability of a Russian government dependent on oil revenue.

Climate "threat multipliers"

Unlike politicians, the military and intelligence communities have been notably clear-eyed about climate disruption's existential threat.

In 2007, a group of US generals and admirals coined the term "threat multipliers" to describe the potential for climate disruption to aggravate the impacts of political, social, and environmental stressors. In a 2014 report, they went further, declaring:

"In many areas [the impacts] will be more than threat multipliers; they will serve as catalysts for instability and conflict." The authors noted that extreme weather in Africa, Asia, and the Middle East are triggering food shortages, desertification, sea-level rise, and population dislocation and mass migration that threaten governments. "We see these trends growing and accelerating," they wrote.[855]

The 2014 Department of Defense *Quadrennial Defense Review* echoed this conclusion, calling climate disruptions impacts "threat multipliers that will aggravate stressors abroad such as poverty, environmental degradation, political instability, and social tensions—conditions that can enable terrorist activity and other forms of violence."[856]

Similarly, in 2019, the US intelligence community, in its annual worldwide threat assessment, wrote that climate hazards "are intensifying, threatening infrastructure, health, and water and food security."[857] And in 2020, a panel of US national security, military, and intelligence experts warned:

> Even at scenarios of low warming, each region of the world will face severe risks to national and global security in the next three decades. Higher levels of warming will pose catastrophic, and likely irreversible, global security risks over the course of the 21st century.[858]

"Market of violence"

Researchers have already found evidence of a strong link between climate disruption and conflicts. One research review concluded that climate impacts such as temperature increases, cropland loss, floods, and droughts are "major pathways by which climate change leads to collective violence."[859]

Sudan is a prime example of a catastrophic conflict triggered by climate disruption, wrote social psychologist Harald Welzer in his book, *Climate Wars*.[860]

Welzer described how Sudan's soaring temperatures, droughts, and spreading desert have shrunken farmland and grazing land, sparking violent conflict between nomadic tribesmen and small farmers.

"There is a critical threshold below which survival interests can be asserted only by force," he wrote. The conflicts there have cost millions of lives and see no end in sight. He cites the mass killings in the Darfur region of Sudan as "the First Climate War," with up to 500,000 people killed and millions fleeing to refugee camps.

The perpetrators were the Janjaweed militia men: "discharged or turncoat soldiers, adventurers, youth gangs, criminals and assorted adventurers," along with, all too often, children and teenagers. They massacred entire villages, burning them and the surrounding land to prevent resettlement.

"What was first reported to Western TV viewers as a tribal conflict between 'Arab horseback militias' and 'African farmers' looks, on closer examination, to have been a war by a government on its own population, in which climate change played a decisive role," Welzer wrote.

Such conflicts can create a self-sustaining "market of violence," that leads to the societal collapse of a failed state. The term, coined by ethnologist Georg Elwert, means that all the players have a vested interest in continuing the conflict.[861] They include warlords, corporations, private security, and military agencies, and Janjaweed—all of whom profit from the status quo and have no interest in peace agreements. Even aid agencies can become complicit, in that they pay protection money to warlords to obtain safe passage for relief supplies.

Heated conflicts

Heat in particular triggers conflict, found environmental policy researchers. They compared the statistical incidence of civil conflicts in the tropics during the hotter El Niño years relative to cooler La Niña years. They gleaned evidence that El Niño "may have had a role in 21% of all civil conflicts since 1950 . . . the first demonstration that the stability of modern societies relates strongly to the global climate."[862]

The researchers also found evidence of a climate-conflict link when they analyzed longer-term historical data on conflicts.[863] They synthesized 60 studies on climate and conflict from 10,000 BC to today. The conflicts ranged from individual violence to group conflict to the collapse of entire civilizations.

They wrote that climate can "have substantial effects on the incidence of conflict, [and] amplified rates of human conflict *could represent a large and critical impact of anthropogenic climate change* [emphasis added]."

Similarly, a study of armed conflicts from 1980 to 2010 found that 9% coincided with such climate shocks as heat waves or droughts. The figure rose to 23% in ethnically divided countries.[864]

Climate impacts don't even have to occur in an affected country to have an impact. In 2011, climate-caused wheat shortages in the Ukraine, Canada, and Australia led to higher prices in Egypt, which is the world's largest wheat importer. That price shock contributed to the uprising of the Arab Spring.[865]

Given that climate disruption will only worsen over the next decades, it follows that so will wars, and political and economic upheaval.

Systemic Collapse

A simple role-playing game in 2015 gave an inkling of the global political and economic collapse that could be wrought by intensifying climate disruption. For the game, the think tank CNA gathered two dozen experts to simulate how governments' behavior might change with more severe climate impacts. This was no naïve group, including renowned scientists, retired military personnel, diplomats, and national security professionals.

Each expert was assigned to play a senior decision-maker for a nation or region. They were tasked with deciding on such policies as limiting carbon emissions. Each turn in the game represented a decade, they were told.

The game did not go well. Around mid-century, the game entered a tipping point, in which the players ceased cooperation and became "selfish, more insular, and more willing to take risks to preserve their status quo." As the game wore on, players showed "a global fatigue with failed states and migrants," and technologists began advocating extreme measures such as geoengineering.[866]

"No one who started the game expected to see a near-total breakdown in cooperation as temperatures rose," wrote authors Alice C. Hill and Leonardo Martinez-Diaz in their account of the game. "And yet, as conditions grew worse, the players resorted to increasingly desperate and unilateral measures, just at a time when cooperation was needed most."[867]

Climate-related political turmoil has already broken out in unstable regions of Africa, Asia, and the Middle East. However, as climate disruption worsens, it would spread to the developed world, including democratic countries. The first inkling of such unraveling of democracies would be their move toward an authoritarian regime.

Given the impending crises from climate disruption "the imperative of survival would then trump democracy, with its procedural dawdling, endless debate, delays, compromises, evasions, and half measures," wrote environmentalist and political scientist David Orr in his book *Down to the Wire: Confronting Climate Collapse.*[868] The mounting stresses would make authoritarianism attractive "and unavoidable should democratic governments fail to respond effectively and quickly to the demands of the long emergency," he wrote.

Such failures easily metastasize beyond national borders because in an interdependent global society, "small disturbances in one place can ripple throughout the world," Orr wrote.

Societal collapse is triggered by the strain on the Earth's carrying capacity and the growing division of society into the rich and the poor, wrote social psychologist Harald Welzer in his book *Climate Wars*:

> As resources start to run out . . . more and more people will have fewer and fewer means to ensure their survival. Obviously this will lead to violent conflicts among those who wish to feed off the same area of land or to drink from the same trickling water source. . . New wars will be environmentally driven and cause people to flee from the violence, and, since they will have to settle somewhere, further sources of violence will arise—in the very countries where no one knows what to do with them, or on the borders of countries they want to enter but which have no wish at all to receive them.[869]

Besides ecological unraveling, a growing gap between rich and poor is a key trigger of collapse, found one modeling study: "Elites eventually consume too much, resulting in a famine among commoners that eventually causes the collapse of society," the researchers concluded.[870]

The conditions for such collapse already exist. Humans have already overshot the Earth's ecological carrying capacity (see Population

Metastasis). And the huge and growing economic inequality within and among countries has been well documented.[871] [872] [873]

Historian Jared Diamond, in his book *Collapse: How Societies Choose to Fail or Succeed*, described the flaws in societies that lead to collapse.[874] He proposed three reasons that societies fail to recognize a looming problem, or to perceive it after it arrives:

- A problem may be imperceptible
- "Distant" managers don't recognize it
- It is a "slow trend concealed by wide up and down fluctuations."

Climate disruption meets all of these criteria—notably that "distant" leaders who live in comfortable financial and environmental cocoons fail to appreciate its impact.

Diamond wrote that seemingly "rational behavior" also causes societies to fail at even attempting to solve a problem like climate disruption:

> Scientists term such behavior "rational" precisely because it employs correct reasoning, even though it may be morally reprehensible. The perpetrators know that they will often get away with their bad behavior, especially if there is no law against it or if the law isn't effectively enforced. They feel safe because the perpetrators are typically concentrated (few in number) and highly motivated by the prospect of reaping big, certain, and immediate profits, while the losses are spread over large numbers of individuals [who have] little motivation to go to the hassle of fighting back.

More than a decade ago, a cadre of science and policy experts described what would happen in a climate-related collapse:

> The collapse and chaos associated with extreme climate change futures would destabilize virtually every aspect of modern life. . . . All of the ways in which human beings have dealt with natural disasters in the past . . . could come together in one conflagration: rage at government's inability to deal with the abrupt and unpredictable crises; religious fervor, perhaps even a dramatic rise in millennial end-of-days cults; hostility

and violence toward migrants and minority groups . . . and intra- and interstate conflict over resources, particularly food and fresh water.[875]

The collapse may arrive even as developed countries enjoy healthy economies. This topsy-turvy economic logic arises because the rebuilding from climate disasters may positively impact the countries' Gross Domestic Product (GDP).[876] Author Jeremy Lent explains:

Devastated communities mean big profits for the companies supplying materials, technology, services, and finished goods for the rebuilding. . . . This disconnect between GDP and the health of our society means that, even when things become more desperate for people as climate breakdown worsens, investors may keep enjoying high returns on their investments.

Thus, developed countries may enjoy being temporary islands of prosperity even as the world collapses around them—until they, too, succumb.

Climate War Outbreak

Climate-caused political upheaval will increase the likelihood of major wars between countries, even a nuclear war. A prime example of such a war would be an India-Pakistan conflict. Its root cause would be melting of the vast glaciers and deep snows of the Himalayas.

Meltwater from the Himalayas flows into the valleys of Kashmir—a region long a source of violent disputes between India and Pakistan. Those disputes have been driven in part by both nations' need to access the waters of the Indus River Basin fed by the Himalayas. India controls the upstream waters critical to Pakistan's food and water supply and power generation. India is building dams on the river, and in 2019 announced its intent to revoke the treaty that gives Pakistan access to the water.

As detailed in an article by physicist Zia Mian, Pakistan has long claimed the territory and has fought multiple wars with India over that claim.[877]

Global heating will drastically reduce the water available, noted South Asian studies researcher Sunil Amrith. He wrote that an analysis of the region:

> . . . suggests that, even with a drastic reduction in carbon emissions, one-third of the Himalayan glaciers are doomed to melt by the end of this century; without a reduction in emissions, that grows to two-thirds. The livelihoods of well over a billion people are directly at risk from this.[878]

Amrith cited studies indicating that the rivers will begin to dry up periodically from 2050 to 2060, "putting at risk the food security of a significant portion of humanity."[879]

The situation is ripe for an escalation to full-scale nuclear war between the countries, wrote Mian. Pakistani media have declared that Pakistan would counter conventional Indian forces with a nuclear response. And India's nuclear doctrine holds that it will retaliate for even a smaller-scale tactical Pakistani nuclear assault with a massive strike on Pakistani cities. In turn, Pakistan has threatened that it will respond with its own massive attack.

What's more, the conflict could draw in the superpowers. Pakistan is forging closer military and economic ties to China, while India is becoming a strategic partner of the US. These alliances may give Pakistani and Indian leaders confidence in escalating a conflict and issuing nuclear threats during a crisis. And the increasingly tense and militarized rivalry between China and the United States could potentially draw them into a broader war.

Nuclear climate disaster

Even a limited regional nuclear war would have devastating global climate effects. India and Pakistan each possess a nuclear arsenal of more than 150 nuclear warheads.[880]

Detonation of just 50 Hiroshima-sized weapons on each side would create devastating consequences, according to modeling analyses.[881] [882] The analyses revealed that the blasts would launch five million metric tons of black carbon soot into the stratosphere, reducing ozone levels by up to half over populated areas—unprecedented in human history. The UV radiation penetrating to the surface would cause widespread damage to human health, crops, and ecosystems. Global surface temperatures would drop to the lowest levels in a thousand years, severely shortening growing seasons for half a decade and dissipating only gradually for a quarter century. The result would be global famine, concluded the study.

A Pakistan-India nuclear exchange would also trigger a multiyear "nuclear Niño," concluded another analysis, referring to the warming Pacific Ocean of an El Niño. Trade winds and ocean circulation would reverse—the latter halting upwelling that would starve surface waters of nutrients that marine life depends on.[883]

Of course, the climate catastrophe from a limited nuclear exchange pales in comparison with the extinction-level "nuclear winter" produced by a nuclear war between the US and Russia.[884]

A Pakistan-India war is only one nuclear scenario. As climate shocks worsen, other conflicts may well arise. The vast size of extant nuclear arsenals reveal the potential consequences of such nuclear conflicts. The total global inventory of nuclear warheads stands at about 13,000, according to the Federation of American Scientists.[885]

At least several hundred of those weapons are held by countries considered political and/or environmental flashpoints. Their unstable governments, regional conflicts, and/or climate vulnerability make them ripe for war, and their security agreements with major nuclear powers like Russia, the US, and China threaten that an initial regional nuclear exchange would metastasize.

As if that weren't enough . . .

Finally, while the climate-related impacts described in this section could cause human extinction, many global hazards not directly related to climate disruption could also trigger our species' demise. They should also be acknowledged. (For a summary, see Appendix 3: As if that weren't enough. . .)

V
The Epidemiology of Society's Failure

Those infected during a viral pandemic may be overwhelmed by the virus, suffering massive, potentially lethal inflammation. Similarly, global heating's effects threaten to be overwhelming and lethal to our species.

Tragically, key segments of society—the mainstream media, scientists, environmentalists, corporations, and politicians—have failed to warn and act against the looming climate catastrophe. That failure in turn has been underlain by our intrinsic human shortcomings. The sections that follow explore the epidemiology of those failures.

Why the Media Failed

The mainstream media's historic failure to cover the climate pandemic is perhaps the most visible. The media are supposedly society's sentinels, ever-alert to warn against dangers to society's well-being. But as this section shows, mainstream media coverage has not conveyed the stark reality of climate disruption's existential threat to humans. (For a discussion of past coverage, see Appendix 1: A history of neglected climate coverage.)

True, in recent years mainstream media coverage of climate disruption has ramped up considerably.[886] That coverage has been prompted by the growing impacts of unprecedented droughts, heat waves, wildfires, floods, and hurricanes. The mainstream media have also used scientific reports on climate studies as pegs for stories highlighting the threat of climate disruption. And the 2021 UN Climate Change Conference, COP26, occasioned a major, but temporary, uptick in coverage.[887]

Mainstream media have also increased the urgency of their climate-related language; for example, using such phrases as "climate catastrophe" and "climate emergency" in their stories.[888]

However, even with such increased attention, mainstream media coverage remains sparse compared with that of other crises. Imagine if the climate pandemic—which is an existential threat to humanity—had received even a fraction of the media coverage of the COVID-19 pandemic, which is not. More relevant, imagine if the climate pandemic received as much coverage as a looming nuclear war that threatened to end humanity.

The mainstream media still fail to cover the complexity of climate disruption. In particular, they largely neglect to make the critically important point that the current disastrous consequences of global heating are already baked in, so to speak. Global temperatures have already risen to levels that will continue to drive heat waves, droughts, wildfires, floods, higher ocean temperatures, and other catastrophes.

It will not get cooler.

The recent increased coverage and new terminology are too little, too late. The past lack of coverage engendered a false sense of security and contributed to the failure to develop meaningful climate policy. It failed to alert the public to climate disruption's dangers and to engender public support for meaningful policy.

Complicit journalistic "guard dogs"

Mainstream media have failed to cover climate disruption aggressively because they are not independent watchdogs looking out for public interest. Rather, they are "guard dogs" for the establishment, wrote environmental communicator Julia Corbett:

> Many citizens and scientists believe (or hope) that mainstream media will (or should) perform this watchdog function for climate change, even though mainstream media are businesses that sell audiences to advertisers and are dependent on the cooperation of the power structure to stay in business. . . . In reporting climate change, guard dog media report selected climate science

findings and international meetings but overall defer to the mainstream values of a dominant fossil fuel culture and the status quo. . . . If news media operate in the interests of status quo powers and not in the public interest, the media will never lead the call for social change regarding climate change.[889]

Journalist George Monbiot wrote of the mainstream media's complicity: "To pretend that newspapers and television channels are neutral arbiters of such matters is to ignore their place at the corrupt heart of the establishment. . . . Why should we trust multinational corporations to tell us the truth about multinational corporations?"[890]

One telling example of dubious corporate-media connections is *The New York Times*' role in producing corporate ads. More than just running externally produced ads for oil companies, the *Times* has an in-house agency, T Brand Studio, that creates such multimedia packages.[891] The agency's ads include those for ExxonMobil and Chevron.[892][893]

The studio website headlines in prominent type its connection with the *Times*, saying its ads are "Inspired by the journalism and innovation of *The New York Times*" and that "T Brand lives inside the New York City headquarters of *The Times*."

In sharp contrast, the ads it produces contain a nearly invisible disclaimer in tiny dark gray type on a light gray background that "The news and editorial staffs of *The New York Times* had no role in this post's creation."

There is no indication that such corporate advertising influences the *Times*' climate coverage. However, environmental groups have called for the newspaper to stop advertising fossil fuel companies. And when environmental journalist Emily Atkin interviewed current and former *Times* employees, they "expressed concerns about the paper's practice of creating and running fossil fuel ads [which] ranged from undermining the *Times*' own climate reporting, to harming *Times* readers' health, to aiding industry attempts to mislead the public about the deadly effects of fossil fuels."[894]

In sharp contrast, as discussed below, specialist climate media do tell the frightening truth to power. But the mainstream media—especially as they suffer disastrously declining revenues—will remain largely the guard dogs of the status quo, sometimes even the lap dogs.[895]

They will likely never fully convey the profound existential peril of climate disruption. And they will certainly not advocate for the drastic societal transformation needed to stave off extinction.

Misguided media managers

The failure of mainstream media coverage is emphatically not the fault of journalists, but rather the editors, publishers, and producers who set coverage priorities and staffing. While they relegated climate coverage to the back burner, journalists, especially environmental journalists, kept the flame burning. They have assiduously reported on climate science, and in fact—as noted in this book's online acknowledgments—played a key role in making this book possible.

In particular, climate news outlets—most notably, Climate Central, Climatewire, DeSmog, and Inside Climate News—have for years offered detailed, authoritative coverage of climate issues.[896] [897] [898] [899] And the journalism initiative Covering Climate Now has aided climate coverage in hundreds of mainstream news outlets.[900]

Journalism groups—most prominently the Society of Environmental Journalists (of which I am a member)—have actively advocated for climate coverage and offered educational programs and resources for journalists.[901] Of the role of media management, journalists Mark Hertsgaard and Kyle Pope asserted:

> The failure of news organizations to adequately cover the story is structural rather than the fault of environmental-beat reporters or climate experts. If anything, those journalists are the drum-beating exceptions to the news industry's problem. The shortfall is everywhere else, as newsroom managers have failed to see the climate crisis as fundamental, all-encompassing, and worthy of attention from every journalist on their payrolls.[902]

Of more recent climate coverage, Hertsgaard and Pope charged that, despite catastrophic fires and storms, "the climate crisis remains a marginal afterthought in most US news coverage. . . . This is media malpractice."[903]

Pigeonholed coverage

Mainstream media managers have largely relegated climate disruption coverage to the narrow environment category. They failed to broaden their perspective to cover climate disruption's catastrophic social, economic, and security impacts. Such a broader perspective would have motivated those managers to extend climate disruption coverage to their politics, business, international, and health sections.

The public does not share managers' narrow view of climate disruption, as revealed in a survey by the Yale/George Mason University climate change communication program. The survey found that respondents did perceive global warming as an environmental issue (79%) or a scientific issue (74%). But they also saw it as an agricultural (66%), severe weather (69%), economic (64%), humanitarian (60%), health (64%), political (60%), and/or moral (49%) issue.[904]

The majority of registered voters would support declaring global heating a national emergency, according to another survey.[905] However, the COVID-19 pandemic drastically changed the priorities of Americans. According to a Harris Poll, it caused climate disruption to plummet from the number one issue facing society to second-to-last among a list of a dozen options, ahead only of overpopulation. Said the pollsters, "the coronavirus didn't elbow aside other issues as muscularly as it did climate change."[906]

Climate not entertaining or profitable

Even amid increased attention and climatre catastrophes, mainstream media still do not give coverage of climate disruption the prominence it deserves, charged Hertsgaard and Pope. They wrote that "Most major news outlets still present climate change as no more important than a dozen other public issues, when the fact is that if the world doesn't get it under control, fast, climate change will overwhelm every other issue."[907]

For television news, the hard reality is that climate disruption does not fit its business model—in which luring viewers is the paramount concern.

"Coverage prioritizes entertainment and sensationalism that keeps people watching the commercial breaks," wrote journalist Molly Taft. "Having an expert explain how climate change made Hurricane Harvey's rainfall worse is important for the future of our planet; showing a reporter struggle in tough winds is entertaining."[908]

She recalled her experience pitching climate disruption segments to television producers: "I sensed that it had been perhaps so hard for me to get scientists on TV partially because hearing about science can be a little dry—bran flakes, not candy."

However, viewers are far more interested in climate disruption than the editors, publishers, and producers give them credit for. When MSNBC anchor Chris Hayes dubbed climate disruption a "ratings killer," climate reporter Zoya Teirstein retorted:

"The reason that newsrooms are failing to bring up climate change has a lot to do with the way major news outlets are structured (profits first, content second) . . . and less to do with people's interest in climate change."[909]

Indeed, large majorities of viewers of major TV news outlets say they are interested in news stories about global warming topics, found a survey by the Yale/George Mason University program. Most survey respondents said the media should do more to address global warming, with fewer than 20% saying they feel "very well informed about climate disruption."[910]

Mainstream media managers have employed only a modest number of science and environment journalists—compared to, say, the number of sports, entertainment, and political reporters. And over the last decades, media have reduced the science and environment journalists in their employ—a part of the overall decline in newsroom staff.[911] [912]

Because of limited staffing and coverage, the vast majority of news of climate discoveries and reports appear in only a few media outlets (as I discovered when searching for articles in developing this book).

Fake climate news

Even major media outlets have inaccurately covered climate science. For example, national us newspapers have published misleading opinion pieces on climate science—including *The New York Times, Wall Street Journal, The Washington Post,* and *USA Today* (see Appendix 2: Major print media published de-nihilist opinion).

Network television news, in particular the Fox News Network, aired bias coverage. In 2013, 72% of the time Fox's coverage of climate disruption was misleading, found the Union of Concerned Scientists. By contrast, 30% of cnn's coverage and only 8% of msnbc's coverage was misleading.[913]

Fox News has continued to run inaccurate opinion articles, such as a 2019 piece by a representative of the Heartland Institute, which asserted that "the available evidence shows that warming is not dangerous and not likely to be catastrophic."[914] The network and other conservative media have continued to dismiss the role of climate disruption in natural disasters—for example in the 2020 wildfires on the us West Coast.[915]

Media have traditionally preferred to structure stories with a hero and a villain, which has led to false balance in climate coverage (see Appendix 1: A history of neglected climate coverage). However, accurately covering climate disruption is more complex than this simplistic storyline. In reality many of its players can be seen as both heroes and villains. Even the convenient "villains" of the fossil fuel industry and the "heroic" environmentalists do not really fit neatly into their categories (see Why the Corporations Failed, Why the Environmentalists Failed).

Climate facts fade fast

The episodic "one-and-done" nature of the daily media has also led to inadequate climate coverage. Reporters who are pressured to produce can usually do only limited stories on new discoveries. They are seldom given the time or space to add context and explore the discoveries' larger ramifications.

And journalists are seldom given the chance to maintain the steady drumbeat of climate disruption stories that would keep it foremost in the public mind.

What's more, the facts presented in climate stories tend to fade quickly in their influence on public perceptions. One study explored this fading effect by asking some 3,000 volunteers to read articles about climate disruption, followed by other articles that included ones casting doubt on climate science. The researchers found that, while the accurate articles influenced readers, that influence faded quickly when readers were exposed to media that cast doubt on climate disruption's reality.[916] [917]

Journalists—other than environmental journalists—also tend to see environmentalism as less critical to society's well-being than the oil industry. One telling example is the headlines over news stories in 2021 about climate activists gaining power on the boards of oil companies. Climate journalist Emily Atkin found that 26 headlines read something like "A bad day for big oil," but only 3 headlined the story as a win for activists.[918] Atkin commented that:

> News outlets routinely favor a political framing over an existential framing when it comes to climate stories. In general, the push-and-pull between industry and activists is given greater attention than the fight over everyone's health and economic well-being.

Journalists also find it difficult to cover climate disruption because of its often depressing nature. Studies have shown that readers are turned off by depressing news. One basic problem is "the hope gap" between the stark reality of climate disruption and what people can do about it, said Anthony Leiserowitz, director of the Yale Project on Climate Change Communication, to *Climate Central*. "Perceived threat without efficacy of response is usually a recipe for disengagement or fatalism," he said.[919]

The media do not tend to offer positive solutions that would counteract this fatalism. For example, less than a fifth of major networks' segments on climate disruption mentioned solutions, found a Media Matters analysis.[920]

The media also minimize climate disruption coverage because of the inherent uncertainties in climate science, just as there are uncertainties in all science (see Why the Scientists Failed). As environmental reporter Andrew Revkin commented:

> Implicit uncertainty is one reason global warming remains a bad fit for conventional media. Nuance does not make for a fat headline or big front-page play. . . . you don't get extra space in a newspaper or time on a broadcast because climate science is more complex. In fact, the more complex or conditional a story is, often the less space it is granted.[921]

Finally, mainstream editors, publishers, and producers still tend to view climate disruption as just another story, even amid climate-related catastrophes and dire predictions in scientific reports. To illustrate with a personal anecdote:

As this book was being finalized, I submitted an editorial on climate disruption to a leading science media outlet. The editor responded that the outlet "has had so many op-eds on climate recently that I'm going to have to take a pass."

Perhaps my editorial didn't meet the editor's quality standards. But for any science editor to seriously declare that there could be "so many" editorials on climate disruption reveals an endemic just-another-story attitude.

Why the Scientists Failed

While the mainstream media have failed to adequately cover climate disruption, they are not entirely culpable. After all, the media can only cover what climate scientists are willing to communicate. This section details how scientists—climate scientists and others who should have spoken out—have failed in that communication.

True, climate scientists face a massively daunting challenge to understand the intricate, ever-changing global climate, with its multitude of diverse environments.

They are certainly indefatigable and ingenious. Some scientists embark on ocean voyages aboard instrument-laden research vessels.[922] Others analyze cores from probes drilled thousands of meters into the

Antarctic ice sheets.[923] Still others feed masses of such data into supercomputers to construct intricate mathematical models of Earth's climate.[924]

They are meticulous in their research, and their findings are as complete and accurate as they can make them.

We quite properly trust these scientists. One survey found that 71% of the respondents "strongly" or "somewhat" trusted climate scientists as a source of information.[925]

That said, trust in climate scientists depends heavily on political affiliation. A Pew Research Center survey found that only 15% of conservative Republicans trust climate scientists to "give full and accurate information about the causes of climate change." More trusting were moderate/liberal Republicans (32%), moderate/conservative Democrats (45%), and liberal Democrats (70%).[926]

Although climate scientists are trustworthy, they do have flaws. Those flaws have played a central role in their ultimate failure to do their full measure of effort in warning society about climate disruption. Some of these flaws arise from the fundamental nature of science; others from scientists' personal tendencies.

Scientists are never certain

The nature of science dictates that scientists must always be tentative. Their discoveries may seem definitive in media reports, but a new scientific paper can force scientists to revise or even abandon a conclusion. Such tentativeness is a natural and valuable part of the scientific process. It serves scientists well in the laboratory or the scientific meeting. However, the lay public may misinterpret uncertainty as ignorance or evasiveness.

Debating scientific findings is also critical for scientific advance, but scientists tend not to recognize that their internal debates are now public, thanks to the internet. Wrote environmental journalist Andrew Revkin:

> Conflicting findings can make news coverage veer from one extreme to another, resulting in a kind of journalistic whiplash for the public. . . . Scientists see persistent disputes as the normal stuttering journey toward improved understanding of how the world works. But many fear

that the herky-jerky trajectory is distracting the public from the undisputed basics and blocking change.[927]

Scientists also *don't know what they don't know*, which presents another inherent obstacle to communication.

As climate disruption historian Spencer Weart puts it: "In an area as difficult as climate science, where all is complex and befogged, it is hard to see what one is not prepared to look for."[928]

A few examples of such scientific fog:

- Scientists are still unsure how the collapse of the massive Antarctic Thwaites Glacier will affect sea levels (see The Inexorable Melt).[929]
- Methane emissions from oil and gas wells and other sources are being constantly revised upward by new studies (see Mounting Methane).[930] [931] [932] [933]
- Human-made reservoirs are the source of a surprising amount of methane from bacterial breakdown (see Dam Surprising).[934] [935]
- The mass bleaching of Australia's Great Barrier Reef has shocked scientists (see Ravaged Shores).[936]
- Computer models that attempt to predict when species will go extinct are often unrealistic and unreliable (see Mass Extinction).[937]
- Vicious northern winters and massive snowfalls may—or may not—be due to global heating (see Superstormy Weather).[938]

Despite this limitation in understanding, science's rigor still makes it the most reliable source of human knowledge.

Of course, this book relies on scientific papers whose findings are by nature tentative. So, some findings may be proved wrong and others may require revision. However, like a digital image, in which some picture elements change but the overall image persists, these findings form an unequivocal, tragic picture of our potential extinction.

Scientists have a "low-dimensional" view in a "high-dimensional" world

Scientists lead relatively insular lives, spending most of their time in a relatively narrow "low-dimensional" realm of laboratory, seminar room, and field station. They mostly interact with other scientists—collaborating, mentoring, teaching, and supervising. They actually need little contact with laypeople to advance in their careers—when they apply for grants, do experiments, publish scientific papers, and give scientific talks.

Their professional focus is also low-dimensional. For example, in their field studies, they aim to gather narrowly defined data on specific phenomena—whether climate effects on trees or the Greenland ice sheet melting.

Similarly, scientists design narrowly defined laboratory experiments that try to hold constant all elements of a system except one—like evolving a recipe for perfect bread by varying only one ingredient at a time. Even computer modelers, who use a multitude of inputs in their models, cannot possibly encompass the broader complexity of the natural environment, or the social, political, and economic factors that affect it.

Seldom penetrating this professional shell are the broader social, economic, and/or political implications of their research. They have a limited ability to engage the far more complex "high-dimensional" world of politics, media, and the public arena.

Compare this insular lifestyle with that of doctors, lawyers, and politicians. Their professional advancement depends on their ability to communicate with laypeople and to grapple with the moral and political dimensions of their actions. Doctors must explain their diagnoses; lawyers must explain the law to clients and juries; and politicians must persuade voters.

Scientists' instruments also limit their vision. For example, in the remote Arctic, the lack of ground-based automated instruments means that researchers can't precisely measure winter CO_2 emissions. The region is too remote for scientists to make detailed ground measurements in the frigid, dark winter months. This lack of winter measurements is critical because scientists need to understand how soils warmed by global heating are emitting CO_2.[939] [940]

Scientists neglect the human factor

Climate scientists' largely technical approach to their field recalls the saying, "to a man with a hammer, everything looks like a nail." To the environmental scientists, climate disruption looks like a purely environmental problem. They see it as a problem that they can solve—for example, predicting the effects of limiting CO_2. But climate disruption is a stunningly complex *human* problem since it has ultimately arisen from human needs. As climatologist Bill McGuire put it in his book *Hothouse Earth*:

> So complex and intertwined are the interactions and relationships between the climate, the natural world and human society and economy that—despite meticulous and comprehensive modelling—the nature, scale and breadth of climate breakdown impacts later in the century, and beyond, can only be guessed at.[941]

Sociologists have charged that environmental scientists have neglected the human element in climate disruption. Wrote sociologists Riley Dunlap and Robert Brulle in their book *Climate Change and Society*:

> From the very beginning of the climate change research effort, the social sciences have been and continue to be marginalized. Consequently, from a natural science perspective, human activities remain in their black box, largely inaccessible.[942]

They pointed out that only 3% of scientific papers dealing with climate disruption have come from sociologists. When natural scientists do address climate disruption's human elements, they mistakenly emphasize "the role of individuals in generating carbon emissions—who are thus held responsible for reducing them," wrote Dunlap and Brulle. They wrote that stressing individual behavior:

> . . . thus leaves the institutions that structure everyday life and individual practices unexamined [and] obscures the extent to which governments sustain unsustainable economic institutions and ways of life, and the extent to which they have a hand in structuring options and possibilities.

Consequently, they warned that "efforts to address climate change . . . are unlikely to succeed without greater knowledge of human behavior and societal dynamics supplied by social science."

A prime example of climate disruption's human impacts is rising temperatures's perils (see IV. Viral Human Consequences). Economists Tamma Carleton and Solomon Hsiang described them:

> Temperature . . . exerts remarkable influence over human systems at many social scales . . . heat induces mortality, has lasting impact on fetuses and infants, and incites aggression and violence while lowering human productivity.[943]

Our failure to understand the human side of climate disruption means that we will fail to forge a path to solutions. After all, it is our human nature that underlies culture, politics, and economics—all of which must be taken into account in any solutions.

Scientists are occupational optimists

Imagine you are trying to build a machine, and it fails miserably time after time. You're in deep trouble because you've already claimed that it *will* work to those who funded your machine.

Each day you tweak and test and rethink a new design; and each day the machine dishearteningly fails again. Finally, after years of failure, you get the machine to function! But when you submit an article describing your success, the publisher enlists anonymous reviewers—perhaps your rivals—to criticize the design. Their criticisms force you to tweak the article again and again. Finally, you are allowed to unveil your machine to the world, but you know that at any moment a rival may invent a new, improved version that will render yours obsolete.

Welcome to the world of scientists, who toil in a profession in which they fail at the vast majority of experiments they try. In a *Scientific American* article, a young biologist, Maryam Zaringhalam, wrote frankly that:

> Scientists seldom speak of false starts. While we all have stories about failure, the scientific narrative is dominated by bold questions that begat experimental triumphs. . . . If failure is mentioned, it is only in the past tense, listed

as a steppingstone to discovery. . . . But mediocre failures—the mistakes and errors that lead to nothing—have
no place. . . . Nearly everything that happens in the lab
will never make it to print.[944]

To win funding in the first place, scientists must project a determined
optimism in their research proposals. They must project a confidence in
inevitable success. Almost certainly, no scientist has ever submitted a
research proposal declaring, in essence: "We'll give it our best shot, but
we suspect we won't find anything."

Scientists plunge ahead driven by dedication, passion, and optimism. However, this mask of optimism sometimes slips, as climate
scientists revealed on the website Is This How You Feel? The website
contains their letters telling how they feel about the prospect of climate disruption. A poignant example came from climatologist David
Griggs, who wrote:

"How do I feel about climate change?
- I feel confused that many people seem unable to see what seems
  so obvious to me, that we need to act urgently on climate change.
- I feel frustrated that those with the power to affect the transformation we need seem oblivious to the need to act.
- I feel occasionally optimistic when I see progress in renewables
  or companies embracing sustainable practice.
- I more often feel depressed when I think how much we need to
  do and how little time we have to tackle climate change.
- I feel guilty about not achieving more to solve the problem and
  helplessness to know what more to do.
- I feel a great sense of loss for the species that have become extinct
  on our watch and the many more we are set to lose.
- I feel privileged to have worked with so many intelligent, hard-
  working, ethical, and thoroughly nice people who have dedicated
  their lives to making the world a better place.
- But most of all I feel so very sorry for my children's and my
  (hypothetical) grandchildren's generation, for all the beautiful
  things in the world that they will miss."[945]

Scientists self-censor

Climate scientists historically tended to mute their public voices and downplay the severity of climate disruption. Their self-censorship stemmed from their innate scientific reserve and denunciations—even persecution—by de-nihilists, who reject climate science. As climatologist Kevin Anderson wrote in 2015:

> In several important respects, the modeling community is self-censoring its research to conform to the dominant political and economic paradigm. . . . We simply are not prepared to accept the revolutionary implications of our own findings. . . . And even when we do, we are reluctant to voice such thoughts openly. Instead, my long-standing engagement with many scientific colleagues leaves me in no doubt that whilst they work diligently, often against a backdrop of organised scepticism, many are ultimately choosing to censor their own research.[946]

Terming such timidity "scientific reticence," climatologist James Hansen wrote in 2016 that "I believe, the affliction is widespread and severe. Unless recognized, it may severely diminish our chances of averting dangerous climate change."[947]

Hansen cited cases in which scientists reviewing his papers before publication objected to his use of the word "dangerous" to describe the consequences of global heating. The reviewers suggested that the word be enclosed in parentheses, or be changed to "potentially dangerous," or rephrased as "could be dangerous."

"There is a very important issue at play here," wrote Hansen. "The relevant scientific community, in our opinion, has been exercising self-censorship in its warning to the public about the danger of human-made climate change."

Hansen, even as he suffered de-nihilists' attacks, has by no means been reticent himself. He has played a seminal role in bringing public attention to the reality and dangers of climate disruption—most notably in 1988 testimony to a US Senate Committee. In that testimony he bluntly warned that the Earth is warming; that the warming is due to the greenhouse effect; and it will affect summer heat waves.[948] More recently, his program on Climate Science, Awareness and Solutions continues to promote public awareness of climate disruption and to connect climate science to policy.[949]

Because climate scientists self-censored, they allowed de-nihilism to seep into the science, concluded psychologists who analyzed the phenomenon. They wrote:

> In response to constant, and sometimes toxic, public challenges, scientists have over-emphasized scientific uncertainty, and have inadvertently allowed contrarian claims to affect how they themselves speak, and perhaps even think, about their own research. . . . This "seepage" has arguably contributed to a widespread tendency to understate the severity of the climate problem.[950]

Because of scientists' perceived need to speak in a single voice, they have underestimated the pace of climate change, asserted Naomi Oreskes, Michael Oppenheimer, and Dale Jamieson. They dubbed the phenomenon "univocality," writing:

> Many scientists worry that if disagreement is publicly aired, government officials will conflate differences of opinion with ignorance and use this as justification for inaction. Others worry that even if policymakers want to act, they will find it difficult to do so if scientists fail to send an unambiguous message.[951]

The authors also wrote that scientists worry that, if they *overestimate* a threat, they will lose credibility; but if they *underestimate* the threat, they will suffer little if any impact on their reputation:

> In climate science, this anxiety is reinforced by the drumbeat of climate denial, in which scientists are accused of being "alarmists" who "exaggerate the threat." In this context, scientists may go the extra mile to disprove the stereotype by downplaying known risks and denying critics the opportunity to label them as alarmists.

What's more, wrote the authors, scientists are reluctant to make any estimates when data are internally contradictory. These tendencies can lead scientists to "minimalist conclusions that are weak or incomplete."

"Erring on the side of least drama" is how Oreskes and colleagues characterize scientists' inclination to downplay dramatic, alarming, or upsetting results, such as Arctic ozone depletion and the disintegration of the West Antarctic ice sheet. The melting of the ice sheet would constitute a major catastrophe, raising sea levels many feet.[952]

And as climate scientist Katharine Hayhoe succinctly said of her peers, "If they say something's bad, you know it's probably a lot worse than they said."[953]

Even amid their self-censorship, though, climate scientists have expressed an overwhelming and carefully documented consensus supporting the reality of human-caused climate disruption and global heating.[954] Essentially all climate scientists accept the scientific certainty of human-caused climate disruption.

The catch is that only about one in every five Americans know how strong that consensus is—that 90% of scientists think global heating is happening.[955] It is just as likely that Americans don't know that 31 of the world's scientific societies signed a letter reaffirming the reality of climate disruption.[956]

In their self-censorship, scientists tended to delude themselves that they have done their full duty to society by publishing their findings in scientific journals. However, they failed to understand that facts don't communicate themselves; that they require dissemination, explanation, and aggressive advocacy.

While this self-censorship has recently waned amid growing climate-related catastrophes, it rendered scientists inadequate sources of information on climate disruption's dangers.

Scientists build imperfect, but useful, climate models

In a large windowless room in Greenbelt, Maryland, sits a phalanx of black, monolithic computer cabinets. Rows of furiously blinking indicator lights reflect the pace of computation going on within their 129,000 processors. This is the Discover supercomputing cluster at NASA's Center for Climate Simulation.[957] It is among a multitude of centers worldwide that enlist supercomputers to model the global climate.

Researchers construct climate models—intricate networks of equations—based on fundamental physical principles. Then, in an effort to predict the future course of climate disruption, they their feed their models data on such phenomena as solar radiation; greenhouse gases; and aerosols emitted from fossil fuels, fires, and volcanoes.

The models then produce scenarios of possible future climates—including temperatures, precipitation, snow and ice cover, winds, and atmospheric and ocean circulation. The climate modelers then compare those outputs with measurements from the real world. They then "tune" their models' equations until they match real-world measurements. Once they decide their models adequately reflect reality, they begin to pose "what-if" questions to seek to predict future climates.[958]

Models are hellishly complex, controversial, and ever-changing. They can be every bit as mutable as the SARS-COV-2 coronavirus. Their assumptions are continually brought into question. For example, one criticism has been leveled that current models vastly overstate the production of coal and that resulting scenarios project implausible extreme climate impacts.[959] [960]

Nevertheless, such models underpin the efforts to create policies to mitigate climate disruption by the UN Intergovernmental Panel on Climate Change (IPCC). And while the models are impressive and valuable, they have inherent shortcomings that limit their ability to reliably predict future climate disruption.

These shortcomings are not the fault of the scientists who create the models. They arise because of lack of data and understanding of the extremely complex, dynamic global climate—both past and present. And the models are based on scientific theory, which is always subject to revision. Wrote climate scientist Zeke Hausfather:

> Models are necessarily imperfect and cannot foresee all of the technological or societal changes that will happen over the coming century. For example, models used to struggle to reach 2°C targets before they started including large-scale negative emissions technologies—though these still largely exist only in the models, rather than in real-world deployments at scale.[961]

"Discrepancies between model forecasts and subsequently observed data are expected—indeed, they are the *source* of progressive improvements in understanding," wrote Kathleen Hall Jamieson, Dan Kahan, and Dietram Scheufele. "By design, dynamic modeling enlarges knowledge through its *failed predictions* as much as through its successful ones."[962]

A major problem with climate models is failure to communicate their uncertainty, the authors wrote:

> Not only did the science communicators fail to make this element of climate science clear to the public, but over the past decade, many of them adopted communication "strategies" that elided it. To promote the urgency of action, they depicted the projections of the [IPCC reports] as extrapolations from settled and incontrovertible scientific findings. But because this framing was selected to accommodate the popular understanding that science warrants confidence based on experimentally "proven" facts, it made climate science more vulnerable to attack by those intent on undermining public confidence in it when, as was anticipated by scientists themselves, actual data diverged from the climate science model forecasts.

The range of uncertainty in climate models doesn't mean they're wrong. If you rammed your car into a tree, there would be a range of uncertainty about whether you would survive. But ramming your car into a tree would still be a calamity.

The upshot seems to be, scientists really don't know for sure which models are good and which aren't.

Scientists "tune" their models

As mentioned earlier, scientists tune their models to improve them. As journalist Paul Voosen explained: "When the equations miss the mark and the model strays from the known climate, scientists . . . bring it back into harmony by adjusting [their models]." Such tuning is, and will remain, ad hoc and limited, wrote Voosen: "Indeed, whether climate scientists like to admit it or not, nearly every model has been calibrated precisely to the 20th century climate records."[963]

The human element is very much part of the climate modeling "equation." Climatologist Michael Oppenheimer and colleagues termed expert judgment "an unavoidable element" of climate models.[964]

Oppenheimer commented that "scientists working in climate change know that the models used throughout climate research have shortcomings . . . the procedure by which experts assess the accuracy of models projecting potentially ruinous outcomes for the planet and society is *surprisingly informal* [emphasis added]."[965]

However, here's a key message to climate de-nihilists: Such tuning does not reflect uncertainty about the *reality* that global heating is happening. That reality is irrefutable.[966] Rather, the tuning relates to uncertainty about the *speed and magnitude* of temperature rise, sea-level rise, and other phenomena.

Scientists' models look backward with blurry vision

In their modeling, scientists often look backward in order to look forward—using historical data to test their models. But their rearview vision is far from 20/20. In reality, scientists aren't really sure *what* historical global temperatures were. There simply wasn't enough instrumentation. So, historical global temperatures are calculated by blending the few temperatures measured over land with the few measured over ocean, wrote climate scientist Ed Hawkins. These measurements could only be obtained where there were thermometers on land and ships on the ocean. Thus, the measures are "sparse, differently measured changes of temperature over time," he wrote.[967]

For temperature measures before thermometers existed, scientists rely on "paleoclimate proxies." These are temperature-indicating materials preserved within the geologic record, including everything from plankton to cave deposits. Analyzing them to deduce ancient temperatures is technically challenging and subject to interpretation.

Scientists' models are blind to abrupt changes

Another climate model shortcoming is that they do not take into account data on the sometimes-drastic changes in the paleoclimate. Such data could significantly improve climate models' accuracy, noted one study. The authors wrote that "Although the latest Earth system models offer an unprecedented number of features, fundamental uncertainties continue to cloud our view of the future."[968]

Scientists' blurry view of the paleoclimate means that climate models are ill-equipped to predict future abrupt changes. As the *National Climate Assessment* stated:

> [Climate models] do not include all of the processes that can contribute to feedbacks ... compound extreme events, and abrupt and/or irreversible changes. For this reason, future changes outside the range projected by climate models cannot be ruled out .... Moreover, the systematic tendency of climate models to underestimate temperature change during warm paleoclimates suggests that climate models are *more likely to underestimate than to overestimate the amount of long-term future change* [emphasis added].[969]

Abrupt changes arise from events like major volcanic eruptions or "tipping points"—irreversible transitions triggered by rising temperatures (see Climate Monsters). These tipping points cause feedback that drives even greater temperature rise. They include massive methane release from frozen subsea deposits called clathrates; uncontrolled burning of peat bogs; and massive release of CO_2 from decay of thawing permafrost.

In cataloging such tipping points, researchers have found shortcomings in climate models. Wrote climate physicist Sybren Drijfhout:

> Most climate models still don't even factor in how vegetation will respond to changes in climate [which] would probably lead to more predictions of land-based "tipping points." Likewise, ice sheet collapses and carbon and methane release from thawing permafrost could

also lead to abrupt transitions but aren't yet included in climate models.[970]

For example, current climate models don't agree on how fast Arctic permafrost will thaw because they don't reproduce such surface features as thermokarst lakes, said the 2021 IPCC report on the physical basis of climate change.[971] Vast numbers of such lakes produced by thawing permafrost dot the Arctic.[972] The IPCC report found that "not representing thermokarst-inducing processes in ice-rich terrain leads to a systematic underestimation of the rapidity and magnitude of permafrost thaw."

When researchers did create a model that took the effects of new lake formation into account, they found that by 2100 the increased permafrost thawing could add millions more metric tons of methane to the atmosphere per year than other models predicted.[973]

Carbon emissions from warming soils is another important CO_2 source left out of climate models because of high uncertainty (see Respiring Soils). In one study, when ecologists analyzed the results of field experiments in which test plots were artificially warmed, they calculated that up to 50 billion metric tons of carbon could be released from warming soils by 2050. They noted that their estimates have "considerable uncertainty," but that "the direction of the global soil carbon response is consistent across all scenarios."[974]

"It's of the same order of magnitude as having an extra US on the planet," co-author Thomas Crowther told *The Washington Post*. "The entire magnitude of this feedback was removed from several of the Earth system models, the models that inform [the IPCC] because of its massive uncertainty," he said.[975]

Scientists' models can't handle feedback

Feedback—in which change triggers more change—is a fundamental property of such tipping points. Climate models fall short in taking into account feedback mechanisms, both the *National Climate Assessment* and individual researchers have asserted.

One important such mechanism is carbon-cycle feedback. The carbon cycle comprises the chemical and physical processes by which carbon is exchanged among the atmosphere, land, ocean, and organisms. It governs how much emitted CO_2 is absorbed by the oceans and land.

While the oceans and land currently absorb about half of emitted CO_2, this absorption drops with rising global temperature. Feedback arises because warming oceans and soil can hold less CO_2. And more CO_2 is released by dying trees, wildfires, and thawing permafrost. This CO_2 increase feeds back to trigger higher atmospheric CO_2.

Uncertainties about carbon-cycle feedback constitute a major reason why different climate models yield different results. Such uncertainties could mean major differences in projected warming. Feedbacks could result in up to 25% more warming than in IPCC projections, one study showed.[976]

Scientists' models can't handle multiple disasters

Nor can models handle the complex interactions among multiple climate phenomena. As climatologist Katharine Hayhoe commented at a scientific meeting when discussing the report the *National Climate Assessment*:

> Even though we know our climate models incorporate most of the important processes . . . we know they don't include all the processes that can contribute to these vicious cycles—to these types of compound extreme events, where you have heat and drought, or flood and heat happening at the same time—and abrupt or irreversible changes. And so we conclude that future changes outside the range projected by climate models cannot be ruled out.[977]

And as the *Assessment* itself pointed out, these effects "can be greater than the sum of the parts."[978]

The future will see more multiple, simultaneous climate disasters, concluded a research review by Camilo Mora Mora and colleagues.[979] They compiled data on such hazards as heat waves, drought, floods, storms, and fires. They concluded that by 2100, the world could be exposed to three such simultaneous hazards if emissions are not aggressively reduced. Some tropical coastal areas could face up to six simultaneous hazards, they projected. Mora told *The New York Times* the prospect is "like a terror movie that is real."[980]

Scientists' models are dehumanized

Because climate scientists have neglected to see climate disruption as a human problem, as discussed earlier, their models reflect this neglect. For example, climate models have not included the interaction between the "Earth system" and the "Human system," noted researchers led by Safa Motesharrei. They define the Human system as including growth in resource use, land-use change, emissions, and pollution.

"This makes current models likely to miss important feedbacks in the real Earth-Human system, especially those that may result in unexpected or counterintuitive outcomes," the researchers wrote.[981]

Scientists' models can conflict with each other and with reality

Computer models' shortcomings can arise from their inability to reflect the reality revealed by actual measurements.

For example, models tend to underestimate how much fossil-fuel particulate emissions reach the Arctic. Understanding these emissions is important because carbon soot from burning fuels and farm waste lofts high into the atmosphere and spreads worldwide, including in the Arctic. Such soot increases atmospheric temperatures by absorbing sunlight and also coats the white Arctic ice with a layer of heat-absorbing grime, increasing melting.

Researchers led by Yousuke Sato developed an improved model of soot's effects that will lead to more realistic climate simulations.[982] However, he said, while the new approach "reduced the underestimation, it did not completely eliminate it."[983]

Researchers must also adjust their models to accommodate new field measurements—for example, of CO_2 emissions from lakes and waterways. Models currently calculate such emissions indirectly using physical laws. However, when researchers took actual measurements of emissions over a reservoir, they found that emissions may be up to 40% greater than previously believed—meaning that models miss a significant CO_2 source.[984]

Models are also deeply inadequate in assessing how clouds affect global heating. As the 2021 IPCC report on the physical basis of climate change put it:

> Clouds and aerosols continue to contribute the largest uncertainty to estimates and interpretations of the Earth's changing energy budget. . . . Climate models are incorporating more of the relevant processes than at the time of [the 2014 report], but confidence in the representation of these processes remains weak.[985]

Indeed, climate modeler Ellie Highwood has dubbed clouds "infernally infuriating."[986] [987]

Some studies suggest that clouds cool the Earth, with their loss having catastrophic effects. One modeling study concluded that future high CO_2 levels expected over the next century could cause cooling stratocumulus clouds to dissipate, triggering a massive 8°C heating over that caused by greenhouse gases alone. Clouds would only reform once CO_2 levels drop, which could take centuries.[988]

Such cloud-cooling assumptions are a major cause of "too hot" models that climate scientists wrestle with how to combine with other models.[989] Wrote authors of a commentary on hot models, even if researchers knew precisely future greenhouse gas emissions:

> . . . we would still not know exactly how warm the planet would get. This is because human-caused global warming is an enormous experiment that has no precedent, and feedback processes, such as changes to cloud cover, will affect the pace and magnitude of warming.[990]

On the other hand, other studies suggest that clouds *amplify* global heating. These studies, based on actual measurements of cloud characteristics, predict that warming temperatures make the Earth cloudier, triggering feedback of more heating.[991] [992] [993] [994]

Even given the shortcomings of global climate models, they have done quite a good job so far of tracking the inexorable rise of global temperatures.[995] However, "past performance is no guarantee of future results," as the standard disclaimer on financial documents puts it.

Earth has entered a new regime rife with catastrophic peril.

Putting you in a climate scientist's shoes

Imagine you're a climate scientist. Your research tells you that the world undoubtedly faces ecological ruin if governments fail to take drastic steps to battle climate disruption. While you feel a moral obligation to advocate for action, you face intimidating barriers to that advocacy.

For one thing, you don't have the time. To serve your career, you must write extensive proposals to win research funding. Because you live in a "publish or perish" world, you must spend huge amounts of time writing scientific papers to share your findings.

You also must spend time analyzing data, attending seminars and conferences, managing experiments, teaching classes, mentoring students, attending administrative meetings, and reviewing scientific papers for journals.

You may mount field expeditions to measure tree rings, take cores of glacial ice, sample ocean water, probe ocean currents, explore coral reefs, or chip at sedimentary rock layers.

On top of all that, keeping your sanity requires a social life, family time, and recreation.

What's more, you are not trained for communication skills. You have likely never taken a course in communication, so you aren't practiced in the arts of persuading audiences, telling engaging stories, or creating vivid metaphors.

Unlike doctors, lawyers, and politicians, as mentioned earlier, explaining your work to the public is not a basic part of your profession. Your only lay-level explaining is teaching to an essentially captive audience of students—very different from persuasively explaining to an audience for whom listening to you is entirely voluntary.[996]

You are milquetoasted

When you do communicate with the public, your job situation forces you to be "milquetoasted"—muting your voice and moderating your opinions.

You can be summarily fired for speaking out if you work for a private company, such as a government contractor. If you are a public university scientist, you must take great care with any public advocacy, scrupulously separating it from your work. The Climate Science Legal Defense Fund (CSLDF) cautions such scientists who would advocate publically to:

- Use only personal email and phone for any advocacy activities because work emails may be subject to Freedom of Information Act release
- Only do advocacy outside of work and business hours
- Do not give your title in documents, and list your affiliation "for identification purposes only."[997]

If you are a government scientist, you risk your career by speaking out—especially given that your agency is headed by a political appointee. Public advocacy can lead to budget cuts, reassignment, and/or your projects being relegated to a back burner.

Although universities do have a tradition of academic freedom, it only goes so far. If you don't have tenure, you risk your career because of the "inconvenience" your activism might present for your institution. After all, universities depend on money from donors, corporate partners, alumni, and parents; and these groups likely include people who deny the reality of climate disruption.

Even if donors and corporations do accept climate disruption, they may be reluctant to invest in research by an outspoken climate advocate who might violate confidentiality agreements. And by speaking out, they may see you as violating a university culture that values public reserve.

If you find yourself in legal hot water, your university's lawyers do not necessarily have your best interests in mind. After all, their job is to defend the institution, not its employees. The CSLDF advises you to hire your own lawyer if you find yourself subject to threats, congressional inquiries, subpoenas, or record requests.

For public universities, politics adds another element of doubt about whether the university will protect scientist-advocates. Your Board of Regents may renounce, or at least fail to support, an activist scientist.

You must also consider more than just your own career in deciding whether to advocate. You likely work in a team of scientists inside and outside your institution. Your activism could reflect negatively on the team and damage any collaborative projects. Even those collaborators at private institutions protected from state government interference may still fear that their association with you will leave them vulnerable to such privacy invasions as having their emails made public.

You work in a climate of fear

You could face personal hazards just for publishing your work in scientific journals, as has climatologist Michael Mann. He is co-author of a famous scientific paper showing that compared to past millennia, global temperatures have recently soared upward like the blade of a hockey stick.[998] Because of that "hockey stick graph," he has received death threats against him and his family, and even experienced the horror of opening an envelope full of a white powder that could have been anthrax. It turned out to be cornstarch.[999] He has also fought a protracted legal battle against climate science de-nihilists seeking to obtain his emails.[1000]

Environmental activist Bill McKibben has found himself stalked by videographers from right-wing organizations and his archives copied.[1001] In her book *Saving Us*, climatologist Katharine Hayhoe describes the persecution she has suffered:

> Communist, libtard, lunatic; Jezebel, liar, and whore; high priestess of the climate cult and handmaiden of the Antichrist, I've been called it all . . . . Nearly every day I receive angry, even hate-filled, objections to the work I do as a climate scientist: tweets, Facebook comments, even the occasional phone call or handwritten letter. "You make your living off climate hysteria," reads one tweet. A multipage, single-spaced manifesto in my university

mailbox starts, "You Lie!!!!" A Facebook message screams, "Get aborted you human-hating c***."[1002]

Another barrier to effective advocacy is that you are not particularly politically influential. "Scientists have little political power: they are small in numbers, rarely sufficiently financially wealthy to use money as a political tool, and often politically naïve or poorly networked," wrote climatologist Peter Gleick.

Climate scientists face unfriendly legislators when testifying at hearings, wrote Gleick: "The hostility of some policymakers to scientific evidence and information—especially the federal level—has . . . turned them into events more akin to political theater than educational and informational opportunities."[1003]

And as a climate scientist, your public voice has been muted by poor mainstream media coverage (see Why the Media Failed). For example, science makes up only a couple of percent of the news coverage in traditional media, found one study.[1004]

Scientists lack the advocacy gene

Besides such daunting personal barriers to advocacy, most scientists possess a natural disinclination to involve themselves in messy political controversy. While they readily debate scientific facts and findings, debate over politics is not as built into their DNA.

Nor do scientists like to "perform" before an audience, using what they may see as unseemly theatrics to compellingly make their case—even though such stagecraft is fundamental to engaging audiences. So, they prefer to write reports, letters, and op-eds, rather than giving passionate speeches, lobbying, or holding news conferences.

Despite scientists' ambivalence about advocacy, they are generally positively disposed toward public communication. One survey of scientists found that an impressive 87% agreed that "Scientists should take an active role in public policy debates about issues related to science and technology." However, 56% consider media coverage of their research unimportant.[1005] [1006]

Scientists' commitment to advocacy may well be increasing due to the rising urgency of climate disruption and an anti-science political climate. For example, the March for Science events have certainly been salutary and praiseworthy events.[1007] That said, it's worth noting that it took the presidency of Donald Trump and a virulently anti-science administration to spur scientists to leave their laboratories and demonstrate.

Perhaps the marches signal an upswing in scientists' political involvement. But scientists will never be able to mount the kind of well-funded efforts of corporate lobbyists.

Scientists are cool-blooded

We humans are emotional creatures, which has served our species well. While our intellect has fueled our success as a species, our emotions are the spark that ignites our drive for survival. Scientists, however, tend to see themselves, wrongly, as purely intellectual creatures, whose principal motivation is cool, emotion-free curiosity.

True, scientists are not most rewarded in their careers for passionate advocacy of their theories, but for dispassionate analytical communication of their findings. Their scientific papers are understated, dry, and conservative in vernacular—sometimes to the point of absurdity.

An example of such absurdly low-key prose is scientists' description of their geoengineering proposal to reduce global temperatures by injecting sulfur into the atmosphere.[1008] The scheme by Ulrike Niemeier and Simone Tilmes is distinct in its unworkability and peril. In the deadpan prose of their scientific paper, the authors cite "uncertain" aspects that include the level of injection and distribution patterns.

However, the kicker comes when they dryly cite that injections would have to continue for 160 years, require spewing eight million metric tons of sulfur a year into the atmosphere, from 6,700 airplane flights a day, at a cost of $20 billion a year. The authors' ability to cite such statistics without exclaiming the scheme's foolhardiness is breathtaking (see Geoengineering Quackery).

Scientists communicate blandly

Scientists' public documents are similarly understated, often to the point of vapidity. A prime example is an open letter from National Academy of Sciences members after Donald Trump's nomination. The letter was dry and bloodless—despite the outrageousness of Trump's claim that climate disruption was a hoax and his threat to withdraw from the Paris Agreement on climate change.

For one thing, the Academy letter was not from "shocked," "dismayed," or "astonished" scientists, but from "concerned members" of the Academy. And it only called climate disruption a "real, serious, and immediate problem" that "poses significant risks." The letter blandly declared that "it is of *great concern* [emphasis added]"—and not even of "greatest concern"—that Trump advocated US withdrawal from the Paris Accord.[1009] You can imagine how little impact this letter had amid the high emotions of the campaign.

Scientists' tendency to tamp down passion in their communications has compromised their role as a source of accurate information because true accuracy requires emotional context. Scientists are fact-driven, while the public is driven more often by emotion, and politicians by political calculation, with facts often taking a back seat.

The authors of *The Psychology of Climate Change Communication* leveled a charge back in 2009 that in my experience is still true today:

> Many of the highly publicized graphs and charts showing global climate change data . . . fail to inspire a sense of urgency in many audiences. They do not help convey the deep concern scientists have that efforts to abate and adapt to climate change are a near-term necessity if humanity is to avert the worst effects.[1010]

Scientists tend to be similarly passionless when they give talks to lay audiences. As one who has sat through a multitude of their lay-level talks, I can attest that scientists are too often lackluster performers—low-key, low-energy, and data-spouting. As discussed earlier, unlike lawyers and politicians, they shy away from using the dynamic stagecraft that makes for effective presentations. This lack of emotion may arise from their teaching role, where they see their primary job as imparting facts to students, not engaging their interest. But it certainly arises from scientists' lack of an explanatory culture.

Scientists cling to the deficit model

Scientists tend to be "factivists"—enamored of the belief that they need only feed their audiences facts, and those audiences will readily adopt the rational view of such topics as climate disruption. However, reaching the public and policymakers means not only transmitting scientific information, but interpreting its policy implications and advocating for that interpretation—even, God forbid, showing passion.

In their communication, scientists have long embraced a theory called the "deficit model." The model holds that to correct wrong-headed thinking only requires giving people more information.

However, this "most widely held, and simplest model of what audiences need from science communication . . . is wrong," as was so pithily expressed in the publication *Communicating Science Effectively: A Research Agenda*.[1011] The authors wrote that research on communication:

> Shows that audiences may already understand what scientists know but, for diverse reasons, do not agree or act consistently with that science. . . . People rarely make decisions based only on scientific information; they typically also take into account their own goals and needs, knowledge and skills, and values and beliefs.

Another problem with the deficit model is that corrective information quickly fades, concluded studies by political scientists Brendan Nyhan and colleagues. Their experiments tested the durability of corrective information like fact checks. They found that the corrections "frequently seem to decay or be overwhelmed by cues from elites and the media promoting more congenial but less accurate claims," wrote Nyhan.[1012]

The irony is that data-loving scientists—in uncritically embracing the deficit model—ignore *data* from psychological studies disproving the model's effectiveness. As microbiologist Amanda Freise wrote:

The reluctance of some scientists to accept the failure of the deficit model approach indicates that pure information isn't enough to convince them, either—otherwise, they would acknowledge the research and look for new ways to talk to the public.[1013]

Studies have conclusively shown that more information does not lead to "enlightenment." Psychologists found that political beliefs tended to trump knowledge when they measured the science literacy of 1,540 people, then asked them for their opinions about climate disruption. Conservative subjects who knew the most about science tended to believe that climate change posed the lowest risk. The researchers concluded that facts took a back seat to people's personal interest "in forming beliefs in line with those held by others with whom they share close ties."[1014]

Many science groups have mounted efforts to help scientists progress beyond mere data transmission. The Office of Government Relations of the American Association for the Advancement of Science helps scientists advocate for research.[1015] And the COMPASS science communication program trains scientists to build advocacy into their communication.[1016] The American Geophysical Union offers its members resources and training to enable them to advocate for Earth and space science.[1017] The Union of Concerned Scientists offers workshops that teach scientists how to influence decision-makers, talk with the media, and work with communities.[1018]

Nevertheless, the erroneous deficit model will continue to rise zombie-like to stalk the scientific community. The hallmark of its undead presence will be naïve assertions by scientists that they seek to "educate" and/or "inform" the public and/or policymakers to enlighten them about the truth of a scientific theory—whether it is climate disruption or another partisan issue.

Scientists are wishy-washy worded

Scientists' milquetoasted communications have included the words they use. In choosing descriptive words, climate scientists downplayed the seriousness of climate disruption, charged climatologist James Risbey.

In a 2008 article, he wrote that climatologists tended to dismiss as "value-laden" such terms as "catastrophic," "rapid," "urgent," "irreversible," "chaotic," and "worse than previously thought"—even though climate change can be legitimately described as such. At the same time, scientists did not label as value-laden milder terms that are just as subjective, Risbey wrote.

"This asymmetry in use of the charge of 'value-loading' is a form of scientific reticence and weakens scientific communication in the face of actual threats to the public," he wrote.[1019]

A classic example of inadvertent wishy-washy wording is the title of Bill McGuire's book *Hothouse Earth: An Inhabitant's Guide*.[1020] The word is weak, in that a hothouse is a warm building meant to grow plants out of season—in other words, a *comfortable* environment. Thus, a "hothouse flower" was grown in a sheltered environment. The phrase "Hellscape Earth" would more aptly describe the true catastrophic impact of global heating (see Hellscape Earth).

As alarm over climate disruption has grown, some scientists have begun using appropriately urgent language to describe its dangers. In 2020, one group warned of "a ghastly future of mass extinction, declining health, and climate-disruption upheavals."[1021] And in 2021, a group of more than 14,000 scientists warned of a "climate emergency," citing "mounting evidence that we are nearing or have already crossed tipping points associated with critical parts of the Earth system."[1022]

However, this evolution in language is arguably too little, too late.

Scientists are word-deaf

Scientists are also "word-deaf," tending to resort to arcane jargon when speaking to nonscientists. Climate communicator Susan Hassol counsels using more lay-friendly substitutes for such jargon, like "human-caused" instead of "anthropogenic" and "time" instead of "temporal." She wrote:

> Saying human activity "contributes" to global warming
> makes it sound like human activity might be only a minor
> contributor. It would be more accurate to say "most of

the warming" . . . Avoid using the word "debate" in connection with climate change . . . try something like "the urgent challenge of human-induced climate disruption," rather than "climate debate."[1023]

As shown in this table, there are myriad other terms that scientists use that mean very different things to the public.

When scientists say:	They mean:	But the public thinks:
enhance	intensify	improve
aerosol	suspended particles	spray can
positive trend	upward trend	good trend
positive feedback	self-reinforcing cycle	good response, praise
theory	body of data	speculation
uncertainty	range	ignorance
error	difference from exact number	mistake
values	quantities	ethics, monetary values
manipulation	changing a condition to study its impact on an experiment or model	exploitation
scheme	systematic plan	devious plot

Table 1. The same words can mean very different things to scientists and the public.[1024] [1025]

The word "uncertainty" is among the most misleading such words used in climate science to the public. They see the word as denoting ignorance rather than merely a statistical term denoting the range of possible values of a measurement.

For example, a summary for policymakers of the 2021 IPCC report used the words "uncertain," "uncertainty," or "uncertainties" some 16 times in its 41 pages.[1026]

The IPCC report said that, even though wide ranges of uncertainty likely encompassed true values of climate effects, "wide intervals were interpreted by lay people as implying subjective uncertainty or lack of knowledge on the part of scientists."[1027]

In one study, psychologists found that IPCC scientists failed to communicate effectively the risk level of climate disruption effects. The psychologists surveyed lay-level respondents on their interpretation of risk-communicating sentences from the IPCC reports. While the reports explicitly defined "very likely" to mean a greater than 90% probability, most of the respondents took "very likely" to mean down to 65% or less.[1028]

This critical perception gap means that policymakers could well believe that the scientific evidence for global heating is weaker than it really is.

Scientists made a terminal terminological error

By far the most egregious and damaging examples of scientists' word deafness has been their uncritical adoption of the terms "climate change" and "global warming." Scientists introduced both terms in early technical papers, and they went on to be adopted as de facto standards. The term "climatic change" apparently appeared for the first time in a 1956 paper by physicist Gilbert Plass.[1029] And "global warming" was popularized by a 1975 paper by geochemist Wallace Broecker.[1030]

Both these terms reflect scientists' penchant for bland understatement, as well as a lack of appreciation of the wider impact of their words. And ironically—given scientists' pride in using precise technical terms—both phrases are imprecise.

"Climate change" is a neutral term that fails to reflect its profound global impact. The innocuous word "change" seems to signify a natural, evolutionary process, rather than an abrupt alteration. Its adoption as the default term has certainly given climate disruption de-nihilists an opening big enough to drive a tanker truck through. They often use the term to make the invalid point that the climate has always been "changing."

The term "climate disruption" is more accurate and informative. It conveys the idea of an unnatural global climatic discontinuity. Certainly, de-nihilists could not argue that the climate has always been "disrupting."

The term "climate disruption" has been used occasionally by such distinguished scientists as Paul and Anne Ehrlich, John Holdren, and Stuart Pimm. [1031] [1032] [1033] However, it is not in widespread usage.

The term "global warming" is just as misleading. It evokes a benign, even pleasant, process, rather than the existential threat it really is. For example, we "warm" ourselves to feel more comfortable when we are cold. We give people a warm welcome because we have a warm personality.

This book uses "global heating," as have such groups as Greenpeace to more accurately describe the dangerous temperature rise from increased greenhouse gases.[1034]

By perpetuating the inaccurate terms "climate change" and "global warming," scientists inadvertently sabotaged their own efforts to convey the urgency of action to prevent ecological disaster.

As a result of the shortcomings laid out in this section, scientists' voices have been tragically muted on climate disruption. They have failed to convey the peril of the climate pandemic.

Why the Environmentalists Failed

While scientists must overcome daunting barriers to communication, environmental groups have seemed unfettered in their crusade against climate disruption. Supported by donors and driven by their sense of justice, nothing seemed to stand in their way of leading society into a carbon-free future.

Nonetheless, the environmental movement has failed, as evidenced by the policy vacuum in governments and the continuing unrestrained momentum of the fossil fuel economy (see II. The Carbon Contagion).

Some blame accrues because the movement allowed itself to be painted into a green corner—pigeonholed narrowly as a movement to save polar bears and reduce air pollution. As George Marshall wrote in his book *Don't Even Think About It*: "The visual and metaphorical language that surrounds climate change marks it, irredeemably, as an environmental issue." He charged that the images "detach climate change from the issues—such as employment, economy, crime, and defense—that people care more about."[1035]

Using the polar bear as the ubiquitous symbol of climate disruption constituted a classic case of this environmental hyper-focus, pointed out Marshall:

> There are no bears of any kind in the materials of human rights, refugees, health charities, trade unions, business organizations, or faith groups. . . . An issue that suffers from a lack of proximity has chosen as an icon an animal that could not be more distant from people's real life.

Asserted environmental justice advocate Robert Bullard: "The icon should be a kid who is suffering from the negative impacts of climate change and increased air pollution, or a family where rising water is endangering their lives."[1036]

The narrow environmental definition of climate disruption, ". . . enables some people to shrug it off as something only environmentalists need to worry about. But climate change . . . will have an impact on nearly every human system, including health, the economy, and national security," pointed out the authors of *The Psychology of Climate Change*.[1037]

Co-opted environmentalists

Some environmentalists and environmental groups have also displayed a disconcerting split personality regarding the fossil fuel industry. On the one hand, they have cast it as the ultimate villain. For example, former Vice President Al Gore used a boxing match metaphor to declare:

> "In one corner of the ring are Science and Reason. In the other corner: Poisonous Polluters and Right-wing Ideologues . . . trampling all over the 'rules' of democratic discourse."[1038]

At the other extreme, some environmental groups allowed themselves to be co-opted by industry. The groups adopted industry-friendly policies, and even invested in fossil fuel enterprises. These groups came to be lumped together under the rubric Big Green. Wrote Naomi Klein in her book *This Changes Everything*:

> "Several of these groups have consistently, and aggressively, pushed responses to climate change that are the least burdensome, and often directly beneficial, to the largest greenhouse gas emitters on the planet."

The groups have raised funds on the promise of saving the environment, "and yet some have turned around and invested that money with companies that have made it abundantly clear, through their reserves, that they intend to extract several times more carbon than the atmosphere can absorb with any degree of safety," she wrote.[1039]

The Nature Conservancy represents a prime example of a group that allied itself with industry in a way that some have argued co-opts a mission to combat climate disruption.[1040] For example, the Conservancy accepted funding from the bank JPMorgan Chase, which is also the largest funder of the fossil fuel industry (see Why the Corporations Failed).[1041] The millions in funding to the Conservancy is minuscule compared to the hundreds of billions of dollars the bank invests in fossil fuels.

Environmental groups have also failed because they functioned largely as an archipelago of organizations, collaborating too rarely to make themselves a more powerful and politically persuasive movement. While groups have periodically joined to fund reports and support legal actions, these have been far too few to present a united front against climate disruption.

Imagine how impactful a congressional hearing would have been in which a phalanx of environmental group leaders gave testimony advocating climate legislation. However, there is no obvious indication that this ever happened.

However, in the end, even if environmentalists had overcome their shortcomings, they were destined to fail at fomenting the radical societal changes needed to avoid extinction. They have faced the Sisyphean task of battling the overwhelming momentum of the fossil-fueled energy system and our own nature (see II. The Carbon Contagion and Why We Failed).

That said, they will continue play a critical role in resisting the assaults of climate disruption and preserving Earth's ecology (see Palliate the Planet). They remain deserving of the most dedicated support.

Why the Corporations Failed

We can thwart a viral pandemic with straightforward measures like vaccines and antiviral drugs. However, to overcome the climate pandemic we would have to re-engineer the entire economic body of corporations and government—like engineering the human body to live on Mars. The corporate-based economic system, whether capitalist or socialist, has been enormously successful in generating wealth. However, that system possesses fundamental flaws that prevent a climate-saving transformation.

Political scientist David Orr pithily summarizes the underlying flaw of corporations:

> Corporations are bundles of capital dedicated to near-term profitability of stockholders, not to the long-term sustainability of the human enterprise. . . . The cardinal rule of capitalism is to make money, and no amount of greenwashing can hide that fact.[1042]

Deceptive greenwashing

Corporations have long attempted to disguise their climate-damaging nature by greenwashing—conveying a false eco-friendly image. Perhaps the most notorious example is the promotional campaign mounted by British Petroleum. In 2000, the company heralded its new eco-consciousness by rebranding itself as BP, adopting a new slogan "Beyond Petroleum." To signify this evolution, it adopted a new sunburst "Helios" logo, named after the Greek god of the sun to "suggest heat, light, and nature."[1043]

But on April 20, 2010, BP's greenwashing campaign literally blew up.[1044] An explosion on the Deepwater Horizon oil rig in the Gulf of Mexico killed 11 workers, sank the rig, and unleashed 134 million barrels of oil before it was capped. It was the largest marine oil spill in US history.[1045] Investigations revealed the disaster was due to the rig's poor safety practices.[1046]

Another greenwashing tactic is to announce what appear to be major climate initiatives that turn out to be like patching an arterial bleed with a Band-Aid. One example is the seemingly major billion-dollar clean energy investment announced in 2016 by the corporate group, the Oil and Gas Climate Initiative (OGCI). [1047] The investment was in carbon-capture research, methane emission reduction, and energy efficiency over a decade by ten of the world's largest oil and gas companies. The billion-dollar commitment would seem gargantuan. Except that it is not. Geologist Stuart Haszeldine commented that splitting the billion dollars among ten companies, then again over 10 years makes the $10 million-per-year amount for each company trivial:

> This group proudly proclaims that they are responsible for 20% of global oil and gas production, so we should expect something big, commensurate with the size of the problem, right? Wrong. . . . The response is to combine together funds from OGCI members and invest—*in themselves* [emphasis added].[1048]

Jeremy Leggett, former chairman of the Carbon Tracker Initiative, pointed out that, "given that the world has to mobilize trillions of dollars a year for clean energy . . . if the Paris goal is to be realized, this is quite simply nowhere near good enough."[1049]

Another report suggested that limiting global temperatures to 2°C would require investing about $1 trillion a year in clean energy. This level is about four times the current level and needs to total $36 trillion by 2050, the report noted.[1050]

Another major greenwasher is the meat industry—a major and growing greenhouse gas source. The industry's greenwashing efforts were investigated by the journalism website DeSmog.[1051] Its review of company and trade association documents found that the industry sought to portray itself as climate-friendly by

- Downplaying livestock farming's climate impact; for example, by narrowing the definition of its emissions by excluding emissions from grazing and animal feed crop cultivation.
- Casting doubt on meat alternatives' climate-change-reducing effects
- Promoting meat's health benefits, ignoring the industry's environmental footprint
- Exaggerating how much agricultural innovations could reduce the industry's ecological impact.

In one blatant and amusing example, a Danish meat producer mounted a media campaign declaring that its pigs were "more climate-friendly than you think." The company labeled its pork products as coming from pigs that were "climate-controlled."

Two-faced corporations

Even the most assiduous greenwashing has not disguised fossil fuel companies' willful ignorance of climate disruption's reality.

For decades, ExxonMobil and the American Petroleum Institute lobbying group were acutely aware of the climate disruption's impacts, but chose to ignore their own scientists' findings, found investigations by Inside Climate News and the *Los Angeles Times*.[1052] [1053] [1054] [1055]

A documentary by PBS's *Frontline* revealed that the industry not only ignored those findings but actively worked to sow doubts about the science, to thwart climate-saving policy, and to delay the transition to renewable energy.[1056]

There was a dramatic disconnect between ExxonMobil's private and public stance on climate disruption. While 80% of the company's scientific papers and internal documents acknowledged climate disruption's reality, only 12% of the company's paid "advertorials" did, with most expressing doubt. This finding arose from an analysis of nearly four decades of ExxonMobil documents by science historians Geoffrey Supran and Naomi Oreskes.[1057]

Over decades, fossil fuel companies and their front organizations spent heavily on misleading advertisements casting doubt on climate disruption, they found. The ads had headlines such as "Who told you the earth was warming . . . Chicken Little?" and "Lies they tell our children."[1058]

The fossil fuel industry "has subjected the American public to a well-funded, well-orchestrated disinformation campaign about the reality and severity of human-caused climate change," wrote Supran, Oreske, and their colleagues in a report *America Misled: How the Fossil Fuel Industry Deliberately Misled Americans about Climate Change*.[1059] The industry's efforts to challenge the scientific evidence included "cherry picking, fake experts, and conspiracy theories—[that] come straight out of the tobacco industry's playbook for delaying tobacco control."

The public-private disconnect of fossil fuel companies extended to the political arena. For example, in one revealing undercover video, ExxonMobil lobbyist Keith McCoy admitted that, while the company publically supported a carbon tax, it was merely a greenwashing tactic. He said that the company knew the carbon tax was a "non-starter" that "gives us a talking point." The video was made by a Greenpeace UK representative.[1060]

Banks have also been guilty of two-faced greenwashing. In 2020, JPMorgan Chase & Co announced "a financing commitment that is aligned to the goals of the Paris Agreement." The commitment included financing a Center for Carbon Transition to give clients access to sustainability-focused financing and a 100% renewability target.[1061]

But at the same time, the company remains the largest financer of fossil fuels, according to the report *Banking on Climate Chaos*. In the period from the 2015 Paris Agreement to 2021, the bank provided more than $382 billion in fossil fuel financing. Overall, the world's 60 largest banks invested nearly $4.6 trillion since the adoption of the Paris Agreement, said the report.[1062]

"A lot of what passes for sustainability is actually nothing more than public relations," declared Paul Argenti, a professor of corporate communications, regarding the banks' policies.[1063]

Split corporate personalities

While not all corporations have been as overtly culpable as BP, Exxon, and JPMorgan Chase, almost all have failed to consistently and vigorously support measures to stop climate disruption. At the very least, they have had a split corporate personality, simultaneously advocating for climate solutions and working to undermine them.

For example, more than 50 corporations that publicly claim to be climate friendly are members of lobbying groups that opposed the 2021 US budget bill that contained major climate initiatives.[1064]

"Major corporations love to tell us how committed they are to addressing the climate crisis and building a sustainable future, but behind closed doors, they are funding the very industry trade groups that are fighting tooth and nail to stop the biggest climate change bill ever," Kyle Herrig, president of group Accountable.US that compiled the analysis told *The Guardian*.[1065]

Nearly all of the world's largest companies are members of at least one trade association with lobbying practices misaligned with the Paris Agreement, found the organization InfluenceMap.[1066]

Such policies have been devious, charged the Union of Concerned Scientists (UCS) in a report that analyzed corporate influence on climate policy.[1067] In another report examining the statements and actions of 28 US companies, the UCS noted:

> Even while cultivating a climate-concerned image in more public settings, these corporations have sown doubt about climate science both directly (such as by challenging climate science in government filings) and indirectly (e.g., by supporting politicians, trade groups, and think tanks that misrepresent the scientific consensus on climate change and oppose action to address it).[1068]

In yet another analysis, UCS scientists quantified how much of the global temperature and sea-level rise can be attributed to specific fossil fuel companies. Their analysis revealed that the 90 largest carbon producers were responsible for more than half of the CO_2 increase between 1980 and 2010, up to half of the global surface temperature rise, and up to 32% of the global sea-level rise.[1069]

Placebo corporate climate commitments

Many corporations have announced programs to reduce their greenhouse gas emissions, even to net zero.[1070] However, such commitments are largely placebos—ineffective but giving a comforting appearance of activity.

Some have joined the Science Based Targets initiative, committing to emission reductions to reduce greenhouse gas emissions. As of this writing, more than 1,000 corporations have committed to such targets.[1071] However, as of this writing, none of the major fossil fuel companies have committed to the targets.

Such corporate commitments are all too often only window dressing, Alberto Carrillo Pineda, a founder of Science Based Targets, told *The New York Times*:

"You can look at a company's website and see their sustainability report and it will look great. . . . But then when you look at what is behind it, you'll see there is not a lot of substance behind those commitments or the commitments are not comprehensive enough."[1072]

Indeed, an analysis of the emissions-reduction progress of 9,300 companies found that, as of 2021, they were only two decades away from depleting their emissions budget for keeping global temperature rise below 2°c.[1073]

In any case, corporate climate initiatives invariably fade, found management scientists. Analyzing climate initiatives by five large corporations over a decade, they found that the initiatives erode under the pressure of business as usual. They identified three stages of erosion:

- *Framing*: The corporation identifies climate disruption as an urgent social and strategic business issue, seeking strategies to benefit both the environment and the economy.
- *Localizing*: Managers try to apply the strategies with such efforts as energy conservation.
- *Normalizing*: Criticism from managers and shareholders cause the initiatives to be scaled back, in favor of maximizing shareholder value.

"Our research highlights an inconvenient truth, if you will, for politicians and businesspeople alike: we can't simply depend on corporations and markets to address one of the gravest threats to our collective future," concluded the researchers.[1074] [1075]

"Humanity by the throat"

Contributing significantly to the climate crisis have been the vast sums corporations have spent advertising their products, according to the report *Advertising's Role in Climate and Ecological Degradation*.[1076] The report concluded:

... that the advertising industry indirectly contributes to climate and ecological degradation through its encouragement of materialistic values and goals, the consumption-driving work & spend cycle, and the consumption of two illustrative products, namely beef and tobacco.

The report concluded that "in the presence of a large volume of advertising, many people come to want to work, shop, and consume relatively more than to rest, recreate, and relate with others."

Advertising indirectly contributes to climate and ecological degradation by encouraging such intensively carbon-emitting practices as buying SUVs and taking leisure airline flights, concluded the report.

Specifically, the energy industry and its trade associations have spent massively to promote their products and greenwash their image. As UN Secretary General António Guterres put it:

We seem trapped in a world where fossil fuel producers and financiers have humanity by the throat. For decades, the fossil fuel industry has invested heavily in pseudo-science and public relations—with a false narrative to minimise their responsibility for climate change and undermine ambitious climate policies.[1077]

Chief among the US trade groups has been the American Petroleum Institute (API).[1078] The API alone accounted for almost half of the $1.4 billion spent by energy-related trade associations on public relations and advertising during 2008–2018, found an analysis by the Climate Investigations Center.[1079]

During 1986–2015, the five largest fossil fuel corporations spent a combined $3.6 billion on advertising—mainly touting the benefits of fossil fuels, found another study. Those expenditures ramped up significantly over that period—from about $35 million a year through 1996, to an average $217 million a year during 2008–2016.

The authors wrote that the advertising "essentially amounts to fossil fuel corporate propaganda," and that "it can have a major impact on the perceptions of the public and major stakeholders regarding the need for legislative action to address climate change."[1080]

Public relations firms have played an influential role in such propaganda, found sociologist Robert Brulle and colleague Carter Werthman.[1081] For example, the firms created catchphrases including "clean coal," "renewable natural gas," "coal country," and "carbon footprint," that shaped public perception of climate change, they found.

"The fossil fuel industry's obstruction of climate action goes beyond misinformation and climate denial," said Brulle. "PR firms are a big part of the corporate propaganda machinery that guides the way Americans think about the issue," he told DeSmog.[1082]

One particularly active group thwarting climate regulation during the 1990s was the international Global Climate Coalition. It represented a broad cadre of fossil fuel, utilities, steel, and rail industries. The PR company it hired conducted an aggressive media campaign casting doubt on climate disruption—including placing quotes, pitching op-eds, providing backgrounders and contacting journalists. The firm also paid climate de-nihilists to give speeches and write op-eds.[1083]

Corporations ignored climate risks

Corporations have certainly been warned that climate disruption could wreak havoc on their bottom line. One report found that 93% of the equities analyzed faced some degree of climate-related risk.[1084]

"Because of this ubiquity, investors cannot diversify away from climate risk; instead, they must focus on managing it," noted the report by advisors on sustainability's financial impacts.

However, corporations have traditionally had major "adaptation blind spots" that rendered their risk assessment unrealistic, asserted a review of the adaption plans of more than 1,600 corporations.[1085] The review found that the companies estimated their financial risk as being in the *billions* of dollars, but in reality are in the *trillions*.

Even insurance companies—for whom climate disruption presents perhaps the most direct financial risk—have been largely blind to its impacts. Only a third of 80 of the largest insurers in one survey reported that their approach to investing is "climate-aware." And they have allocated only about 1% of their assets to low-carbon investment.[1086]

Instead of planning wisely, insurance companies and other corporations will likely confine themselves to such meaningless actions as supporting the "Business Call to Action: Build Back Better," of the Coalition for Environmentally Responsible Economies. The declaration by more than 300 businesses advocates for Congress to adopt a "strategy that recognizes the need for a resilient, clean energy economy."[1087]

However, "these sorts of toothless statements are often undercut by corporate actions that do have teeth," wrote science historian Naomi Oreskes and businessman Auden Schendler in a *Harvard Business Review* article. "It's not enough to sign a pledge. You have to fight for that pledge too, something that even progressive corporations have been generally unwilling to do," they wrote.[1088]

Corporations finally face climate risks

Amid growing climate catastrophes, corporations have begun to grasp climate disruption's profound financial risks. JPMorgan Chase—the same bank that is the largest investor in fossil fuels—issued a report warning that "we cannot rule out catastrophic outcomes where human life as we know it is threatened."[1089] The report asserted that carbon emissions "will continue to affect the climate for centuries to come in a way that is likely to be irreversible," and that cutting emissions "is a global problem but no global solution is in sight."

However, the company pointed out that the research team behind the report was "wholly independent from the company," which suggests that the bank's investment strategy will see little change.

Also, one of the largest insurers, Swiss Re, has warned that climate disruption could reduce global economic output by about 10% by 2050—as much as a $23-trillion reduction.[1090]

The investment community has proven more aggressive than corporations in calling for climate action. In a 2019 letter to G20 global leaders, 477 investors with $34 trillion in assets declared that the goals of the Paris Agreement needed to be implemented "with the utmost urgency." The letter urged the leaders to phase out coal plants, put a price on carbon, and phase out fossil fuel subsidies.[1091]

However, US corporations and investment firms have suffered backlash for their climate-saving policies, from Republican legislators, state officials, and their allies. Those groups have passed legislation to punish climate action and used media appearances, television ads, and billboards to threaten companies that divest from fossil fuels, said an article in *The New York Times*.[1092]

Insurmountable barrier to green growth

Even if corporations and investors were to magically adopt climate-saving policies, economists have found no evidence that "green growth" in the economy is even possible. Green growth assumes that economic expansion can still foster a sustainable environment. Such green expansion would require a "decoupling" of economic growth from environmental degradation.

One review of 179 scientific papers on decoupling concluded that there is "no evidence of economy-wide, national/international absolute resource decoupling." And "no evidence of the kind of decoupling needed for ecological sustainability." The study concluded that "in the absence of robust evidence, the goal of decoupling rests partly on faith."[1093]

Another analysis by economists also concluded that "there is no empirical evidence that absolute decoupling from resource use can be achieved on a global scale against a background of continued economic growth. . . . We conclude that green growth is likely to be a misguided objective."[1094]

Climate economic catastrophe forecast

Even as corporations were ignoring climate disruption's hazards, myriad studies were documenting its profound impacts.

As far back as 2010, a *Climate Vulnerability Monitor* report estimated that inaction on climate disruption had already cost the world economy 1.6% of global Gross Domestic Product (GDP), totaling $1.2 trillion.[1095]

Climate disruption caused an average of 400,000 deaths a year "mainly due to hunger and communicable diseases that affect, above all, children in developing countries," concluded the report. And the report linked the carbon-intensive energy system to an estimated 4.5 million deaths each year due to air pollution, hazardous occupations, and cancer.

A 2016 analysis found that a business-as-usual approach to climate disruption would risk $2.5 trillion in assets. And even if the world could manage to limit warming to 2°C, financial assets valued at $1.7 trillion would be wiped out.[1096]

Climate disruption could devastate the stock market, according to *The Economist*.[1097] Its report concluded that by 2100, climate change could cause global stocks—currently valued at $143 trillion—to lose $4.2 trillion, or "roughly on a par with the total value of all the world's listed oil and gas companies or Japan's entire GDP." The study found that 6°C of warming would cause value losses of roughly 10% of the entire stock of manageable assets.

Of course, stock market losses in a 6°C world would be the least of the human species' concerns, as we barreled toward extinction.

For the US, "With continued growth in emissions at historic rates, annual losses in some economic sectors are projected to reach hundreds of billions of dollars by the end of the century—more than the current gross domestic product (GDP) of many U.S. states," concluded the 2018 *National Climate Assessment*."[1098]

In a blunt warning, the US Commodity Futures Trading Commission declared that "climate change poses a major risk to the stability of the US financial system and to its ability to sustain the American economy."[1099] Its report asserted that "a world racked by frequent and devastating shocks from climate change cannot sustain the fundamental conditions supporting our financial system."

Climate disruption's economic impact will be the result of damage from hurricanes, droughts, floods, wildfires, and ocean heating and acidification. In the US alone, such economic losses currently amount to about $240 billion a year—or about 40% of the economy's economic growth, found a report by the Universal Ecological Fund. The report estimates that this loss will grow to about $360 billion a year by the next decade.[1100]

Decarbonizing could be profitable

On the other hand, mitigating climate disruption could yield large economic benefits, studies have shown.

Climate-friendly investment and policies "could yield a direct economic gain of US$26 trillion through to 2030 compared with business-as-usual," found an analysis by the Global Commission on the Economy and Climate. It was likely a conservative estimate, the report noted.[1101]

Investing in sustainable industries often pays off better than investing in, for example, fossil fuel companies, found a Morgan Stanley study of more than 11,000 mutual funds. The report concluded that "there is no financial trade-off in the returns of sustainable funds compared to traditional funds, and they demonstrate lower downside risk."[1102]

Also, as discussed later, investing in greater energy efficiency offers considerable payback, although such investment is largely neglected in the financial and policy communities (see Energy Inefficiency).

In the end, corporations have failed to play a significant part in thwarting climate disruption because of their focus on short-term profits. As Naomi Oreskes and Auden Schendler put it in a *Harvard Business Review* article:

> The idea of business leading the charge was flawed, because as consumers we cannot take companies at their word. Like the scorpion who asks the frog for a ride across the river and then stings him, killing them both, it is simply *in corporations' nature* to internalize profit and externalize costs.[1103]

Why the Politicians Failed

Picture this scene: An up-and-coming politician is announcing a Senate candidacy. The candidate mounts the auditorium stage with a photogenic family: an attractive spouse and two charming children. The reporters switch on their cameras and recorders to capture the announcement. Supporters chant the candidate's name, cheering and hoisting campaign signs.

The candidate smiles and waves, and after effusive thanks to supporters and family, launches the campaign pitch:

> I will dedicate myself as your senator to meeting the foremost threat facing our country. It's not the economy, a pandemic, or terrorism. It is climate change. The disastrous droughts, wildfires, heat waves, and floods we are suffering are proof that we are in a climate emergency. We must avoid the dire consequences of climate change for the future of our children and grandchildren.
>
> So, I will seek to dismantle the fossil fuel industry and transition our economy to renewable energy; to implement a carbon tax; to eliminate the billions of dollars a year in subsidies of the fossil fuel, meat, and dairy industries; and to increase subsidies for fruit and vegetable production.
>
> I recognize that these policies will mean higher natural gas and gasoline prices and higher prices for meat and milk. I know that millions of workers in those industries will lose their jobs. But I hope that many will get jobs in the renewable energy and other industries boosted by my policies.
>
> These changes will mean drastically changing our lifestyles. We will have to switch to electric cars and bicycles. We will have to eat less meat and dairy, and more vegetables. We will have to reduce our energy consumption and live more frugally and in harmony with the demands of global sustainability.
>
> To remain independent, I will refuse contributions from the fossil fuel or meat industries, or from any donor that does not fully recognize the need to stop global warming.

Stunned silence greets the speech. The candidate's poll numbers immediately plummet to single digits, marking a campaign dead in the water. The candidate will not be the senator from the great state of "Mythigan."

The campaign was doomed because it violated cardinal rules of politics. The candidate foolishly:

- Sought to be a political *leader*. Politicians are really *followers*—adhering religiously to voters' current desires, and often more important, donors' desires.
- Made climate disruption a top priority. Even with new recognition of climate disruption's dangers, it is relatively low on voters' priorities. Ranked higher are dangers like the COVID-19 pandemic, the economy, and terrorism.
- Called for sacrifice. Voters hate sacrifice, especially in the service of some future goal.
- Called for new taxes. Voters hate taxes.
- Advocated a policy that would cost jobs—a politically radioactive position. Politicians never mention job losses. For example, the economic recovery and climate plans put forth by President Joe Biden stressed the jobs that would be created, without mentioning the jobs that would be lost.[1104] [1105] [1106]
- Vowed immediate, specific action. Successful politicians make only vague promises on the stump to maximize support.
- Declined to accept interest group donations. "Money is the mother's milk of politics," as the late California politician Jesse Unruh put it.

The failure of politicians to pursue aggressive climate policies also arises from their personal characteristics:

- They tend not to look beyond the next election cycle.
- They tend to be older, less disposed to look beyond the shorter horizon of their own lifetimes at the long-term dangers of climate disruption.
- They are wealthier. They tend to see themselves as financially insulated from the vicissitudes of climate disruption.
- They likely owe that wealth to special interests—whether the fossil fuel industry or other corporations that feel threatened by climate-preserving policies.
- Many of them are de-nihilists (see Co-infection by De-nihilism).

- They are urban. They are insulated from nature, not likely to experience the damage to the natural world from climate disruption. And they don't appreciate the "ecosystem services"—ranging from rainfall to a productive ocean—that nature provides and that civilization depends on.
- They are people. They share the same human shortcomings that have prevented all of us from grasping climate disruption's dangers (see Why We Failed).

Importantly, these principles apply globally, not just to the US. Politicians worldwide have failed for these same fundamental reasons.

Political structural failure

Politicians' failure to address climate disruption is also due to structural shortcomings of all governments.

For one thing, all governments are naturally fragmented organizations, not integrated to cope systematically with complex, long-term threats like climate disruption. Wrote political scientist David Orr in his book *Down to the Wire: Confronting Climate Collapse*:

> The environment is a complex, interactive, and nonlinear system. But the structure of the Constitution favors "decentralized, fragmented, and incremental law-making" in legal scholar Richard Lazarus' words. . . . As a result, laws, policies, agencies, and whole government departments often work piecemeal and at cross-purposes, without due regard for long-term consequences.[1107]

Historically, national governments have evolved away from a culture that could address climate disruption, wrote Orr:

> Beginning with the onset of the Cold War, government became increasingly shrouded in secrecy and organized to accelerate the exploitation of natural resources, subsidize corporations, treat the symptoms of environmental problems without touching their root causes, alleviate some aspects of poverty without solving deeper problems, and protect the interests of the wealthy.

What's more, wrote psychologist Per Espen Stoknes, government officials are not likely to take concerted action:

> Public servants have no incentive in advocating for costly measures or risky climate-related investments. They don't get rewarded for recommending risky new green technologies even if they turn out successful, but their personal reputation will certainly suffer if it goes badly.[1108]

Just another political issue

In the US, the Biden administration sought to create a more integrated, comprehensive approach to climate policy than had past administrations. It aimed to infuse climate policy into every agency and every relevant legislation.[1109] It sought to re-establish energy standards and make climate a central element in economic policy. Biden appointed climate-related personnel, including a national climate adviser and a special international envoy for climate change.[1110]

The administration has achieved considerable climate legislative success. The approximately $1 trillion Infrastructure Investment and Jobs Act of 2021 did include an investment in climate-related projects. They included upgrading the electric grid, building electric vehicle charging stations, supporting renewable energy projects, developing battery technology, and improving energy efficiency.[1111] [1112]

And the Inflation Reduction Act of 2022 includes tax incentives for electric vehicles and renewable energy, and penalties for methane leakage. However, in a classic case of two steps forward but one step back, it also includes support for natural gas pipelines, oil drilling leases, and carbon capture.[1113] [1114]

Overall, while the two pieces of legislation will ultimately reduce US CO_2 emissions, that reduction will still leave the US as among the world's largest greenhouse gas emitters.

Globally, the disorganized response to the COVID-19 pandemic offers a bleak lesson about the prospect of an effective response to climate disruption, declared political scientist Jason Bordoff. He wrote in *Foreign Policy* that "the very same barriers preventing an effective

COVID-19 response continue to keep climate change action out of reach." He predicted that governments will fail to take the necessary collective climate action, fail to achieve public understanding and buy-in, and fail to carry out decarbonization that could cause economic damage.[1115]

In short, the pressures of coping with multiple factions and challenges has caused climate disruption to become "just another political issue."

Time-delaying politicians

Even when politicians do commit to action, they readily embrace the distant time frame—around mid-century—that climate scientists typically posit in their modeling. As George Marshall wrote in his book *Don't Even Think About It*:

> Politicians are all too happy to talk about climate change in these terms so that they can postpone difficult decisions as far into the future as possible. . . . Governments have proven to be extremely unwilling to incur costs in the short term but perfectly willing to accept far greater costs in the future. The larger measures that might achieve the target are safely placed . . . always just over the horizon.[1116]

Politicians are also reluctant to act because they seek credit for the results. Wrote Ian Bremmer in his book *The Power of Crisis*:

> Few elected leaders are eager to take responsibility for policies that impose near-term pain, especially knowing that future leaders will claim the credit when positive results emerge. Leaders also know that they get more credit for addressing local problems than global ones. It's easier to kick the carbon can down the road and make it someone else's problem.[1117]

In contrast to politicians' reluctance, voters eagerly support climate-friendly policies. One survey found that majorities of US voters support funding renewable energy, levying a carbon tax, and requiring electrical utility companies to generate 100% of their energy from clean sources by 2040.[1118]

However, climate disruption is still relatively low on US voters' priorities. Before the 2020 election, climate disruption ranked second from last in a list of priorities, found a Pew Research Center survey. Ranking at the top were the economy, healthcare, Supreme Court appointments, the COVID-19 outbreak, and violent crime. Given this low ranking, it is likely that climate disruption will continue to have a lower priority in politicians' agendas.[1119]

Special interests at the controls

Another major political barrier to aggressive climate policy is that unelected special-interest groups, rather than elected officials, are often operating government's machinery. In the US, such groups, rather than congressional staff, are guiding much policy and even drafting laws.

"With few exceptions, our policymaking institutions are losing the ability to think for themselves. In some cases, it's already gone," wrote political scientists Lee Drutman and Steven Teles in *The Atlantic*. Budget cuts have crippled government's capacity to keep up with the gangs of lobbyists and well-funded special-interest groups, they asserted.[1120]

These special interests spend heavily to achieve their goals. Oil, gas, and coal companies spend more than $100 million a year on lobbying, according to OpenSecrets.org. Overall, US companies and other organizations now spend more than $3 billion a year on lobbying.[1121] This expenditure is greater even than the approximately $2.5 billion in federal funding for both the Senate and the House of Representatives.[1122]

"Today, the biggest companies have upwards of 100 lobbyists representing them, allowing them to be everywhere, all the time," wrote Drutman in another *Atlantic* article. "For every dollar spent on lobbying by labor unions and public-interest groups together, large corporations and their associations now spend $34."[1123]

Special interests are allowed to donate vast amounts of money to congressional campaigns, thanks to the 2010 *Citizens United* Supreme Court decision, which rejected limits on corporate donations.[1124] As a result, the coal, and oil and gas industries have poured large sums of money into campaign coffers, the majority going to Republicans.[1125] [1126] The resulting atmosphere, wrote Rhode Island Senator Sheldon Whitehouse in *The Washington Post*:

> Has quashed any Republican effort on climate change, silenced serious climate debate in Congress and ended progress, as desired and directed by the fossil-fuel industry. . . . Republicans are trapped. The merciless might of the fossil fuel industry's new post-*Citizens United* political armaments is directed at them.[1127]

Whitehouse wrote that, while publicly declaring their support for carbon pricing, the oil companies are "using all their quiet lobbying muscle to crush any threat of bipartisan action on the carbon pricing they claim to espouse."[1128]

In one telling example, an ExxonMobil lobbyist was caught on hidden camera boasting how he had influenced lawmakers to delete climate change policies from the 2021 US infrastructure bill. The recording was made by an undercover Greenpeace UK reporter. The lobbyist Keith McCoy said that he would "bait" Congressmen by talking about climate-related issues. Then, he would "reel them in" to persuade them to limit infrastructure to traditional infrastructure like roads and bridges.[1129]

What's more, multiple Biden appointees either met with oil and gas industry representatives about the infrastructure package and/or had ties to the fossil fuel industry before their appointments, pointed out an article in *The New Republic*.

"It's clear that several administration officials have also been eager to give oil and gas companies a seat at the policymaking table Exxon's lobbyist has now admitted to trying to dismantle," concluded author Kate Aronoff.[1130]

Politicians for hire

The US suffers a particularly dysfunctional democracy because of the golden rule: "he who has the gold makes the rules."[1131]

A telling example is that the Republican senators who urged then-President Trump to withdraw from the Paris Agreement received more than $10 million in oil and coal industry campaign contributions.[1132]

In another case, senators who voted against a 2016 amendment confirming the reality of human-caused climate disruption received more than five times the donations from the fossil fuel industry since 2010, compared to senators who voted for it, found Alec Goodwin of the Center for Responsive Politics.[1133]

US politicians are also particularly loath to offend special interests because many plan to become lobbyists once they leave Congress. The website OpenSecrets.org lists hundreds of former members of Congress and staffers who are now lobbyists.[1134]

The source of politicians' personal wealth can also influence their position on climate disruption. A prime case in point is West Virginia Senator Joe Manchin, whose opposition compromised the Biden administration's climate legislation. Investigations by *The New York Times* documented his long-time opposition to climate legislation and detailed his history of using his political positions to further his financial interests in his coal company.[1135] [1136] As another investigation of Manchin by *The Intercept* concluded:

> Though Manchin's motivations are often ascribed to the conservative, coal-friendly politics of West Virginia, it is also the case that the state's senior senator is heavily invested in the industry—and owes much of his considerable fortune to it. . . . For decades, Manchin has profited from a series of coal companies that he founded during the 1980s.[1137]

Politicians' reluctance to address climate disruption contrasts sharply with public opinion. The majority of voters strongly support climate-friendly energy policies, found a survey by the Yale/George Mason University climate communication programs. And half or more said the political parties, Congress, and local government should do more to address global warming.[1138]

Partisan political ploys

In casting doubt on climate disruption, Republican lawmakers were known to declare, "I am not a scientist."[1139] Indeed, politicians, and not just Republicans, *are* notably unscientific. They practice the "political method," rather than the scientific method. As mathematician John Allen Paulos commented in a *New York Times* op-ed:

[Politicians often] employ rhetorical tricks rather than logical arguments. Both Republicans and Democrats massage statistics, use numbers to provide decoration rather than information, dismiss, or at least distort, the opinions of experts . . . equivocate, derogate and obfuscate.[1140]

David Levitan lists key tactics politicians use to muddy public discussion of climate disruption in his book *Not a Scientist: How Politicians Mistake, Misrepresent, and Utterly Mangle Science.* They:

- *Cherry-pick* an example that supports a position, while ignoring overwhelming facts that don't. For example, emphasizing that one glacier is growing, while the vast majority are shrinking.
- *Cite dubious sources* such as de-nihilist bloggers "with the knowledge that many people simply won't know how to check the underlying science. It's online, so it must be true!" wrote Levitan.
- *Ridicule and dismiss the science* in misleading terms that sound ridiculous. Levitan cites former Arkansas governor Mike Huckabee's speech that dismissed global heating as trivial compared to terrorism. Huckabee said: "I believe that most of us would think that a beheading is a far greater threat to an American than a sunburn."
- *Cite the inherent uncertainties* in the details of climate science to argue that they negate its overall validity.
- *Cite a seemingly damning piece of evidence*, while ignoring follow-up stories that disprove it.
- *Blatantly fabricate information* in the hope that repeated assertions will give it a sheen of accepted fact.[1141]

A prime example of the fabrication tactic is a bogus online petition dubbed the World Climate Declaration. It claimed that "over 1100 scientists and professionals" said that "There is no climate emergency." However, *Inside Climate News* discovered that the vast majority of the signatories had no climate science experience. And the group behind the message had ties to oil money and fossil fuel interest groups.[1142]

The Trump administration mounted a sustained, aggressive attack on climate science and policy that reverberated beyond his presidency. He pulled out of the Paris Agreement, rolled back emission regulations, compromised climate science research, and interfered with publication of scientific reports on climate.[1143] That attack caused large-scale exodus of climate-related scientists from government, hamstringing efforts to implement new climate initiatives.[1144]

However, the impacts of such obstructionist policies, while hindering US climate mitigation efforts, were basically insignificant when placed in a global context.

Democrat deficiency

As discussed earlier, the Biden administration has made significant advances in enhancing domestic climate policy. And the administration and congressional Democrats advanced an ambitious climate plan that envisioned a wholesale revolution in the nation's energy system and environmental policy.[1145 1146] However, these aspirational plans are unrealistic politically, technologically, and economically. As examples of such unrealistic goals, the plans propose to:

- Reach 100% net zero emissions in the US by 2050 (see Decarbonization Delusion)
- Achieve net zero emissions in the electricity sector by 2035 (see Renewable Energy Hype)
- Achieve net-negative emissions during the second half of the century through such technologies as direct air capture (see Carbon Capture Snake Oil)
- Achieve 100% zero-emissions passenger vehicles by 2035 and heavy-duty trucks by 2040 (see Fossilized Transportation)
- Eliminate subsidies and tax breaks for oil and gas companies drilling on public lands (see Bankrolling the Contagion).

Such goals are not politically feasible, especially with a Republican congressional majority. For one thing, conservatives will mount battles against any decarbonization plans. For example, Replublican state attorneys general, conservative legal activists, and a conservative Supreme Court have tried to severely weaken environmental laws and thwart the executive branch's climate policies.[1147]

An example of the US Supreme Court's anti-environment position was its 2022 decision in *West Virginia et al. v. Environmental Protection Agency et al.*[1148] That decision severely limited the agency's authority to reduce CO_2 power plant emissions, leaving specific regulation to Congress. Congress, however, did overcome that barrier in passing the Inflation Reduction Act of 2022, specifically defining CO_2 as a pollutant.[1149]

Lower US courts are also raising barriers to climate legislation and policy, particularly when they threaten energy industries. One example of such judicial barriers was a federal court's blocking in 2022 of a Biden administration policy setting a high "social cost of carbon"—the measure of the damage produced by each additional ton of greenhouse gas emissions. The measure is a key element in creating laws regulating auto emissions, oil and gas lease sales, and construction projects.[1150]

At the US state government level, Republican treasurers mounted a coordinated campaign to punish companies that try to reduce greenhouse gases, found an investigation by *The New York Times*. They used the tax dollars they control to threaten banks and other companies seeking to reduce fossil fuel investments, protecting coal, oil, and gas interests. According to the *Times*:

> The Republican treasurers skirt the fact that global warming is an economic menace that is damaging industries like agriculture and causing extreme weather that devastates communities and costs taxpayers billions in recovery and rebuilding. Instead, they frame efforts to reduce emissions as a threat to employment and revenue, and have turned climate science into another front in the culture wars.[1151]

Globally, the Biden administration did take what steps it could to reestablish US leadership in climate policy. It rejoined the Paris Agreement, although that agreement is fatally flawed (see Paris Agreement: Blind and Toothless).

It also made a formal agreement with China—the other major global source of greenhouse gases—to cooperate to address climate disruption. However, that cooperation is very much subject to the fickle winds of international politics. For example, US-China climate talks were put on hold due to China's objection to US House of Representatives Speaker Nancy Pelosi's 2022 visit to Taiwan.[1152]

Finally, the stark reality is that no governments would be willing to launch an energy revolution that would significantly threaten their fossil fuel industry, given its massive size, political influence, and the resulting economic damage (see II. The Carbon Contagion).

No global energy revolution

Only an unprecedented, wholesale revolution in global economic systems could possibly hope to produce a reduction in emissions.

That revolution would require the global society to focus less on economic growth as a measure of progress and more on societal well-being, pointed out researchers Rick Stafford and Peter J. S. Jones.[1153] Governments would be required to enact a heavy carbon tax that would turn environment-burdening products such as air travel, fossil fuels, and red meat "from everyday items into luxury goods," they wrote. Governments would also have to implement a four-day work week, a universal basic income, and large-scale restoration of natural ecosystems, they concluded.

There is not widespread global support for such a revolution, found the largest survey of public opinion on climate change ever conducted. The People's Climate Vote had 1.22 million respondents worldwide. Of those respondents, 64% said that climate disruption is a global emergency. However, only 59% of *those* respondents said that the world should "do everything necessary, urgently in response." Thus, only 38% overall favored urgent action.[1154]

Nor is there a majority of support in the US for urgent action. A 2021 *Washington Post*-ABC News poll found that only 45% of respondents saw global heating as an urgent problem requiring immediate government action. By contrast, 49% saw it as a longer-term problem requiring more study before action was taken.[1155]

Given the obstacles discussed above, global governments, abetted by corporations, will inevitably fail to enact the revolutionary legislation that could eliminate the threat of an extinction-level climate catastrophe.

The centralization of political and economic power and privilege has led to a "global Zeitgeist whereby development and progress are reduced to economic growth and defined by increasingly narrow financial metrics and indices," wrote authors who analyzed that failure.[1156] They concluded that "the very stability of the current Zeitgeist, with its deep reliance on escalating and centralized energy use, looks *set to be its downfall* [emphasis added]."

More bluntly, environmental activist Greta Thunberg declared:

Build back better. Blah, blah, blah. Green economy. Blah blah blah. Net zero by 2050. Blah, blah, blah . . . . This is all we hear from our so-called leaders. Words that sound great but so far have not led to action. Our hopes and ambitions drown in their empty promises.[1157]

Why We Failed

First of all, *guilt is bullshit.*

You should feel no personal guilt that our species could go extinct just because you didn't recycle that plastic bottle or buy that electric car. One subtext of the decree that you must "Do what you can to fight global warming" is that you should feel guilty for living in a world that you didn't create.

The problem is not *you*; it's *us*. You didn't fail as an individual. Society failed, which could lead to our species failing because of our fundamental nature. Human society will have failed to create the cultural and political mechanisms necessary to avoid climate disruption and to exist sustainably on the planet.

In part, society failed because when natural scientists address the human dimensions of climate disruption, they mistakenly emphasize "the role of individuals in generating carbon emissions—who are thus held responsible for reducing them," wrote sociologists Riley Dunlap and Robert Brulle (see Why the Scientists Failed).

"The stress on individual behavior and change thus leaves the institutions that structure everyday life and individual practices unexamined," they pointed out.[1158]

Climate de-nihilists have used the emphasis on individual behavior to deflect attention from the need for policy solutions, pointed out climatologist Michael Mann.

"This is a deflection campaign and a lot of well-meaning people have been taken in by it," he told *The Guardian*. "This approach is a softer form of denial and in many ways it is more pernicious," he said.[1159]

Corporations have promoted the theme of personal responsibility to shift blame for climate disruption away from them and onto individuals. Historians Geoffrey Supran and Naomi Oreskes found evidence of such a strategy when they analyzed ExxonMobil's climate change communications. Their analysis revealed that "ExxonMobil advertisements worked to shift responsibility for global warming away from the fossil fuel industry and onto consumers." They concluded that:

> Our research suggests warning signs that the fossil fuel
> industry is using the subtle micro-politics of language to
> downplay its role in the climate crisis and to continue to
> undermine climate litigation, regulation, and activism.[1160]

The misleading narrative of personal culpability has made it implicit that we're complicit and has been allowed to dominate our thinking. We have been set up for a lifelong guilt trip toward extinction.

As discussed earlier, our critical institutions failed because of their inherent flaws. But they also failed because institutions are made up of people, and we the people failed as a species. The three-pound miracle of our brain that propelled us to become Earth's dominant species also harbored the seeds of our potential extinction.

Here are some traits that led to our failure:

We are future-blind

Let's say you are offered $250 in cash right now. But if you are willing to wait a year you can receive more money. How much would it take to wait? Subjects in an experiment presented such a scenario demanded about $337—an extraordinary interest rate![1161]

This *hyperbolic discounting* is our tendency to prefer smaller rewards sooner over larger rewards later. Hyperbolic discounting is just one component of our psychological makeup that dooms us to failure to avoid climate disruption. We overvalue such immediate rewards and worry far more about immediate threats than those in the future, like climate disruption.

We don't worry about global heating because "we see it as a threat to our futures—not our afternoons," wrote Harvard psychologist Daniel Gilbert in the *Los Angeles Times*. "Like all animals, people are quick to respond to clear and present danger," not long-term threats.[1162] We also react intensely to threats that we deem *immoral*, wrote Gilbert:

> [Global heating] doesn't violate our moral sensibilities. It doesn't cause our blood to boil . . . Although all human societies have moral rules about food and sex, none has a moral rule about atmospheric chemistry. [Global warming] doesn't make us feel nauseated or angry or disgraced, and thus we don't feel compelled to rail against it as we do against other momentous threats to our species, such as flag burning.

Our brains also react intensely to threats that are *intentional*, wrote Gilbert (before the COVID-19 pandemic):

> We worry more about an underwear bomber—annual death toll: zero—than about influenza: annual death toll in America 40,000 people. Why? Influenza's a natural accident, underwear bombing is an intentional action . . . if climate change were some kind of nefarious plot visited upon us by bad men with worse mustaches, right now we would be fighting a war on warming.

Finally, as discussed earlier, global heating is too slow, wrote Gilbert: "Many environmentalists say global warming is happening too fast. No, it's happening too slowly. It's not happening nearly quickly enough to get our attention."[1163]

We are fact-averse

Our misperception of facts hinders our ability to face the facts about climate disruption. We experience *solution aversion* when we disbelieve facts about a problem when we don't like its solution. Psychologists Troy Campbell and Aaron Kay detected solution aversion in a survey of Republicans and Democrats about climate disruption. They found that Republicans were skeptical in part because the solutions conflicted with their ideology.[1164]

"In our research, we find that people treat facts as relevant more when the facts tend to support their opinions," said Campbell. "When the facts are against their opinions, they don't necessarily deny the facts, but they say the facts are less relevant."[1165]

In extreme cases, people may even resort to "alternative facts"—a term notoriously introduced by then-President Trump adviser Kellyanne Conway. "Alternative facts," of course, are just lies.

Partisans are perfectly willing to assert alternative facts, as evidenced by one fascinating experiment revealing such bias. The researchers showed subjects photos of the Trump and Obama presidential inaugural crowds. They asked half the people which image was from Trump's inauguration and which was from Obama's. They asked the other half which photo showed more people. In both cases, the Trump supporters were far more likely to answer the questions wrong—saying that the Trump inauguration photo showed more people, even though it obviously showed fewer.

"Clearly, some Trump supporters in our sample decided to use this question to express their support for Trump rather than to answer the survey question factually," wrote the researchers.[1166] The Trump supporters were exhibiting *expressive responding*, in which people knowingly give wrong answers to support their side.[1167]

We select convenient facts

Confirmation bias is another way we nourish our preconceived notions. That is, we tend to seek information to confirm our preexisting beliefs, while discounting information that would require us to change our mind. For example, we tend to seek out media stories that bolster our views—whether they be on Fox News or in *The New York Times.*

In the case of climate disruption, confirmation bias might mean that we see hot spells as confirming global heating and cold spells as refuting it. Confirmation bias was at work when de-nihilist Senator James Inhofe notoriously brought a snowball into the senate in winter to bolster his view that global heating is a myth.[1168] Of course, Inhofe was conflating short-term weather with long-term climate.

Such bias is widespread, noted a study led by Robert Kaufmann. The researchers found that people who live in record-hot areas are more likely to believe that the Earth is warming, while those who live in record-cold areas are less likely to believe.[1169]

"When personal experience and expert opinion don't align on a topic not critical to an individual's well-being, they're going to go with their gut rather than what the expert tells them," Kaufmann told *Scientific American.*[1170]

Our bias trumps our knowledge

We have a *bias blind spot* that makes us more readily recognize biases in others while remaining blind to our own. Only one adult out of 661 would admit to being more biased than the average person, found surveys by psychologists. This bias blind spot was regardless of people's intelligence, decision-making capability, or self-esteem. Researchers also found that people with a high bias blind spot are most likely to ignore advice from peers or experts.[1171] [1172]

We can engage in *motivated reasoning,* in which partisans who are given facts counter to their beliefs become even more partisan. Communication researchers found this tendency in experiments in which they showed subjects fictional news stories about climate disruption's health effects. They found that Republicans who read stories highlighting climate disruption's health risks became more partisan than Republicans who did not.[1173]

It is not ignorance of science that makes people more partisan, found psychologists led by Dan Kahan. When they surveyed 1,540 people on their degree of "science literacy" and their attitudes toward climate disruption, they found that people with the least science intelligence were less partisan than those with the most—whether they were believers or non-believers in climate disruption. Their findings contradicted the notion that people who lack science knowledge are the most partisan and rely on emotion for their positions.[1174]

The partisan attitude makes sense, in that people want to fit in with their social group. Wrote Kahan: "A person who forms a position out of line with her cultural peers risks estrangement from the people on whom she depends for emotional and material support."[1175]

Our perceptions weaken our resolve

Our response to climate disruption is limited by our *conceptual frames of reference*—mental cubbyholes that enable us to keep the world in order. As George Marshall pointed out in his book *Don't Even Think About It*, the language surrounding climate disruption "marks it, irredeemably, as an environmental issue," which isolates it from issues such as employment, economy, crime, and defense. This isolation weakens our resolve to take action on climate disruption.[1176]

The very words used to describe climate issues can affect our response. In an experiment with Democrat and Republican subjects, psychologist David Hardisty described a fee as either a carbon "tax" or a carbon "offset." He told the subjects the fee would pay for alternative-energy and carbon-reduction technologies. Hardisty found that while Democrats were willing to pay either a "tax" or an "offset," Republicans were only willing to pay an "offset."[1177]

Our thinking is even affected by how energetic or loud a message is. We naturally pay more attention to messages delivered in passionate "outdoor voices" than more subdued "indoor voices." That's why TV pitchmen and politicians are so over-the-top outspoken. Scientists, meanwhile, tend to use low-key "indoor voices" in their communications (see Why the Scientists Failed).

Our mental mechanisms limit action

We may exhibit the *bystander effect*, in which we bow to social pressure, paralyzing our inclination to act on climate disruption. "The more people we assume know about a problem, the more likely we are to ignore our own judgment and watch the behavior of others to identify an appropriate response," wrote Marshall.

Also, we might feel that if we've performed one virtuous act, we are *morally licensed* to offset it with less virtuous acts. "Research has found repeatedly that people who buy energy-efficient lights and appliances tend to use them more. People who insulate their houses then turn up the thermostat," wrote Marshall.

Our responses to climate disruption might also be limited by our tendency to believe that doing one thing means we've done our part, wrote psychologist Elke Weber.[1178] So, this *single-action bias* might kick in when we buy an electric car, and we no longer feel a need to write our legislator, campaign for a carbon tax, or install solar panels.

Although worry can prompt action, we have a *finite pool of worry*, wrote Weber. We can only fret over a limited number of things at a time. So, our worry pool may well have been filled to overflowing by the COVID-19 pandemic and the resulting economic upheaval. Added worry about climate disruption could go down the drain of our worry pool.

Fearmongering fails

Fear will not motivate us to pay attention to climate disruption or to alter our behavior, noted researchers Susanne Moser and Lisa Dilling. Publishing fear-provoking articles, "even if they succeed in getting attention . . . might still fail if it triggers denial or repression of a problem perceived as overwhelming." Such repression would contribute to passivity, and "if dire predictions do not immediately materialize, [it may give listeners] official permission to turn attention away from recurring alarming news," they wrote.[1179]

Fear can even lead to anger: "Anger and violence toward the environment as a maladaptive response to fear, pain, or despair can often be spiteful or even have the flavor of revenge—all in the name of reasserting one's power," Moser and Dilling wrote.

The failure of fear to motivate was clearly revealed in sociologists' experiments, in which they presented subjects with images depicting climate change.[1180] The images included factory smokestacks, starving children, a biting mosquito, a field of sunflowers, and wind turbines. They asked subjects to sort the images into groups that reflected how important the images made climate disruption seem, and how the images made them feel about coping with climate disruption.

While the negative images made the subjects fearful, they also enhanced feelings that thwarted action. The researchers concluded that:

> The very images that made participants have the greatest sense of climate change being important were also disempowering at a personal level [driving] feelings of helplessness, remoteness, and lack of control. Equally, the images making participants feel most able to do something about climate change did not hook their interest in the issue and were more likely to make people feel that climate change was unimportant.

Fearmongering can lead us to become *psychically numbed*—failing to generate any emotional response. Emotion drives people to action, and its lack raises a significant psychological barrier to action.

"You can only take in so much," Moser told *Grist*. "If in one year we had a huge fire, floods in the Midwest, several hurricanes hitting the East Coast and the Gulf . . . I think it would be very difficult in that context to still feel as horrified about the last death as about the first death."[1181]

Taking action also means taking the time to pay attention to climate disruption. We don't necessarily take that time, wrote Moser and Dilling. "Classic time management literature . . . tells us that humans spend most of their time on issues or demands perceived as urgent, such as responding to telephone calls or email. . . . Inattention to global warming can thus be seen as yet another example of this classic time management problem."

Our many versions of aversion

Besides *solution aversion*, our *ambiguity aversion* thwarts action because of uncertainty. In the case of climate disruption, we fail to act because of uncertainty about future impacts. Wrote researchers led by Stephan Lewandowsky:

> The "doing something about climate change" options appear laden with unknown probabilities . . . whereas the "business as usual" . . . option gives the appearance of being associated with a known outcome. . . . We prefer to take a gamble on what we "know" . . . rather than on what we do not know.[1182]

Loss aversion biases us to be more sensitive to losses than gains—a tendency identified by economists Daniel Kahneman and colleagues.[1183] [1184] To illustrate loss aversion, Kahneman tells his classes that he will toss a coin, and if it comes up tails, they would lose $10. He then asks how much they would have to win to accept that gamble. Most people would demand more than $20.[1185]

Climate disruption is a perfect trigger for loss aversion, Kahneman told George Marshall: It's far in the future, and it means sacrificing now for uncertain future losses.[1186]

We also fail to act on climate disruption because the lessons from climate disasters tend to fade rapidly. In one survey, political scientists found that the increased concern about climate disruption by people who had experienced heat waves, droughts, floods, or hurricanes largely disappeared after just a few months.[1187]

Our responses to *dread risk* and *unknown risk* are perhaps the most powerful psychological barriers to climate action. Dread risk, as described by psychologists, is a threat that is potentially catastrophic, fatal, and offers no chance of control, like nuclear weapons. Unknown risk is invisible, unprecedented, and delayed in its effects—like chemical pollution. Dread risk tends to produce a sense of powerlessness, and unknown risk triggers anxiety. Nuclear radiation and climate disruption are doubly paralyzing in that they are dread as well as unknown.[1188]

Weak drivers to action

Counterbalancing the strong tendencies that cause us to avoid action are weaker tendencies to act.

Generativity is one of these weaker, action-oriented tendencies. First described by psychologist Erik Erikson, it is our concern for fostering and guiding the next generation.[1189] Parents might be expected to have a strong generativity-driven concern about climate disruption. However, George Marshall cited studies to the contrary in his book *Don't Even Think About It*. Having a child means that parents have an *optimism bias* concerning climate disruption, he noted, in which they emphasize their personal reasons for having children and suppress knowledge of the precarious world those children are being brought into.[1190]

Guilt is another possible action-motivator, although Marshall stated that guilt tends not to be a good motivator. For one thing, he wrote, climate disruption triggers "lukewarm narratives of guilt" that don't lead us to accept personal responsibility. But more importantly, he noted, there is no way to alleviate that guilt.

"The climate change narrative contains no language of forgiveness," he wrote. "It requires people to accept their entire guilt and responsibility with no option for a new beginning."

In fact, guilt thwarts action, wrote Sarah Jaquette Ray in her book *A Field Guide to Climate Anxiety*: "Guilt is self-interested; alleviating the unpleasant feeling of guilt becomes more important than alleviating the suffering of others." She wrote that it is ineffective for spurring action, "although it's used as an affective strategy in most environmentalist messages."[1191]

Convenience rules

Our *materialism* and *love of convenience* also thwart our ability to re-engineer our lives to stop climate disruption. For example, Americans love large cars. Even though Americans can now buy fuel-efficient hybrid and electric cars, we still flock to bigger cars, trucks, and suvs.[1192]

In the US at least, we love spacious houses. The size of the average American house has steadily increased over the last four decades, studies have found, even though the size of the average household is shrinking.[1193]

And although we may be willing to support climate-friendly policies, we aren't disposed to put up our own money. In one survey, only 57% of respondents said they were willing to pay even one dollar more on their electric bill to combat climate disruption.[1194]

All this is not to single out Americans as energy villains. Globally, energy consumption per capita has risen steadily over the last century and continues to rise at an increasing rate.[1195] [1196] This increase has happened even in the face of new energy-saving technology. For example, even though LED lighting enables major savings on outdoor lighting costs, satellite data have revealed that such savings are undermined because globally, outdoor lighting has increased over recent years.[1197]

The bottom line: Our basic psychology has caused our failure to be motivated to take the radical action to head off our own extinction.

Co-infection by De-nihilism

Just as viral pandemics can spawn dangerous secondary bacterial infections, the climate pandemic has been co-infected by "de-nihilists." They are so named because of their nihilistic rejection of established science and their destructiveness.

They are by no means a major percentage of the population. One survey found only about 9% of respondents are "dismissive" of global heating.[1198] However, their disinformation campaigns have warped media coverage and hindered progress toward effective legislation.

Irrationally, de-nihilists manage to hold two contradictory beliefs without suffering the pangs of cognitive dissonance: On the one hand, they are perfectly willing to accept the science of meteorology and weather forecasting. But on the other, they reject climate science and climate projections—even though both meteorology and climate science arise from the same fundamental geophysical principles and use the same scientific methodology.

The massive research effort to understand climate disruption shows how illegitimate is de-nihilists' dismissal of climate science:

- Tens of thousands of scientists have traveled the globe on field expeditions and gathered input from millions of sensors and instruments to compile many libraries' worth of scientific data.
- Over many decades, they have published their analyses of those data in thousands of detailed scientific papers, critiqued those papers, and debated their conclusions.
- They have used this vast store of knowledge to create an unequivocal picture revealing that climate disruption and global heating are human-caused and extremely dangerous.
- They have worked continuously to fill in missing elements of this picture. When findings turn out to be wrong, climate scientists gather still more data to refine or correct them.

The science of climate disruption is universally accepted by responsible organizations. For example, national academies of science worldwide have formally acknowledged that humans are responsible for climate disruption, with not a single academy disputing that reality.[1199] And 31 scientific societies have issued a consensus letter reaffirming the reality of human-caused climate disruption.[1200] Also, almost all climate scientists agree that humans are causing global heating, with the level of consensus being greater among scientists with greater expertise.[1201]

By contrast, the willfully ignorant de-nihilists have not gathered any valid data; and almost none lack the training to authoritatively analyze climate data or scientists' conclusions from those data.

Dissecting the de-nihilists

De-nihilists can be divided into three overlapping groups: the political, the paid, and the paranoid.

The *political* de-nihilists had their intellectual origins some four decades ago, as detailed in the book *Merchants of Doubt,* by historians Naomi Oreskes and Erik Conway.

Back then, a cadre of free market ideologues and Cold-War-era scientists became motivated to oppose environmentalism by the reality that the market system does not take into account what economists call "negative externalities." These externalities include the environmental and human damage from climate disruption. Oreskes and Conway wrote:

> Accepting that byproducts of industrial civilization were irreparably damaging the global environment was to accept the reality of market failure. It was to acknowledge the limits of free market capitalism. . . . So our Cold Warriors . . . who had dedicated their lives to fighting Soviet Communism, joined forces with the self-appointed defenders of the free market to blame the messenger, to undermine science, to deny the truth, and to market doubt. People who began their careers as fact finders ended them as fact fighters.[1202]

Political de-nihilists can be distinguished by their shrill rhetoric. They denounce "climate alarmists," "global warming hysteria," "liberal elites," and "bureaucratic mandates." They charge that climate science is a self-enriching industry that supports shaky science.

The Republican Party is the US home of political de-nihilists. Over the years, the partisan gap between Democrats and Republicans has widened, polls have found. Far more Democrats than Republicants accept the reality of climate disruption.[1203] [1204]

As a result, Democrats and Republicans have far different policy priorities. One survey found that the vast majority of liberal Democrats (88%) and moderate/conservative Democrats (68%) think global warming should be a high or very high priority. However, a much lower percentage of liberal/moderate Republicans (38%) and conservative Republicans (12%) believe so.[1205] Republicans have ranked climate disruption at or near the bottom of policy priorities for more than a decade, according to Pew Research Center surveys.[1206]

Globally, right-wing parties are also hostile to climate-saving policies, found an analysis by researchers Ben and Matthew Lockwood. Measuring right-wing representation in countries, they found that the greater such representation the weaker the countries' climate policies.[1207] Said Matthew Lockwood:

> Conventional center-right political parties have always been more reluctant to adopt strong climate policies, but

the rise of right-wing populist parties and movements represents a threat of a different order. Our research suggests that while right-wing populists taking over mainstream center-right parties is relatively rare, when they have done so, as with Donald Trump in the US, the impacts on climate policy have been strongly negative.[1208]

Political de-nihilists have falsely claimed that mitigating climate disruption would devastate economies. However, environmental economists found that the health benefits alone of mitigating climate disruption would far outweigh the costs.[1209]

Their computer models included emissions, air quality, and the monetary value of health impacts—revealing that "the health co-benefits substantially outweighed the policy cost of achieving the target for all of the scenarios that we analysed." Epidemiologist Philip Landrigan commented on their findings in *The Lancet*:

> Political and economic arguments *against* [emphasis added] climate mitigation and pollution control are typically based on short-sighted, one-sided, and self-serving calculations that consider only the tangible, concrete, and relatively easily counted costs of controlling emissions. This report's carefully crafted conclusion that the health and economic benefits of climate mitigation significantly outweigh its costs provides a powerful rebuttal to those arguments.[1210]

A UN report estimated global health savings from limiting temperature rise to 2°C at about $54 trillion, compared to the $22 trillion cost of achieving the necessary greenhouse gas reduction.[1211]

And as discussed earlier, investing in decarbonizing the world economy could have yielded considerable profit (see Why the Corporations Failed).

Conservative de-nihilism's deep roots

Political de-nihilism is rooted in political conservatism. It is the same conservatism that fueled denial of the COVID-19 pandemic, wrote economist Paul Krugman. He summarized the right-wing media view on the pandemic:

> It's a hoax, or anyway no big deal. Besides, trying to do anything about it would destroy the economy . . . it's very similar to the Trump/right-wing line on climate change. Here's what Trump tweeted back in 2012: "The concept of global warming was created by and for the Chinese in order to make US manufacturing noncompetitive." It's all there: it's a hoax, doing anything about it will destroy the economy, and let's blame China.[1212]

The psychology of conservatives also drives political de-nihilism, wrote political philosopher Adrian Bardon in his book *The Truth About Denial*.[1213] While conservatives believe in small government, preventing climate disruption invariably requires large-scale government action, wrote Bardon. Thus, working to prevent climate disruption "presents a clear and present threat to the heart of this small-government ideology," he wrote.

There is also a deeper psychological basis for conservative de-nihilism, wrote Bardon. Studies have shown that "conservatives are more sensitive to risk, to threatening stimuli, and to negative images and messages," he wrote. They are also "more likely across a wide range of issues to favor conventional social attitudes and oppose scientific progress." And their "protective response to threatening information is to circle the ideological wagons."

This fear is exemplified by then-President Trump's attitude toward environmental activists, as when he declared:

> These alarmists always demand the same thing: absolute power to dominate, transform and control every aspect of our lives. We will never let radical socialists destroy our economy, wreck our country or eradicate our liberty.[1214]

Fundamentally alien groups

The fact that scientists tend to be liberal adds to the gulf between conservatives and researchers, noted Bardon. Conservative politics, de-nihilist media, and a closed culture produce a "self-reinforcing feedback loop of increasing emotional commitment to a (counter)-factual world view," he wrote. Political differences render each group "fundamentally alien" to the other, wrote Bardon.

As wildfires, floods and other disasters rendered climate disruption's impacts more obvious, many political de-nihilists have turned to blaming immigration for environmental damage. They claim that immigrants from developing nations who ruined their own countries threaten to do the same in developed nations. Wrote environmental reporter Oliver Milman in *The Guardian*:

> This wrapping of ecological disaster with fears of rampant immigration is a narrative that has flourished in far-right fringe movements in Europe and the US and is now spilling into the discourse of mainstream politics.[1215]

Blaming of immigrants for environmental degradation has been dubbed "ecobordering" by political scientists who analyzed the communications of 22 European far-right parties. They wrote that the blaming

> . . . seeks to obscure the primary driving causes of the ecological crisis in the entrenched production and consumption practices of Global North economies, whilst simultaneously shifting blame on to migration from the Global South where ecological degradation has been most profound.[1216]

Dollars for de-nihilists

The *paid* de-nihilists include individuals, elected officials, and groups supported by the fossil fuel industry and conservative donors and foundations.[1217] [1218] The fossil fuel industry, of course, stands to lose immense amounts of money if climate policies lead to reduced fossil fuel use. The most prominent de-nihilist conservative and libertarian groups include:

- American Enterprise Institute
- Americans for Prosperity
- American Legislative Exchange Council
- Beacon Hill Institute at Suffolk University

- Cato Institute
- Competitive Enterprise Institute
- Heartland Institute
- Heritage Foundation
- Institute for Energy Research
- Manhattan Institute for Policy Research [1219] [1220] [1221]

These organizations have aimed to distort communications about climate disruption, as documented by sociologist Justin Farrell. He analyzed more than 40,000 printed texts of 164 such organizations. He found that the disinformation from corporate-funded organizations significantly polarized the discussion of climate disruption.[1222] [1223]

De-nihilists denouncing "warmism"

The *paranoid* de-nihilists are those for whom "warmists," as they pejoratively call climate advocates, are heretical, much as the church saw Galileo as a heretic for his assertions that the sun was the center of the solar system. Like Galileo, "warmists" are upsetting de-nihilists' deeply held beliefs in the primacy of fossil fuels and invalidity of climate science.

Psychologist Per Espen Stoknes described the paranoid de-nihilists' beliefs in his book *What We Think About When We Try Not To Think About Global Warming*:

> They claim there are active attempts to silence them from voicing their honest opinion against the mainstream. They see a dogmatic climate fundamentalism that strangles free thought. And that peer review of scientific journals works just like Stalinist censorship in stifling legitimate dissent. In their own eyes, they are victims persecuted by the dogmatic majority. But they have the courage to stand up for what is now politically incorrect.

Even though paranoid de-nihilists are a freely vocal group, "they still fancy a story about themselves as victims of suppression," wrote Stoknes. "The most active of them like to view themselves as the lone dissident voices, articulate clearheaded heroes, mavericks, and fearless guardians of the obscured and abused Truth."[1224]

Paranoid de-nihilists also tend to be conspiracy theory buffs who reject science in general, found a survey by psychologists. Such conspiracists are emphatically not open to evidence, commented the researchers, who wrote: "Providing additional scientific information may only amplify the rejection of such evidence, rather than foster its acceptance."[1225]

In another survey, researchers found that "endorsement of a cluster of conspiracy theories (e.g., that the [FBI] killed Martin Luther King, Jr.) predicted rejection of climate science as well as other scientific findings."[1226]

De-nihilists have also embraced the conspiracy group QAnon's theories, found analysts tracing de-nihilist social media posts. Said Michel Khoo, an author of the study, "We've observed climate deniers shift their focus over several months from climate change to QAnon greatest hits, such as COVID-19 conspiracies and anti-Black Lives Matter content and disinformation."[1227]

US conservatives are particularly prone to both de-nihilism and conspiracy theories, found a global survey of more than 5,000 people in 25 countries about their belief in four popular conspiracies:

- That John F. Kennedy was assassinated as part of an organized plot
- That Princess Diana was murdered
- That an elite group was attempting to create a New World Order
- That the US government had foreknowledge of the 2001 World Trade Center attack.

The survey found that US conservatives—compared to those in any other nation—showed the strongest correlation between climate de-nihilism and belief in the conspiracy theories.[1228]

Paranoid de-nihilists have wrongly claimed that climatologists are publishing only results that support climate disruption and hiding evidence against it. One study refuting that claim examined 1,154 experimental results from a sample of 120 papers, finding no evidence of this publication bias.[1229] The biologist conducting the analysis found that all results were reported, even those that were not statistically significant or that showed no positive effects.

Co-author John Hollander wrote in *The Conversation* that "we reject the accusation made by climate change sceptics and can confirm that there is no publication bias in climate change research."[1230]

Of course, the paranoid de-nihilists are not likely to accept the study, given that it was published in a scientific journal.

Manufacturing uncertainty, spreading falsehoods

A major weapon in the de-nihilist arsenal of deceit is manufacturing uncertainty about climate disruption, wrote sociologists in the book *Climate Change and Society*:

> Over time, manufacturing uncertainty has evolved into "manufacturing controversy," creating the impression that there is major debate and dissent *within* the scientific community over the reality of anthropogenic climate change. . . . By creating the appearance of controversy within the *public realm*, denialists are able to appeal to values such as freedom of speech, fairness to both sides, and respecting minority viewpoints to add legitimacy to their claims—thereby bypassing the scientific realm in which peer review and accumulating knowledge eventually lead to the rejection of discredited claims.[1231]

A prime de-nihilist tactic is to use patently false assertions to seek to discredit climate science. An example is a deception-riddled Heartland Institute commentary titled "The 6 Biggest Reasons I'm a Climate-Change Skeptic—And Why You Should Be a Skeptic Too." The Heartland commentary questioned climate scientists' predictive ability, the validity of their climate models, and the accuracy of their data. It even asserted that a warming climate might be a good thing.[1232]

Author Ethan Siegel, who documented numerous patent falsehoods in the commentary, commented: "If the only way you can make your argument for your desired policy position is to tell lies or distort what we actually know, then no amount of reasoning will change your mind."[1233]

Fake climate experts

Unqualified "experts" provide ammunition for de-nihilists in misleading books, reports, and non-peer-reviewed articles. The authors of such material have never done research on climate disruption and lack academic credentials. Or, if the "expert" is a journalist, they have never covered climate disruption for a reputable outlet.

A good example of fake expertise is a fallacious report *What Rising CO_2 Means for Global Food Security* by the de-nihilist CO_2 Coalition. Declaring CO_2 a "miracle molecule," the report asserted that the continuing increase in CO_2 levels "is essential for securing future food security" and that slowing the increase "because of the risks of predicted climate changes must also consider the risks of limiting its benefits to agricultural [sic], nature and humanity."

The report ignores the catastrophic effects of higher CO_2 levels, such as drought.[1234] It also ignores that CO_2's fertilization effect decreases over time as plants adapt; and that increased CO_2 spurs growth of weeds that compete for water and fertilizer (see Epidemic of Hunger).

De-nihilists media also tout scientific-sounding journal articles, despite their flaws. One such article purported to prove that global heating is natural. It was published in the journal *GeoResJ* by researchers John Abbot and Jennifer Marohasy.[1235]

The paper had the impressive-sounding title "The Application of Machine Learning for Evaluating Anthropogenic Versus Natural Climate Change." The authors listed affiliation with the authoritative-sounding Institute of Public Affairs and the Climate Modeling Laboratory.

However, the Institute is not a scientific organization but an industry-funded de-nihilist think tank. And the Climate Modeling Laboratory lists only three members, including Abbot and Marohasy.[1236] Its cited publications deal almost entirely with rainfall forecasts rather than climate modeling. Abbot also listed James Cook University as an affiliation, but is no longer affiliated with the university. And the journal *GeoResJ* has ceased publication.

The paper was criticized as "junk science" by climate researchers contacted by reporter Graham Readfearn. Readfearn quoted climate modeler Benjamin Henley as saying: "The paper is seriously flawed and should be retracted by the journal"; that the authors used an "extremely unscientific approach"; and that "the conclusions are not supported by the results."[1237]

In reality, only a few percent of scientific papers in legitimate journals reject the reality of global heating. And those are almost certain to be invalid. For example, when physicist Rasmus Benestad and colleagues analyzed the 38 such papers, they found all of them to be flawed.[1238]

"Every single one of those [papers] had an error—in their assumptions, methodology, or analysis—that, when corrected, brought their results into line with the scientific consensus," co-author Katharine Hayhoe was quoted as saying.[1239]

De-nihilists also compile lists of patently fake experts who espouse their views. One such list was the headline-making letter signed by 300 so-called scientists urging then-President Trump to abandon the Paris climate agreement. When Abraham investigated the list, he found that "hardly anyone on the list was a climate scientist; many were not even natural scientists. It is almost as though anyone with a college degree . . . was qualified to sign that letter."[1240]

Academic de-nihilists discounted

There does exist a very small cadre of academic de-nihilists with scientific credentials whose work is cited by de-nihilist bloggers and politicians. Their work has been discounted by reputable climate scientists and is not considered a legitimate contribution to the field.

One such academic, physicist Henrik Svensmark, has published papers contending that cosmic rays and sunspots are the major climate disruption causes. However, his critics point out that the effect is infinitesimally small and can be discounted.[1241]

Two other de-nihilist academics are climate scientists John Christy and Roy Spencer. Their published research papers have used satellite sensor data to claim that the Earth is not warming as fast as other researchers have found. However, their work has major errors that have rendered their conclusions invalid, as documented by climate scientist and journalist John Abraham. He pointed out that satellite data are unreliable for measuring global temperatures because of their poor calibration and other technical shortcomings.[1242]

In one paper, Spencer outlined his arguments against climate disruption, declaring that "the science of global warming is far from settled" and "uncertainties over the possible role of Mother Nature in recent warming all combine to make climate change beliefs as much faith-based as science-based.[1243]

In analyzing that white paper, scientist/journalist Dana Nuccitelli exposed Spencer's arguments against climate disruption as "a variety of long-debunked myths." For example, Spencer argued that CO_2 cannot be harmful because it is a trace gas in the atmosphere. Of that assertion, Nuccitelli wrote:

> No scientist should ever claim that carbon pollution is benign because it's only present in the atmosphere in trace amounts. For example, arsenic can be deadly if present in trace amounts in water; Spencer probably wouldn't drink from a water source with 400 ppm of arsenic. This is an easily refuted, scientifically useless argument whose sole purpose seems to be fooling non-experts.[1244]

The website Skeptical Science lists and debunks many other de-nihilist climate myths:[1245]

- The climate has changed before, so the latest increase is not significant.
- There is no scientific consensus on climate disruption.
- Global heating is not really bad.
- Global temperature measurements are unreliable.
- Climate models are unreliable.

Theoretical physicist Steven Koonin is perhaps the most seemingly authoritative academic de-nihilist. His book *Unsettled: What Climate Science Tells Us, What It Doesn't, and Why It Matters* calls into question the conclusion of almost all climate scientists that climate disruption is a major and existential threat.[1246] The book asserts that:

- "Humans exert a growing, but physically small, warming impact on the climate . . ."
- "The results from the multitude of climate models disagree with, or even contradict each other . . ."

- "Government and UN press releases and summaries do not accurately reflect the reports themselves . . ."
- ". . . the science is insufficient to make useful projections about how the climate will change over the coming decades, much less what effect our actions will have on it."

While conservative organizations, media, and academics praised the book, climate scientists denounced it as inaccurate, as well as Koonin's other claims over the years.[1247]

Environmental economist Gary Yohe charged Koonin with "making distracting, irrelevant, misguided, misleading and unqualified statements about supposed uncertainties that he thinks scientists have buried under the rug," in an article in *Scientific American*.

In the article, Yohe refuted Koonin's misstatements about heat waves, global temperature increases, ice sheet melting, climate disruption's economic impact, sea-level rise, and wildfires.[1248]

Koonin is an outlier—one of the extremely rare de-nihilist academic voices amid thousands of climate scientists who have spent their professional lives in detailed study of the climate.

And while Koonin accuses climate scientists as overplaying the effects of climate disruption, the truth is that they have historically downplayed it (see Why the Scientists Failed).

Malignorant media

Sympathetic media have aided and abetted de-nihilist misinformation. Their reach not only includes the outlets themselves, but their social media presence. For example, an analysis of media Facebook posts by the Center for Countering Digital Hate identified what they called "The Toxic Ten." Those publishers are responsible for 69% of all users' interactions with de-nihilist content on Facebook, found the Center. The ten media outlets are:

- Breitbart
- The Western Journal
- Newsmax

- Townhall Media
- Media Research Center
- *The Washington Times*
- The Federalist Papers
- The Daily Wire
- Russian State Media
- The Patriot Post

These outlets had 186 million followers and garnered millions of dollars in ad revenue, found the Center's study.[1249]

Facebook and other social media have allowed these and other de-nihilist sources to spread climate misinformation with little oversight, charged Greg Bensinger in *The New York Times*:

> Even with the rapid shift in public opinion and the outward signs of global warming in recent years, social media companies have been slow to adapt, allowing sometimes blatant disinformation to flourish unchecked on their sites. Under Facebook company guidelines, climate content may be categorized as opinion and subject to no more scrutiny than peer-reviewed scientific research.[1250]

One analysis of Facebook posts documented the extensive reach of such misinformation. Climate misinformation had been viewed from 818,000 to 1.36 million times daily, and only 3.6% of the content had been fact-checked, found an analysis by the group Stop Funding Heat.[1251]

Twitter has also been an insidious purveyor of de-nihilist misinformation. When the investigative journalism website DeSmog analyzed more than 300,000 tweets between 2005 and 2020, it a change from outright denial of climate disruption:

> Our research found that climate denial has evolved into a softer, more insidious type of misinformation, one that focuses on denying urgency and action, one that targets the solutions more than anything else. Key elements of this strategy include promoting confusion, doomist perspectives, conspiracy theories, and fabricating lies to convince the public that there is no real need for climate change policy . . .[1252]

De-nihilist echo chambers

De-nihilist blogs and books also serve as de-nihilist echo chambers. The blogs largely cite one another, as exemplified by a study by biologists.[1253] They analyzed how 90 climate blogs—both scientific and de-nihilist—covered the status of polar bears and retreating sea ice. They found that the de-nihilist blogs drew material mostly from their fellow bloggers rather than scientific papers. And 80% of those blogs drew from one blog by a purported polar bear expert who "has neither conducted any original research nor published any articles in the peer-reviewed literature" on polar bears, wrote the researchers.

Similarly, de-nihilist books constitute exercises in journalistic self-stimulation. In seeking to make a case against climate science, they heavily reference de-nihilist articles, blogs, and websites. They cite few, if any, peer-reviewed scientific papers and government and scientific association reports.

The bad science promoted by de-nihilists and their media has translated into bad policy. Then-President Trump's decision to abandon the Paris Agreement was based on unsound arguments originally made by the oil and gas industry decades ago. These arguments include that the agreement would be bad for the US economy, would exacerbate poverty, and would fail to reduce global heating. They were based on deeply flawed reports by economists in the pay of the American Petroleum Institute (API).[1254]

The API has heavily supported a long-term effort to mislead the public about climate science—as revealed in a Union of Concerned Scientists (UCS) report *The Climate Deception Dossiers*.

The UCS report cites an API "Global Climate Science Communications Plan" as evidence the API sought to mislead on climate science. The plan declared that:

"Victory will be achieved" when "uncertainties in climate science . . . become part of the conventional wisdom"; when media coverage recognizes "the validity of viewpoints that challenge the current 'conventional wisdom'"; and when industry leaders "understand uncertainties in climate science, making them stronger ambassadors to those who shape climate policy."[1255] [1256]

Of course, the "uncertainties" that the plan sought to promote were actually API-manufactured falsehoods about the reality of climate disruption.

De-nihilists harassing scientists

De-nihilists have attacked the characters of climate scientists by promoting fake conspiracies and casting false aspersions. One example is the myth that climate scientists are biased because of their funding support. Former Senator Rick Santorum exemplified this baseless position when, he declared on CNN: "If there was no climate change, we'd have a lot of scientists looking for work. The reality is that a lot of these scientists are driven by the money that they receive . . . from people who support their agenda."[1257]

Of course, the government grants supporting climate science are not predicated on any position on climate disruption. And scientists are not reaping large financial rewards by garnering lucrative government grants. In dismissing that myth, journalist Anthony Sherwood wrote, "there's not much gravy on this train." In reality, such grants pay for equipment, supplies, and a salary incredibly modest by comparison to, say, that of oil company executives.[1258]

De-nihilists also level personal attacks on climate scientists (see Why the Scientists Failed). Climate scientist Michael Mann described the strategy of such attacks:

> On the eve of a critical congressional vote, hearing, or climate policy summit, a late-breaking "scandal" suddenly erupts. Individual scientists are typically charged with claims of misconduct, fraud, or data manipulation, and soon enough, right-wing blogs, climate-denying websites, and the conservative establishment media are trumpeting the accusations. In time, more objective media outlets are forced to cover the uproar, lending it credibility and oxygen, even as it is responsibly dissected.[1259]

The harassing legal tactics de-nihilists use on climate scientists are exemplified by a 2016 incident involving then-Congressman Lamar Smith. He subpoenaed the correspondence of states' attorneys general and environmental groups such as the UCS regarding the investigation of ExxonMobil's knowledge of the risks of climate disruption.[1260]

"Mr. Smith makes no claim that our organization violated any law or regulation; he simply demands to see our correspondence," wrote then-president of the UCS Ken Kimmel in *The New York Times*. "This is a deeply troubling request. It is, in effect, a bullying tactic that threatens the work that advocacy groups like mine do under the protection of the First Amendment."[1261]

A classic case of individual harassment was the filing of a suit by the attorney general of Virginia to obtain Michael Mann's emails, as well as the bringing of subsequent legal action against him.[1262]

"In all, I've been through roughly a dozen investigations prompted by climate change deniers," wrote Mann in *The Washington Post*. "Each time, I've been exonerated. Investigators find that my methods are sound and my data is replicable. (And, indeed, I've been recognized by the scientific community with numerous awards and accolades for my work.) But by then, much time has been lost, expense has been incurred and I've endured abuse and vilification."[1263]

While de-nihilists have sought to thwart policies to avoid climate disruption, they have *ridden* the societal wave of climate science denial, rather than *powered* it. The energy source for that wave has been the vast power of the fossil fuel industry (see II. The Carbon Contagion).

The False Hope Nostrum

During the COVID-19 pandemic, then-President Trump notoriously touted the antimalaria drug hydroxychloroquine as an antiviral treatment. It was unproven for that purpose. Similarly, "false hope nostrums" are being promoted by many advocates in the climate pandemic. They promote these nostrums with little proof that our species can "cure" the climate pandemic by inventing new technology, vanquishing anti-climate forces, marshaling political will, and/or having an optimistic outlook.

Author George Marshall dubs these people "bright-siders" in his book *Don't Even Think About it.*[1264] Marshall wrote that the bright-siders believe that:

> Climate change is a challenge, but it is also a great opportunity. Humans have always triumphed over adversity and come through stronger. Our ingenuity, technology, and capitalism have created unbelievable progress and will continue to do so. We can be anything we want to be, so the real enemy is negativity and despair, which must not be allowed to poison this positive vision.

Bright-siding, wrote Marshall, "replaces uncertainty with confidence... And it compensates for the taint of failure and self-doubt that hangs around climate change with an overstated confidence in technology and economic growth."

Scientists have been among the most prominent proponents of the false belief that we can invent our way out of a climate disaster. In part, they are inclined to false hope because of their innate professional optimism (see Scientists are occupational optimists).

Another motive may have been their reluctance to be the bearer of tragic news. As with all of us, they may have been reluctant to face the hard reality of our future as a species. For some there may even have been an element of disingenuousness behind their promulgation of false hope.

Hope springs infernal

Many climate scientists have asserted that there is "still time left" to avoid climate disruption's most catastrophic dangers—prime examples of their blind acceptance of the false hope nostrum. For example, after release of a 2022 IPCC report on climate disruption mitigation, climate scientists declared in concert that there was still time left to avoid major impacts.[1265] [1266]

However, climate scientists are neither engineers, economists, nor political scientists. They discount the massive technological, economic, and political barriers to stopping the massive momentum of our fossil-fuel-driven society. Whistling past a graveyard does not mean the graveyard is not still there.

Evidence of this false hope is evident in the multiple lines in the sand scientists have drawn in past years—deadlines for averting a climate crisis. These past deadlines were:

- *2021*: In 2018, the Global Commission on the Economy and Climate declared that "The next 2–3 years are a critical window when many of the policy and investment decisions that shape the next 10–15 years will be taken."[1267]
- *2020*: In 2017, prominent climate scientists warned that the world had three years to begin major decarbonizing to meet the two-degree target. They hopefully declared, "Let us stay optimistic and act boldly together."[1268]
- *2017*: A 2011 International Energy Agency report stated that "If stringent new action is not forthcoming by 2017, the energy-related infrastructure then in place will generate all the emissions allowed in the [two-degree] scenario up to 2035, leaving no room for additional power plants, factories and other infrastructure unless they are zero-carbon . . ."[1269]

Only more recently have climate scientists begun to contemplate the possibility of climate catastrophes. For example, in a 2022 paper, a group of climate scientists declared:

> Prudent risk management requires consideration of bad-to-worst-case scenarios. Yet, for climate change, such potential futures are poorly understood. Could anthropogenic climate change result in worldwide societal collapse or even eventual human extinction? At present, this is a dangerously underexplored topic. Yet there are ample reasons to suspect that climate change could result in a global catastrophe . . . It is time for the scientific community to grapple with the challenge of better understanding catastrophic climate change.[1270]

"Disney version of environmental science"

A key belief of the false-hopers is that technology will rescue society. A prominent proponent of this belief is Microsoft founder Bill Gates, who authored the book *How to Avoid a Climate Disaster: The Solutions We Have and the Breakthroughs We Need*.[1271]

The book is a contradictory mix of realism and false hope. On the one hand, Gates does realistically present the massive barriers to implementing decarbonizing technologies. He covers renewable energy, nuclear power, industrial processes, agricultural practice, carbon capture, and geoengineering. His conclusions, in fact, closely track those found in this book (see VI. Grasping at Climate Panaceas). Nevertheless, he hopefully declares:

> We need to accomplish something gigantic we have never done before, much faster than we have ever done anything similar. To do it, we need lots of break-throughs in science and engineering. We need to build a consensus that doesn't exist and create public policies to push a transition that would not happen otherwise. We need the energy system . . . to change completely and also stay the same. *But don't despair. We can do this* [emphasis added].

Gates admits, "I think more like an engineer than a political scientist, and I don't have a solution to the politics of climate change."

Nor does he have economic solutions, only saying offhandedly, "we know it will require a massive investment."

Such optimists "have failed to grasp the nature of either Earth systems or the political economy that bears upon them," wrote journalist George Monbiot. "These men are not climate deniers; they are politics deniers." Monbiot charged that they spin "a simple story with a happy ending, telling power what it wants to hear, this is the Disney version of environmental science."[1272]

Battling dark forces

Other false hope advocates believe simplistically that mainly dark forces of politics and greed stand in the way of overcoming climate disruption. These false-hopers include climatologist Michael Mann.

In his book *The New Climate War: The Fight to Take Back Our Climate*, Mann wrote that climate progress requires overcoming "the forces of denial and delay—the fossil fuel companies, right-wing plutocrats, and oil-funded governments that continue to profit from our dependence on fossil fuels." Those groups are "engaging in a multipronged offensive based on deception, distraction, and delay. This is the new climate war, and the planet is losing."[1273]

While these forces are indeed at play, as this book shows, far more important are the massive momentum of the fossil fuel industry and of greenhouse gas emissions (see II. The Carbon Contagion and III. Plague on the Environment).

Environmental groups have adopted the "overcoming-dark-forces" theme for both financial and philosophical reasons. Financially, they find it a productive fundraising strategy to warn of climate enemies, but to declare that generous contributions will fuel their success in thwarting those enemies. And philosophically, lack of hope undercuts the groups' optimism that activism will yield success. Apocalypse doesn't sell.

Hope-filled, uncritical media

Optimistic false-hopers have included some media. Many media stories have uncritically reported scientists' "just a little time left" declarations without questioning their basis.

Other uncritical media stories have touted advances in technologies such as solar panels and batteries, but downplayed key caveats (see Renewable Energy Hype). They mentioned only deep in the story that an advance was only laboratory-scale, or that it faced major technical and economic barriers to commercialization.

Other such stories have hailed record *increases* in solar energy deployment without mentioning that the increase was from a *very small base*. Similarly, many stories declaring solar energy to be cheaper than coal did not mention the major barriers to their massive deployment.

Some media have published breathlessly Panglossian articles such as "Our Amazing Clean Energy Future Has Arrived," by Vivek Wadhwa and Alex Salkever. The authors declared that "the evidence of a great green wave is now overwhelming," but failed to credibly analyze that evidence, as this book does (see Renewable Energy Hype). Nor do they appear to have the professional credentials to do so. Neither author is a science or environmental journalist or has a scientific education. The former holds an MBA, and the latter a degree in political science and Russian language and literature.[1274]

Even as false-hopers promulgate positive views of the climate future, they denounce articles and books that paint a less-than-rosy image. For example, a largely negative reception was given a portentous article, "The Uninhabitable Earth," by David Wallace-Wells. The article's opening lines:

"It is, I promise, worse than you think. If your anxiety about global warming is dominated by fears of sea-level rise, you are barely scratching the surface of what terrors are possible."[1275] (The article has since been expanded into a book.[1276])

The article was roundly criticized by scientists—for example, in an article quoting climatologist Michael Mann in *The Washington Post*:

"The evidence that climate change is a serious problem that we must contend with now, is overwhelming on its own. There is no need to overstate the evidence, particularly when it feeds a paralyzing narrative of doom and hopelessness."[1277]

Hopeful politicians

Politicians are major purveyors of optimistic false hope because hope is a fundamental ingredient of a successful campaign. Bill Clinton was known as "The Man from Hope"—only partly because he was from Hope,

Arkansas. George W. Bush's campaign slogan was "A Safer World and a More Hopeful America." And, of course, Barack Obama's presidential slogan was that one word, "Hope."

Like other bright-siders, Gore typically picks the ripest cherries of good news—citing positive statistics without providing the proper context. For example, in a *New York Times* op-ed, he declared that wind and solar energy are becoming cheaper than fossil fuel plants. However, he failed to include that they remain a minuscule percentage of overall energy sources, and that their advantage disappears as that percentage grows (see Renewable Energy Hype).

Gore wrote that "several American utilities have announced plans to close existing natural gas and coal generating plants." But he did not include that huge numbers of such new plants are being constructed (see Fossil Fools). He cited a 450% increase in the number of electric vehicles without noting that this increase is from a minuscule base (see Fossilized Transportation).[1278]

Gore has moderated his bright-siding somewhat as the tragic consequences of climate disruption have unfolded. Nevertheless, he still exudes a determined optimism, declaring in an interview with *The Atlantic*:

"We just have to be clear-eyed about it—and we have to be brave about it—in acknowledging that for some of these consequences, it's already too late, but for the most serious of them, it is not too late."[1279]

De-nihilist false-hopers

Even de-nihilists have bought into the optimistic false hope nostrum in their own way. They espouse "an unlimited faith in technological development . . . to overcome any potential resource limits and readily solve any (minor) environmental problems," wrote sociologists Riley Dunlap and Aaron McCright.[1280]

De-nihilists' false hope is also driven by the frightening specter of climate disruption's dire implications. As psychologist Per Espen Stoknes wrote in his book *What We Think About When We Try Not To Think About Global Warming*:

"The concept of denial is reserved for those issues that are emotionally and morally disturbing and therefore—if not dealt with—generate an uncomfortable inner splitting."[1281]

Corporations indirectly propagate optimistic false hope, motivated by their profit orientation, limited time horizon, and innate inertia (see Why the Corporations Failed). Corporate executives focus laser-like on profits in the next quarter, not survival of the human species in the next centuries. And, they focus on the technology required to successfully create a new product, not to create a sustainable society.

Finally, we readily buy in to false hope because of what psychologists call our "optimism bias." That is, we overestimate the likelihood of positive events and underestimate the likelihood of negative events. This trait reduces our stress and anxiety about the future, wrote psychologist Geoffrey Beattie: "Some argue that optimism bias may help explain why we don't do anything about the threat of climate change. It's not personal, it won't affect us, it's others that need worry."[1282]

Given this false hope, and our institutional and psychological shortcomings, it is no wonder that our society has downplayed the profound obstacles to overcoming climate disruption.

VI
Grasping at Climate Panaceas

As discussed earlier, surviving the climate pandemic would require an unprecedented political, economic, technological, and societal revolution in our energy system. This section explores the overwhelming obstacles to achieving that revolution. It will show the profound shortcomings of the Paris Agreement, renewable energy, carbon capture, geoengineering, and nuclear power; as well as the obstacles to enhancing energy efficiency and decarbonizing transportation and agriculture. The proposed solutions are all illusory panaceas.

And finally, it will address the agonizing reality of the climate pandemic's threat to our survival and how we might cope with that threat.

Paris Agreement: Blind and Toothless

You may recall from an earlier chapter the hapless senatorial candidate who proposed a politically disastrous, aggressive climate platform (see Why the Politicians Failed). Let's say the candidate somehow ended up in office.

Now, the maladroit congressman is holding a news conference to announce introduction of a bill to fight a major threat to the constituency. The congressman mounts the stage before a gaggle of media gathered for the announcement. The congressman begins:

"Today, I am announcing a proposal for sweeping legislation to halt a threat to our very civilization. I recognize that my law is wholly inadequate to meet that goal, but I am proceeding anyway, with the hope that we can somehow do better in the future."

Asks a reporter: "What are the penalties for noncompliance?"

"Well, there are none. Compliance is voluntary," replies the congressman.

"So, there's no way to enforce the law?"

"No, we actually don't have any legal jurisdiction," is the answer.

"How about policing? How will you know that people are obeying the law?" asks another reporter.

"It's up to them to tell us that they are obeying it. We can't do any patrolling to check."

"So, it will be up to them to report whether they are violating it?"

"Well, actually, they may not even know that they're violating it. They might not have good enough information on their own compliance."

"But at least they will have committed to obeying the law as written, right?" asks a reporter.

"Not really," admits the congressman. "They can decide to change their commitment at any time. We hope they decide to be more rigorous about obeying the law, but they may decide to be more lax."

"So, will they be tempted to reduce their commitment?"

"Yes, unfortunately. They will find it very hard to obey the law. It will require them to spend enormous amounts of time and money. They could endanger their economic well-being, and they would have to drastically change their behavior."

The reporters chuckle, shake their heads in disbelief, and leave the room to produce their stories about the congressman's preposterous proposal.

In this scenario, substitute "Paris Agreement" for "law," and you have precisely the features of the international climate agreement adopted in December 2015. The UN Paris Agreement entered into force in November 2016 when a majority of participating nations ratified it.[1283]

The agreement was formulated at the 2015 United Nations 21st Conference of the Parties (COP21). It seeks to hold "the increase in the global average temperature to well below 2°C above preindustrial levels and to pursue efforts to limit the temperature increase to 1.5°C above preindustrial levels."

2°C fabrication

First of all, the 2°C limit is not a *scientific* number, but a convenient *political* measure with a highly dubious scientific provenance. One might think the number originated from a careful analysis of a vast amount of scientific data on global temperatures, historical records, glacial melting, ecological impacts, and so on. But it didn't.

Rather, the notion of a 2°C limit first arose casually in the 1970s, when economist William Nordhaus suggested it in two discussion papers. The papers were not even formally reviewed and published in scientific journals.[1284] [1285] And his suggestion was not even based on the ecological impact of a 2°C warming. Rather that was the temperature rise believed to occur if CO_2 levels doubled. In fact, Nordhaus declared that:

> The standards proposed here, as well as the reasoning behind it, are extremely tentative. It must be emphasized that the process of setting standards used in this section is deeply unsatisfactory, both from an empirical point of view and from a theoretical point of view. We can only justify the standards set here as rough guesses.

The 2°C limit was promoted by the Stockholm Environmental Institute in 1990, in perhaps one of the weirdest examples of "scientific reasoning" ever. The report acknowledged that a rise beyond 1°C "may elicit rapid, unpredictable, and nonlinear responses that could lead to extensive ecosystem damage." But since it was too late for society to limit the temperature rise to 1°C, the report elected to settle for a 2°C limit.[1286]

As described in a history of the 2°C limit, the 2°C number continued to propagate as a political measure.[1287] In fact, as climatologist Reto Knutti and colleagues wrote in a critique of the 2°C target:

> This 2°C warming target is perceived by the public as a universally accepted goal, identified by scientists as a safe limit that avoids dangerous climate change. This perception is incorrect: no scientific assessment has clearly justified or defended the 2°C target as a safe level of warming.[1288]

The lower 1.5°C limit, by the same token, was not chosen because it represented some safe level. It was chosen because scientists knew that the damage from climate disruption would be less than for a 2°C increase. The number is certainly not precise, as climatologist Michael Oppenheimer, an author or editor of multiple IPCC reports, told a news briefing:

> Although every increment of warming . . . causes more damage, more lost life, more damage, costly damage to property, when you get above *about* [emphasis added] a degree-and-a-half, these effects start to go non-linear . . ."

Oppenheimer said the 1.5°C limit was "chosen for first, scientific reasons, and second, practical reasons. Practical reasons because it's hard to envision landing the climate at a lower temperature . . ."[1289]

As noted earlier, I do use temperature limits throughout the book as numerical shorthand for "crippling" (1.5°C, 2°C), "devastating" (4°C) and "terminal" (6°C).

Importantly, de-nihilists should not take the imprecision of these numbers as evidence that global heating isn't real. The masses of valid scientific evidence cited in this book point toward a hotter world and climate catastrophe.

Fuzzy verbiage

The Paris Agreement is rife with vague wording, including nebulous phrases, such as that countries should:

- Be "pursuing efforts" to limit temperature increase to 1.5°C above preindustrial levels
- Commit to "put forward their best efforts" to reach peaking of greenhouse gases "as soon as possible"
- Set their own "ambitious" reduction goals that "represent a progression over time."

The agreement allows that "a Party may at any time adjust its existing nationally determined contribution with a view to enhancing its level of ambition . . ."[1290]

To be fair, the agreement is the best that could have been hoped for, given the vastly different goals and interests of the participating countries. As Michael Oppenheimer said in the press briefing:

> As far as enforceability . . . it's the weakness of the Paris Accord. There are no penalties, except for what's called name and shame. . . . I'd feel more comfortable if there were trade sanctions and other penalties as part of the Paris Agreement. It's not there. We got to do the best we can despite that.

Nevertheless, the Paris Agreement epitomizes the failure of the international community to even begin the massive revolution in the global energy system required to address climate disruption.

Climatologist James Hansen, considered a pioneer in the field, told *The Guardian*: "It's a fraud really, a fake. . . . It's just bullshit for them to say: 'We'll have a 2°C warming target and then try to do a little better every five years.' It's just worthless words. There is no action, just promises."[1291] Hansen was also quoted as dubbing the agreement "half-assed" and "half-baked."[1292]

In a paper titled "The World's Biggest Gamble," an international cadre of climate scientists was just as critical. The scientists charged that:

> The scale of the decarbonisation challenge to meet the Paris Agreement is underplayed in the public arena. It will require precipitous emissions reductions within 40 years and a new carbon sink on the scale of the ocean sink. Even then, the world is extremely likely to overshoot. . . . The agreement is void of quantitative emission pathways to reach this goal, and bizarrely, the phrase "fossil fuels" is never used. . . . In reality, despite the progress of the [Paris Agreement], nations are gambling with the stability of the Earth system.[1293]

Even optimists recognize the agreement's failures. Terry Odendahl, head of the philanthropic organization Global Greengrants Fund, charged that COP21:

- "completely failed to address the elephant in the room: that we must stop burning fossil fuels and switch to clean energy."

- "contains false solutions such as 'carbon markets.' Many large global funders are still wedded to false solutions such as fracked gas, mega-dams, clean coal, and carbon capture."
- "failed to adequately address the threat climate change poses to the 'undeveloped' world."
- "failed to address the effect of climate change on marginalized people around the world—indigenous, youth, women, poor, rural, and others who have and will continue to suffer the brunt of the chaos."[1294]

Fantasy scenarios

Even the agreement's "success" will constitute a failure to avoid dangerous, even catastrophic climate disruption over the next decades, concluded multiple assessments of the agreement:

The International Energy Agency (IEA) *World Energy Outlook 2018* concluded that there is a huge gap between the Paris Agreement and sustainable development scenarios. Noted the report: "The projected emissions trend represents a major collective failure to tackle the environmental consequences of energy use."[1295]

Individual countries are not on track to meet their emissions targets either, according to such sources as the Climate Action Tracker.[1296]

Even the UN itself has documented failures year after year in editions of its *Emissions Gap Report*.[1297 1298 1299 1300 1301 1302]

The UN Environment Program called its 2022 *Emissions Gap Report* "a testimony to inaction on the global climate crisis," declaring that "the window of opportunity to limit global warming to well below 2°C, preferably 1.5°C . . . is closing rapidly." In fact, a synthesis of UN reports by one group of scientists concluded that:

> Individual countries are not on track to achieve commitments that were insufficient from the outset and are now woefully inadequate. . . . In 2010, the world thought it had 30 years to halve global emissions of greenhouse gases. Today, we know that this must happen in ten years.[1303]

Particularly poignant was the conclusion of the 2016 *Emissions Gap Report*. It declared that, without urgent action:

> We will mourn the loss of biodiversity and natural resources. We will regret the economic fallout. Most of all, we will grieve over the avoidable human tragedy; the growing numbers of climate refugees hit by hunger, poverty, illness and conflict will be a constant reminder of our failure to deliver."[1304]

These and other reports predict by 2100 an approximately 3°c temperature rise.[1305] [1306]

The un *Global Environment Outlook* concluded that emissions must fall to net zero by around 2070 to meet the 2°c limit.[1307]

Another report by the Universal Ecological Fund basically agreed. It concluded that net zero emissions had to be reached between 2060 and 2075. The report indicated that, even if Paris goals are met, the world would see a 1.5°c rise by the early 2030s, with 2°c reached by 2050.[1308]

These dates may, in fact, be optimistic. The massive momentum of the fossil fuel industry and tipping points may well make them appear absurdly low (see Decarbonization Delusion and Climate Monsters).

Insurmountable shortcomings

The Paris Agreement is beset with insurmountable shortcomings—scientific, technological, economic, logistical, and political. Some examples:

Scientific: The ipcc is likely using the wrong historic baseline from which to measure global temperature increases. It uses the late 1800s to define the preindustrial starting point, but the rise likely began in the 1700s, found climatologists in one analysis.[1309] Said co-author climatologist Michael Mann:

> The ipcc research community uses a definition of pre-industrial that is likely underestimating the warming that has already taken place. . . . That means we have less carbon to burn than we previously thought, if we are to avert the most dangerous changes in climate. . . . When the ipcc says that we've warmed 1 degree c relative to

> preindustrial, that's probably incorrect. . . . It's likely as
> much as 1.2 degrees c.[1310]

Another scientific shortcoming is that emissions budgets have likely not taken into account all the possible greenhouse gas contributors such as methane emissions from thawing permafrost. In one study, researchers who did such accounting concluded that "the world is closer to exceeding the budget for the long-term target of the Paris climate agreement than previously thought."[1311]

Said study lead author Thomas Gasser: "Since we are officially on an overshooting trajectory, we have to prepare ourselves for the possibility that we may never get back to safer levels of warming."[1312]

Technological: The most egregious fantasy in the Paris Agreement is an assumption that "negative emissions technologies" could enable the world to stay below the 2°C goal (see Carbon Capture Snake Oil).

Limiting temperature rise to 2°C would mean sucking between 0.5 billion and 3 billion metric tons of carbon out of the atmosphere *each year* using as-yet-untested carbon-capture technologies, calculated ecosystem researchers.[1313] What's more, they wrote, the system would need carbon storage capacity of between 50 billion and 250 billion metric tons. And that is the best-case scenario.

As discussed earlier, the mirage of carbon capture and storage gives policymakers an excuse to allow temperature overshoot, with the promise that we could remedy the overshoot with negative emissions.[1314]

Economic: Implementing the climate pledges will require a massive global investment of $13.5 trillion in energy efficiency and low-carbon technologies by 2030, found an IEA report. This amount constitutes a full 40% of the total investment in the energy sector.[1315] Also, countries such as Russia will simply not abandon their lucrative oil and gas industry profits to meet the agreement's requirements.

Logistical: Major uncertainties abound in what the signatory countries actually agreed to in their "nationally determined contributions" (NDCs) to reduced emissions. In analyzing the uncertainties, one group of climate policy analysts concluded that "virtually every aspect of the submitted NDCs was decided nationally, and little to no guidance or requirements were given that could focus their scope" to enable comparison and quantification.[1316]

What's more, countries' reports of their emissions constitute a statistical Tower of Babel. An investigation by *The Washington Post* of 196 countries' reports to the UN found a huge gap between their reported emissions and their actual production. The gap ranges from 8.5 billion to 13.3 billion tons a year of unreported emissions. By comparison, the lower number matches the annual emissions of the US; the higher number approaches those of China.[1317] The *Post* investigation concluded that the gap:

> ... is the result of questionably drawn rules, incomplete reporting in some countries and apparently willful mistakes in others—and the fact that in some cases, humanity's full impacts on the planet are not even required to be reported.

Political: Countries do not have the same political and economic interests. As psychologist Per Espen Stoknes wrote in his book *What We Think About When We Try Not To Think About Global Warming*:

> Most countries seem more eager to grind their own mills. The poorer nations want to grow faster, and the old industrialized countries want energy security and continued growth. The oil-rich countries want to continue to sell their black gold. . . . The mad logic is: Better that my nation-state doesn't lose in the short-term race than for all of us to win in the long term.[1318]

Indeed, 2019 negotiations over countries' NDC commitments ended in failure, with the US and other major carbon-emitting nations blocking an agreement to seek more ambitious carbon-reduction targets.[1319] And in 2021, a report on NDCs submitted by participating countries showed that their combined impact would result in a 16.3% increase in greenhouse gas emissions by 2030 above the 2010 level.

In contrast, emissions would have to decline by 45% to meet a 1.5°C increase target.[1320] The report, declared UN Secretary-General António Guterres, "shows that the world is on a catastrophic pathway to 2.7-degrees of heating."[1321]

Another legally nonbinding pact was the 2021 Glasgow Climate Pact at the UN Climate Change Conference, COP26, signed by nearly 200 signatory nations. As with the Paris Agreement, the need for a broad consensus made it wholly inadequate at reflecting the profound hazards of climate disruption.[1322]

For example, the group watered down an early draft that called for a "*phase-out of unabated* coal power . . ." [emphasis added]. The final version called only for a "*phasedown of unabated* coal power . . . [emphasis added]." The word "unabated" was meant to reflect the potential use of untested carbon capture technologies (see Carbon Capture Snake Oil).

The agreement also called for the phase-out of "inefficient" fossil fuel subsidies—a word meant to give some countries an excuse to continue such subsidies (see Bankrolling the Contagion). An early draft of the pact contained the emphatic passage, ". . . that carbon budgets consistent with achieving the Paris Agreement temperature goal are now small and being rapidly depleted." But the final draft weakened the declaration by leaving out the passage.

Despite the failures of such agreements as the Paris and COP26 agreements, many believe that humanity will surely be rescued by technologies such as renewable energy and carbon capture. But as the following sections show, that rescue will not be coming.

Renewable Energy Hype

From my vantage point in an airplane, the sprawling semicircular array of more than 300,000 mirrors of the Ivanpah solar power plant look like some alien transmitter nestled against the rugged brown mountains in the California desert. The mirrors of Ivanpah, the world's largest solar thermal plant, focus the sun's rays on three "power towers." The intense heat created in the towers produces steam to turn turbines designed to generate nearly 400 megawatts of power. On sunny days, the towers glow with a blinding brightness, feeding power to the grid.

Today, the towers are dark, and the mirrors reflect only a wan light. It is cloudy, so neither the towers nor the facility's adjacent array of photovoltaic (PV) panels are producing energy.

The Ivanpah plant is an apt metaphor for the stark realities of renewable energy. It is dramatic, highly visible, and highly publicized. But it is ultimately a disappointment. As this section details, although renewable energy seems a savior in halting the relentless increase in greenhouse gas emissions, it is not.

The plant's technical problems caused its production to fall short of expectations.[1323] And, although the plant has, indeed, prevented millions of tons of CO_2 emissions, it requires burning of significant natural gas to operate.[1324] [1325] The system burns natural gas at night to maintain boiler temperatures, and uses gas turbines as backup generators during cloudy days.

The plant has proven such an economic disappointment by its owner NRG Energy that the company has sold off its renewable energy holdings to focus on fossil fuels.[1326] The similar Crescent Dunes Solar Energy Project farther north also suffered technical problems, failed to be profitable, and declared bankruptcy.[1327]

Advocates unrealistically tout renewable energy as a major future energy source. For example, an International Energy Agency (IEA) report on renewables forecast renewable electricity capacity to grow by over 60% between 2020 and 2026.[1328]

While such statistics make renewable electricity seem highly promising, they are misleading. For one thing, the increase in renewable electricity is from a *very* small base. Also, renewable electricity constitutes only a small portion of the total energy supply.

Globally in 2019, about 14% of total energy came from renewable energy, according to the IEA.[1329] However, more than half that percentage represents burning wood and charcoal for heating and cooking. Only small percentages come from such renewables as hydropower (18%) and wind (6.2%). Even a smaller percentage (3%) comes from combined biogases, renewable municipal waste, solar PV, solar thermal, and tidal.

What's more, renewable energy's share of global energy consumption rose only about 1% per year between 2010 and 2020, according to the International Renewable Energy Agency.[1330]

Currently in the US, wind produces about 8% of electrical generation, hydropower 7%, solar 2%, and biomass just over 1%, according to the US Energy Information Administration (USEIA). In contrast, natural gas generates 40% of electrical power, coal generates 19%, and nuclear about 19%.[1331]

True, by 2050 in the US, renewables' share of electricity generation is projected by the USEIA to reach up to about 44%. However, natural gas will continue to be a major source, with a 34% share, as nuclear and coal drop to, respectively 12% and 10% each.[1332]

Worldwide, almost 28% of electricity is generated by renewables as of 2020, according to the IEA. The largest source is hydropower, with only about 9% generated by wind and solar power.[1333]

Another widely cited—and misleading—statistic is the high percentage of new renewable electrical capacity. For example, almost 95% of new global power capacity added through 2026 will be renewables, projected the above-cited IEA report. However, *additions* to generation capacity do not mean significant *replacement* of the massive existing capacity, which is almost totally fossil-fuel-powered. Indeed, the IEA concluded that an almost doubling of annual additions of PV and wind power would be necessary to meet the IEA's Net Zero Emissions by 2050 Scenario.

Overall, the IEA found that only 2 of 55 technologies—lighting and electric vehicles—key to meeting its Net Zero goal were on track. The 55 key technologies included the power sector, fuel supply, industrial processes, transport, buildings, and energy integration technologies such as energy storage and smart grids.[1334]

Finally, there is little evidence for massive investment in renewable energy projects, despite highly publicized new projects. Analyses have found that such investment has been rising only slowly over time, even suffering a significant drop due to the COVID-19 pandemic in 2020.[1335] [1336]

Rapid PV growth not relevant

Although the falling cost of PV solar installations has spurred rapid growth, *momentum* is not *magnitude*.

Statistics from an MIT study showed how a rapid rise from a minuscule level is still a minuscule level.[1337] While PV solar accounted for about 139 gigawatts of electricity production in 2013, it would require 25,000 gigawatts of zero-carbon energy to avoid significant climate disruption, concluded the study. Reaching this generation level would require a scale-up of 10 to 100 times in PV installations just by mid-century.

What's more, the rated capacity of a PV solar installation is not equal to the energy it will actually produce. Due to solar's actual power output, news reports are misleading that assert that a new installation of a given megawatt capacity is capable of powering a given number of homes. Engineer Jatin Nathwani explained in an article in *The Conversation* why solar comes up short:

> Because of the efficiency of energy conversion, solar energy output tends to be low. For example, the energy produced from a large number of solar arrays combined as 1,000 megawatts (MW) installed capacity will deliver, on average, an energy equivalent of 10 to 12% of its capacity. In contrast, a nuclear plant delivers energy at 80–90% of its rated capacity.[1338]

Some studies do forecast that solar could grow fast enough to ameliorate climate change. One such analysis projected that PV solar could provide 30–50% of global power generation by 2050.[1339] However, that analysis requires an unrealistic perfect storm of solar-friendly regulations and sufficient financing. The massive increase would also require storage technology such as batteries that could incorporate variable PV electricity into a power grid that must operate stably. As discussed below, such economic storage technology does not exist.

Colossal construction needed

One projection by environmental engineers revealed the gargantuan construction effort required for a total global, renewable-powered energy system. The researchers charted roadmaps to transform the energy infra-structures of 139 countries to be powered by wind, water, and sunlight. The roadmaps envisioned 80% conversion by 2030 and 100% by 2050. The researchers calculated that the conversion would require:

- 1.58 million onshore wind turbines
- 935,000 offshore wind turbines

- 1.8 billion residential roof PV installations
- 75 million commercial/government roof PV installations
- 251,000 solar PV plants[1340]

The engineers also created a US version of such a conversion plan.[1341] That plan would require about four centuries to complete at the current rate of renewable generation installation, according to factory construction engineer Tom Solomon.[1342] He calculated that reaching 100% US renewable energy by 2050 would require building nearly 500 huge "gigafactories" for producing solar panels and wind turbines. It would mean building 29 gigafactories every year or two at a total cost of $6.3 trillion.

Massive metal demand, waste generation

A transition to renewables would require a vast increase in production of the metals used in solar panels, wind turbines, and batteries. The metals include aluminum, nickel, cobalt, lead, lithium, silver, neodymium, and indium. Also, the expansion of the electric grid to accommodate renewables, discussed below, will require a massive increase in copper production (see "Gridlocked renewables" below).

For example, an onshore wind plant requires nine times more mineral resources than a similarly sized gas-fired plant, calculated the IEA. And a typical electric car requires six times more minerals than a conventional gas car. The average amount of minerals needed for a unit of power generation has increased by 50% since 2010, as the share of renewables has risen, found the IEA.[1343]

IEA Executive Director Fatih Birol warned that "the data shows a looming mismatch between the world's strengthened climate ambitions and the availability of critical minerals that are essential to realising those ambitions."[1344]

One analysis found that copper demand will increase by up to 350% by 2050.[1345] That increase will mean a major increase in copper mining, with its environmental impacts. An analysis of US copper mines's impacts by the environmental group Earthworks found that:

> . . . 100% had pipeline spills, 92% failed to control
> mine wastewater and 28% had tailings impoundment

failures—polluting drinking water, destroying fish and wildlife habitat, harming agricultural land and threatening public health.[1346]

A total transition to renewable electricity sources could also require silver demand to grow by as much as 105%, indium by 920%, and lithium by 2,700%, calculated economic anthropologist Jason Hickel.[1347] Mining such metals produces such impacts as deforestation, ecosystem collapse, and biodiversity loss, he pointed out. He calculated that just meeting the silver demand could require up to 130 more mines the size of Mexico's Peñasquito mine, which covers nearly 40 square miles. Hickel wrote:

> That operation is staggering in its scale: a sprawling open-pit complex ripped into the mountains, flanked by two waste dumps each a mile long, and a tailings dam full of toxic sludge held back by a wall that's 7 miles around and as high as a 50-story skyscraper.

Hickel's conclusions were based on a World Bank analysis of renewable energy metal requirements.[1348]

Renewable facilities could also generate considerable waste. Without expensive recycling, disposing of decommissioned solar panels could generate 78 million tons of electronic waste by 2050, according to the International Renewable Energy Agency. By then, solar e-waste could amount to 6 million metric tons a year.[1349]

Disposal of wind turbine blades in the US alone will generate up to 370,000 tons a year, with a cumulative 4 million tons by 2050, according to the Electric Power Research Institute.[1350]

Energy additions, not transitions

History also offers sobering lessons about the futility of replacing fossil fuels with renewables. In the past, "the world has never truly undergone an energy transition," wrote energy economist Richard Newell and policy researcher Daniel Raimi.[1351] "Instead, the world has experienced a series of energy additions, where new fuels build atop the old, rising like a skyscraper under construction. . . . These new energy sources—like the ones that came before them—are simply stacking on top of the old ones."

Decades would be required for any energy transition, according to policy analyst Vaclav Smil.[1352] Charting the history of past energy transitions, for example, from wood to coal or oil, he concluded:

> Worldwide the enormous investment and infrastructure needed for any new energy source to capture a large share of the market require two to three generations: 50 to 75 years. . . . Renewables are not taking off any faster than the other new fuels once did, and there is no technical or financial reason to believe they will rise any quicker. . . . Today's great hope for a quick and sweeping transition to renewable energy is fueled mostly by wishful thinking and a misunderstanding of recent history.

Gridlocked renewables

Integrating the increasing amounts of solar and wind generation into the power distribution system will require a profound transformation in the electricity grid, according to the IEA.[1353] [1354]

"Electricity grids could prove to be the weak link in the transformation of the power sector, with implications for the reliability and security of electricity supply," the IEA noted. Given countries' current energy plans, the global need for new transmission lines is "80% greater over the next decade than the expansion seen over the last ten years," found the IEA report.[1355]

An analysis of US policy concluded bluntly that "the current system for planning and paying for expansion of the transmission grid is so unworkable and inefficient it is creating a huge backlog of unbuilt energy projects." Almost 90% of the backlog is for wind, solar, and storage projects, according to the report.[1356]

Transmission costs for wind and solar generation are several times those for coal or nuclear, pointed out energy journalist Gail Tverberg. Because of renewables' variability, transmission lines need to be scaled for maximum output, rather than average output. They need to be longer to bridge the longer distance between generation and consumption.

There is, thus, increased maintenance. Tverberg wrote that renewables' intermittency situation is:

> ... analogous to researchers deciding that it would be helpful or more efficient if humans could change their diets to 100 percent grass in the next 20 years. Grass is a form of energy product, but it is not the energy product that humans normally consume.... The fact that humans have not evolved to eat grass is similar to the fact that the manufacturing and transport sectors of today's economy have *not* [emphasis added] developed around the use of intermittent electricity from wind and solar.[1357]

Large-scale regional power grids could enable wind and solar electricity to be transmitted such long distances, sending surplus electricity to regions that need it. However, in the US, political and economic barriers have stymied such projects. For one thing, the 329 transmission owners in the US evolved to serve their local owners, who resist investing in regional grids, pointed out a report by energy economists.[1358] The report concluded that:

> Market and regulatory failures create perverse incentives that lead to under-investment in the type of regional and interregional transmission that would increase reliability and system-wide efficiency. This failure is widespread across the country.

As energy consultant Susan Tierney told *Science* magazine, "The regional division of power grids means that utility companies and legislators are reluctant to depend on outside power feeds; and communities object to large-scale power lines in their backyards."[1359]

Another complication to running power lines through multiple states is the fact that each will have its own regulations. And approval will be especially difficult for power lines that run through a state but do not supply power to that state.

Concluded an analysis of the power grid by consulting firm ScottMadden, "The general view across the industry is that inter-regional planning processes are at best, stalled, and at worst, ineffective in identifying valuable projects."[1360]

Rosy scenarios of a fully renewable energy future downplay the overwhelming barriers to transforming the energy system and re-engineering the power grid. For example, one such analysis concluded that a fully renewable-powered US grid would be stable with no blackouts.[1361][1362] The modeling study by environmental engineeers imagined a complete electrification of all cars, trucks, heating systems, and other energy users. The plan would more than double electricity use over the next decades, they found.

True, such a profound transformation might be theoretically possible. However, replacing the gargantuan, existing energy infrastructure would require a prodigious, unprecedented feat of legerdemain—political, economic, and technological. And that replacement—scrapping all existing fossil-fueled plants and replacing them with wind and solar—would bring with it wrenching financial disruption.

Another "sunny" study by the National Renewable Energy Laboratory (NREL) found that solar PV could meet much of US power demand, but that curtailment during times of overproduction would become the "new normal." Also, high levels of solar would require considerable energy storage; and conventional generation would still be needed when solar and wind lagged.[1363]

When PV becomes unprofitable

The intermittency and distributed nature of solar PV even mean that it becomes uneconomic at some level due to the need for massive storage and grid re-engineering. An MIT study concluded that:

> Even if solar PV generation becomes cost-competitive at low levels of penetration, revenues per kw of installed capacity will decline as solar penetration increases until a breakeven point is reached, beyond which further investment in solar PV would be unprofitable. . . . Without government policies to help overcome these challenges, it is likely that solar energy will continue to supply only a small percentage of world electricity needs.[1364]

In fact, because they are intermittent, neither solar nor wind will be competitive in the electricity marketplace as their penetration rises, according to economic studies. In one study, energy economist Lion Hirth found that at low market penetration, wind and solar are comparable in value to a constant source such as coal or gas.[1365] However, when wind power reaches 30% of market share, or solar reaches 15%, their value drops well below that of a constant source.

Hirth concluded that "without fundamental technological breakthroughs, wind and solar power will struggle becoming competitive on large scale, even with quite steep learning curves."

A central problem with PV is that it requires massive storage capacity as its percentage in the power grid rises, and a phenomenon known as value deflation kicks in. That is, solar generates so much power during sunny days that its value plummets, even below zero. So utilities must either pay neighboring utilities to take the power or install expensive storage systems. As discussed below, the expense of storage make the system uneconomic (see Battery "derangement" below).

The excess solar power problem is already rearing its head in places such as California, with its large solar power base. Grid managers in the state are actually having to cut solar installations off the grid, to prevent surges during high-solar-output periods.[1366 1367] California utilities have even *paid* other states to take surplus solar power to avoid overloading power lines.[1368] Utility planners worry that increasing solar power will make overproduction during the day even worse.[1369]

One study found that PV costs would have to drop to 25 cents per watt for solar to be truly competitive, given the decreasing value of PV power with increasing grid penetration. "Cost-competitiveness for solar is a moving target," wrote researchers Varun Sivaram and Shayle Kann. "As solar's share of the electricity mix increases, the cost of each new solar project must fall to compete."[1370] The current PV cost is almost $3.00 per watt for residential systems and $1.00 per watt for utility-scale systems.[1371]

A major cost drop is unlikely because while the cost of the panels is falling rapidly, solar installations also require additional fixed-cost hardware such as inverters, installation, and grid connection. Sivaram and Kann concluded that "even with rapid technological advancement, 25 cents per watt may be out of reach by mid-century."[1372]

High percentages of wind power also produce barriers to economic viability on an electric grid. One study concluded that because of the inability to store energy and the need for fast-responding backup capacity, "the indirect costs of wind energy have often been neglected or underestimated." The authors wrote that "The costs of wind power likely exceed the benefits [and] there may be limits to the proportion of electricity that can be generated by wind."[1373]

In fact, storage inadequacies have forced Germany to *pay* customers to consume excess wind-generated power.[1374] Other countries, including Belgium, Britain, France, the Netherlands, and Switzerland have experienced lesser periods of "negative power prices."[1375]

Fossil-powered renewables

Even heavily renewable-powered electrical grids are still mainly fossil-fuel-based. When energy analyst Michael Goff calculated the costs and carbon intensity of electrical grids in 18 leading global economies, he found that:

> Electrical grids with relatively high shares of wind and solar generation are still largely fossil-powered grids. Nations that source 20 to 30% of their electricity from wind, solar, and biomass get up to 60% of their electricity from fossil generation.[1376]

Battery "derangement"

Renewable energy advocates have proposed, unrealistically, that huge banks of batteries could smooth out the hills and valleys of solar and wind generation. They believe that batteries could store massive amounts of excess power during high-production periods and feed that power back into the grid when the sun doesn't shine or the wind doesn't blow.

Proponents of such storage suffer "battery derangement syndrome," contended energy analyst Mark Mills.[1377] They vastly underestimate the magnitude of the batteries that would make up for the lack of solar generation at night.

While factories making lithium batteries currently produce 100 billion watt-hours of storage capacity each year, that production is dwarfed by global electricity use, at *50 trillion watt-hours daily*, wrote Mills. Thus, a pure solar power system with battery backup would require half that amount to make up for nighttime lack of generation. The required battery production "would take 250 years of production from all of today's global battery factories," he wrote.

To meet the 2°C limit, grid storage of about 310 gigawatts (billion watts) would be needed in the US, Europe, China, and India, concluded an IEA report.[1378] By comparison, only about 3 gigawatts of energy storage were added globally in 2019, according to the IEA.[1379]

In the US alone, it would cost some $2.5 trillion to install sufficient battery storage to enable wind and solar to be available when needed.[1380]

Long-duration storage too expensive

A major drawback to battery storage is that it only lasts for a matter of hours. So long-duration energy storage is needed to make wind and solar energy viable during long periods of low generation. However, long-duration energy storage systems are currently far too expensive to compete with natural gas as a backup. These systems store energy as compressed air, hydrogen, and pumped hydro. An economic analysis by MIT researchers found all to be far too expensive.[1381] As energy journalist David Roberts wrote of their findings:

> Their findings on long-duration energy storage (LDES) are daunting and somewhat deflating. In a nutshell: LDES needs to get extremely cheap before it will play a substantial role in a clean grid—cheaper than almost any candidate technology today, and cheaper than any geographically unconstrained technology is likely to get anytime soon.[1382]

That said, the US Department of Energy has set as a goal to reduce the cost of LDES by 90% by 2030, based on its Energy Storage Grand

Challenge.[1383] [1384] However, developing such technologies will take many years, and large-scale deployment many more.

By 2040, LDES could store only up to 10% of global electricity capacity, found an analysis by the management consulting firm McKinsey & Company.[1385] That level is far lower than would be required to support large-scale deployment of intermittent renewable energy.

No Moore's Law for PV, batteries

Some advocates have claimed that PV cells and batteries will plunge in price due to a version of Moore's Law, named after Intel co-founder Gordon Moore. That law predicts that the number of transistors on an integrated circuit will double about every two years, reducing costs and increasing computer power.

While Moore's Law has proved durable in electronics, it is not valid for PV panels or batteries. Moore's Law applies to computer chips because physics allows them to be made smaller and cheaper, pointed out engineer and policy analyst Varun Sivaram.[1386] Solar panels, however, do not have that advantage. Rather, Sivaram wrote:

> Falling costs of silicon solar panels have largely been driven by lower input material costs from scale, lower labor costs through manufacturing automation, and lower waste driven by efficient processing.

Nor will batteries follow Moore's Law. They will remain expensive, even with technological advances, wrote physicist Fred Schlacter:

> The reason there is a Moore's Law for computer processors is that electrons are small and they do not take up space on a chip. . . . Batteries are not like this. Ions, which transfer charge in batteries, are large, and they take up space, as do anodes, cathodes, and electrolytes.[1387]

Because of fundamental physical limits, even the most advanced lithium-ion battery will only reach an energy storage density of about 6% that of crude oil, according to calculations by energy storage researcher Kurt Zenz House. He wrote:

Given other required materials such as electrolytes, separators, current collectors, and packaging, we're unlikely to improve the energy density by more than about a factor of 2 within about 20 years. This means hydrocarbons—including both fossil carbon and biofuels—are still a factor of 10 better than the physical upper bound, and they're likely to be 25 times better than lithium batteries will ever be.[1388]

Realistically modest solar

The stark reality is that worldwide, solar PV and solar thermal systems such as the Ivanpah plant could only supply up to 27% of electricity by 2050, concluded an IEA report.[1389]

But meeting the 2°C temperature limitation of the Paris Agreement would require a tenfold increase in the spread of such low-carbon-emitting technologies as PV systems, concluded a study led by environmental engineer Gabriele Manoli.[1390]

"Radically new strategies to implement technological advances on a global scale and at unprecedented rates are needed," Manoli told *The Engineer.*[1391]

Also, neither PV cells nor batteries are totally "green." Both produce carbon emissions in their manufacture. In the case of PV cells, it may take years to "pay back" that carbon deficit.[1392]

Wind power limited

Wind energy, like solar, will experience a steady cost reduction over the next decades, although not a Moore's Law reduction. The falling costs will be mainly due to the growing size of wind turbines, enabling an economy of scale and enabling capture of more wind energy per unit.

Offshore wind installations in particular are growing rapidly, with a projected production of up to 25 gigawatts by 2030 in the US and 220 gigawatts globally, according to the NREL.[1393] The potential resource is far greater. The US has a potential offshore wind resource of 2,000 gigawatts.[1394]

Despite such growth and such a huge resource, wind generation, onshore or offshore, is not increasing fast enough to meet the IEA's Net Zero Emissions by 2050 Scenario.[1395] And as indicated earlier, wind power becomes uneconomic with increased market penetration.

Even given soaring demand, wind power systems may also be uneconomic in that they may not be profitable for manufacturers. As of 2022, costs of raw materials, supply chain disruptions, and other barriers have led to a "colossal market failure" in the industry, according to Ben Blackwell, head of a wind power trade group.[1396]

It's also possible that wind intensity may decline due to climate disruption. A modeling study by atmospheric scientists found that a warming Arctic will reduce the temperature difference between the Arctic and equatorial latitudes. The result: diminished winds over North America, Asia, and Europe.[1397]

Onshore wind farms are meeting sometimes fierce public resistance as they expand, given their impact on communities. Both onshore wind farms and PV installations are causing controversy in Britain, Germany, and the US.[1398 1399 1400 1401]

This local resistance can kill renewable energy projects because siting requires local or state approvals of such things as the setback requirements of wind projects from buildings. Opponents of wind projects have objected to the noise and "shadow flicker"—the strobing light of windmills on buildings—of such projects. They have also launched aggressive social media campaigns to stop solar and PV projects. These campaigns have gone so far as to push bogus assertions that wind turbines cause cancer and birth defects; that climate disruption is a scam; and that the turbines can dangerously collapse.[1402]

Environmental impacts drive opposition

Such resistance will grow in part due to the huge land requirements for wind farms and PV installations. A full 12% of the continental US land area would be required to meet today's US electricity consumption with wind power, calculated researchers. PV installations would require 1% of the land to meet that need, they calculated.[1403]

Large-scale solar power facilities also produce significant environmental impacts that will drive local opposition. The plants may interfere with wilderness and recreation areas, as well as grazing and farming land. Construction site preparation may cause soil compaction, drainage alteration, increased runoff, and erosion. Thermal solar plants consume water for cooling, straining water resources, especially in desert areas. Chemicals used in solar facilities could contaminate surface or groundwater. All these impacts could adversely affect habitats of native plant and animal species.[1404]

The facilities also directly kill animals. Wind turbines are significant killers of birds, pointed out environmentalist Michael Shellenberger. And the Ivanpah plant has caused the death of hundreds of threatened desert tortoises and thousands of birds a year. In fact, the massive predicted expansion of wind and solar will in some cases lead to extinction-level wildlife deaths, contended Shellenberger.[1405]

Biofuels bust

Biofuels, such as ethanol from corn, are also not an answer. While their energy is not intermittent, producing them uses large amounts of land and water that could be devoted to producing food. Indeed, food grown using land and water currently used for biofuels could feed about 30% of the world's malnourished population, or 280 million people, calculated one study.[1406] And the projected increase in biofuel production based on renewable energy policy would cause a food deficit for 700 million people, said lead author Paolo D'Odorico.[1407]

In fact, the environmental costs of using corn to produce ethanol are significantly greater than the impacts of using the corn for feed, found a study by ecohydrologists. They concluded that producing feed corn is "more energy efficient and less environmentally costly than corn-based ethanol."[1408]

Producing ethanol from corn is not necessarily even significantly lower in greenhouse gas emissions (GHG) than refining gasoline from oil. A 2011 National Research Council (NRC) report found that emissions from ethanol-from-corn production are just 20% less than those from gasoline.[1409] However, a more recent in-depth analysis concluded that corn-produced ethanol would be at least 24% *more* carbon-intensive than gasoline production.[1410]

The 2011 NRC report concluded that "the extent to which [biofuels production] contributes to lowering global GHG is uncertain."

In any case, a major biofuels industry would require massive feedstock production, an IEA report concluded.[1411] The most optimistic production scenario would require 8 billion to 11 billion dry metric tons of feedstock a year by 2050, the report concluded. That scenario assumed that bioenergy would provide only 7.5% of global power generation, 15% of heat used in industry, and 20% used in heating buildings.

The industry would require investing hundreds of billions of dollars for production plants and trillions of dollars for feedstock. However, such an investment is not likely because biofuels are more expensive than fossil fuels, concluded the IEA report.

Hydropower, geothermal inadequate

Hydroelectric power seems a much better bet, given its reliability, low cost, and proven technology. Hydropower already supplies 17% of global electricity generation, behind coal and natural gas, according to an IEA report.[1412]

While the report envisions an increase in hydropower in the next decades, it forecasts that modernizing aging dams will require massive investment. Some $300 billion will be required by 2030 to modernize dams globally, more than double the amount currently planned, said the report. Attracting investment for such modernization projects will be difficult, the report concluded. Investors in new projects will also be discouraged by "long lead times, lengthy permitting processes, high costs and risks from environmental assessments, and opposition from local communities." What's more, the huge dams required for major power production cost up to tens of billions of dollars.

Hydropower is not necessarily a benign, safe source of electricity. Many thousands of older dams have reached the end of their lifespan, needing major repair or replacement. Dams constructed pre-climate-disruption may not be able withstand predicted future extreme floods and river flows.[1413] And, as discussed earlier, dams suffer significant environmental shortcomings (see Dam surprising).

Geothermal energy is only a marginal contributor to electricity and heating demand, and is growing only a few percent a year, according to the IEA. This growth is not enough to meet the agency's Net Zero Emissions by 2050 Scenario.[1414]

That said, there are geothermal technologies in development that could accelerate its use as an electricity source. One company, Eavor Technologies, Inc., has developed a closed-loop system that circulates a working fluid through deep wells, harnessing subterranean heat to generate heating and electricity. The fluid circulates without pumping as a "thermosiphon," in which the heated fluid rises at the outlet, drawing colder fluid into the inlet.[1415]

Overall, renewable energy's bottom line is that it will not live up to its hype. As Richard Heinberg, co-author of *Our Renewable Future*, bluntly wrote:

> While renewable energy can indeed power industrial societies, there is probably no credible future scenario in which humanity will maintain current levels of energy use .... Therefore current levels of resource extraction, industrial production, and consumption are unlikely to be sustained—much less can they perpetually grow.[1416]

Carbon Capture Snake Oil

Carbon capture and storage (CCS) is another supposed savior that will help rescue the world from soaring CO_2 levels. Indeed, CCS is integral to the Paris Agreement's assumptions in its plans to limit emissions (see Paris Agreement: Blind and Toothless).

CCS's major current technology involves extracting CO_2 from fossil fuel power plant exhaust and pumping it deep underground. The broader field of carbon dioxide removal (CDR) encompasses not only CCS, but also sequestering carbon in forests, soils, minerals, and other reservoirs.[1417]

The Petra Nova CCS plant in Texas exemplifies the huge scale of such projects, as well as their just-as-huge drawbacks. Petra Nova aimed to capture carbon dioxide (CO_2) from a coal-powered generating station. The plant cost $1 billion to build, including $190 million in federal support. Far from energy-efficient, the plant required a large natural-gas-fired generating station to supply heat and power to capture the low concentration of CO_2 in the exhaust stream. The captured CO_2 was pumped to a nearby oilfield to boost oil production.

The Petra Nova plant was closed in 2021, the victim of low oil prices and poor performance. The plant missed its carbon-capture targets—which amounted to only a small fraction of the coal plant emissions—and was only operational two-thirds of the time.[1418] [1419]

Another abandoned CCS facility was a "clean coal" project, the Kemper County plant in Mississippi, in 2017. The plant, built at a cost of $7.5 billion, was planned to turn coal from a nearby strip mine into gas for power generation. The CO_2 in the exhaust was to have been captured and piped to a nearby oilfield to use in extracting oil. However, the CO_2 extraction technology failed to perform as planned, so natural gas will be used in the generators.[1420]

Other CCS projects have suffered significant performance shortfalls. In 2021, a Canadian coal power carbon capture plant captured less than half the CO_2 it was meant to because of mechanical problems.[1421] And as of 2021, an Australian CCS project—the Gorgon facility described as the world's largest—captured only a fraction of the five-year target of CO_2 it was designed for.[1422]

So-called CCS successes have come with major caveats. For example, Shell Canada's $1.3-billion Quest CCS project advertised that it met its five-year goal of capturing five million metric tons of CO_2 emitted from processing Alberta tar sands into oil (see Fossil Fools).[1423] Such processing emits CO_2 in generating the hydrogen needed to upgrade the thick bitumen from the sands. However, an investigation by the human rights organization Global Witness found that the plant *emitted* 7.7 million metric tons of greenhouse gases over the same period.[1424]

"Waste of money"

Despite these failures, the US Inflation Reduction Act of 2022 includes billions of dollars in tax credits for CCS projects—dubbed a "counterproductive waste of money, backed by the fossil fuel industry" by environmental engineer Charles Harvey and business executive Kurt House. Writing in *The New York Times*, they said of their own early CCS project "it's clear that we were wrong, and that every dollar invested in renewable energy—instead of CCS power—will eliminate far more carbon emissions." They pointed out that, since almost all the captured CO_2 is used in producing oil or gas, "we consider these ventures oil or natural gas projects, or both, masquerading as climate change solutions."[1425]

In any case, it will take many expensive CCS projects to discover which technologies are viable, concluded political scientist David Reiner.[1426] He said that:

> There's an inherent tension in developing CCS—it is not a single technology, but a whole suite and if there are six CCS paths we can go down, it's almost impossible to know . . . which is the right path.[1427]

Indeed, the US Department of Energy invested hundreds of millions of dollars in CCS plants that were never built because they were uneconomic, according to a report by the Government Accountability Office (GAO). The GAO charged that the Department had used a "high-risk selection and negotiation process" in selecting the projects.[1428]

Such technological gambles would need to be made at a breakneck pace because the 2°C limit would demand construction of large-scale CCS facilities on an extremely short timescale. In fact, the International Energy Agency (IEA) concluded that the technology is "well off track" to meet its Net Zero Emissions by 2050 Scenario.[1429]

Major capture creates major impacts

The million-ton removal scale of current demonstration plants is trivial compared to the 0.5 *billion* to 3 *billion* metric tons of carbon each year that will have to be sequestered to meet the 2°C limit, according to study by Thomas Gasser and colleagues.[1430]

That limit will require thousands of CCS plants to deliver a total of 94 billion metric tons of CO_2 reductions just by 2050, according to an IEA report. Even avoiding a higher 4°C limit would require capturing 19 billion metric tons by 2050, said the report. And in any case, CCS would not likely make fossil plants completely carbon-free, the report noted.[1431]

Almost half of the CO_2 needed to be captured by 2050 would be from industrial processes, not power generation, another IEA report pointed out. Industrial sources are far more difficult to fit with carbon capture systems.[1432]

An ambitious 1.5°C limit would require even greater capture, according to a 2018 IPCC report. The limit would require capturing from 100 billion to a trillion metric tons of CO_2 during this century.[1433]

By 2050, a CCS infrastructure of facilities and pipelines some two to four times larger than the current global oil industry would be required to absorb a significant amount of CO_2, calculated a team of engineers.[1434]

Since CCS would not be profitable, "the taxpayers of rich countries would have to pay for huge capital costs and significant operating burdens of any massive CCS," wrote energy policy analyst Vaclav Smil.[1435]

A massive CCS infrastructure in itself would have major environmental impact, asserted a report by the Center for International Environmental Law.[1436] The report pointed out that a large CO_2 pipeline network poses risks similar to those of fossil fuel pipelines:

> To date, the heavy environmental footprint and safety and health hazards associated with CCS infrastructure have been largely overlooked. . . . Effective transport through pipelines requires that CO_2 be shipped at very high pressure and extremely low temperatures, demanding pipelines capable of withstanding those conditions. The presence of moisture or contaminants can make this

condensed CO_2 corrosive to the steel in those pipelines, increasing the risk of leaks, ruptures, and potentially catastrophic running fractures.

CCS's "unmet expectations"

The IEA has asserted that without CCS, "reaching net-zero [emissions] will be virtually impossible." However, the agency has concluded that "the story of [CCS] has largely been one of unmet expectations: its potential to mitigate climate change has been recognized for decades, but deployment has been slow and so has had only a limited impact on global CO_2 emissions."[1437]

Relatively few large-scale CCS projects are planned or underway. As of 2022, there were 30 projects in operation, with 11 under construction and 153 in development, according to the Global CCS Institute, which advocates for CCS.[1438] Even this group has conceded that current CCS development is inadequate. Limiting temperature rise to 2°C would require capturing and storing more than 5.6 *billion* metric tons of CO_2 a year by 2050—compared to the 40 million metric tons being captured today. Meeting the IEA sustainable development scenario would require deploying 2,000 large-scale facilities by 2050, costing up to $1.3 trillion in investment, according to the Institute.

The timeline is incredibly short for large-scale deployment of CO_2-removal technologies in general, concluded environmental scientists Christopher Field and Katharine Mach. Decarbonizing scenarios "bet the future on CDR technologies operating effectively at vast scales within only a few decades," they wrote. The economics of such efforts are "crude for such scales," and "the risks are high."[1439]

Half-baked bioenergy

Field and Mach's analysis included "bioenergy with carbon capture and storage" (BECCS). This process involves growing massive acreage of biomass—trees and crops—burning it for energy, and capturing and storing the CO_2 underground.

BECCS is just as burdened with shortcomings as CCS, they wrote. For one thing, the IPCC peak-and-decline scenarios assume that BECCS could store some 12 billion tons of CO_2 a year by 2100, more than a quarter of current emissions.

Field and Mach called the assumption a "truly massive use of a technology with little real-world experience and poorly known economics."

Such BECCS deployment would require vast amounts of land, they calculated—ranging from 25% to 80% of the total global cropland, or up to 8% of the entire land area of Earth.

"Converting land on this staggering scale would pit climate change responses against food security and biodiversity protection," they wrote. "Massively expanding managed land for [CO_2 removal] could crash through the planetary boundary for sustainable land use."

In another analysis, climatologists Kevin Anderson and Glen Peters wrote:

> The scale of biomass assumed in [the IPCC computer models]—typically, one to two times the area of India—raises profound questions about . . . carbon neutrality, land availability, competition with food production, and competing demands for bioenergy from the transport, heating, and industrial sectors.[1440]

They noted that the quantities of biomass required would be "equivalent to up to half of the total global primary energy consumption." They concluded: "Despite BECCS continuing to stumble through its infancy, many scenarios assessed by the IPCC propose its mature and large-scale rollout as soon as 2030." They called such technologies "not an insurance policy, but rather an unjust and high-stakes gamble."

Biomass production also uses immense amounts of water. Global water stress could greatly increase from irrigation of large-scale biomass plantations, concluded bioenergy researchers.[1441] Their modeling of water needed for plantations large enough to significantly limit global heating "suggest that both the global area and population living under severe water stress . . . would double compared to today and even exceed the impact of climate change."

Similarly, an IPCC report concluded that large-scale BECCS would threaten global food production, water supplies, and natural biodiversity.[1442] [1443]

Growing enough biomass to supply BECCS to counteract the current CO_2 trajectory would require "eliminating virtually all natural ecosystems," calculated researchers in another analysis.[1444]

In the US, a limited 30% of potential biomass could be used for BECCS, given the lack of underground CO_2 storage sites and long-distance transportation networks, calculated environmental engineers in another analysis.[1445]

Expensive direct capture

Direct air carbon capture and storage (DACCS) of CO_2 using absorbing chemicals has also been proposed as a removal technology. However, this approach would be stunningly expensive, given the low atmospheric concentration of CO_2.

The Global CCS Institute has calculated that the cost of DACCS, including transport and storage, would range from $137 to $412 per metric ton. The Institute noted that "Because DACCS is a pre-commercial technology, the cost is highly uncertain."[1446]

Thus, for even the lowest estimate, sucking the billions of metric tons out of the air required to meet CO_2 limits would cost trillions of dollars.

The company Carbon Engineering, funded by fossil fuel companies, has claimed an estimate of $94 to $232 per metric ton, based on a pilot project.[1447]

However, that estimate comes with so many caveats as to render it meaningless. The process involves trapping CO_2 as calcium carbonate, then heating it to 900°C to release the gas. The heat would come from burning natural gas; and the process itself would create half a ton of CO_2 for each ton captured, found energy analyst Michael Barnard.[1448] What's more, asserted Barnard:

> The total CO_2 load for the energy required for capture, processing, compression, storage, distribution, and

sequestration is almost certain to be greater than the CO_2 removed from the atmosphere.

Carbon Engineering has proposed that the captured CO_2 could be used to produce fuel. But Barnard calculated that such fuel would be at best 25 times the cost and create 35 times the emissions of an electric vehicle.[1449] Nor would the company's proposal to use the CO_2 as an industrial feedstock be viable. Barnard concluded:

> Carbon Engineering's solution is only useful in tapped-out oil wells and as greenwashing for fossil fuel companies. No wonder three fossil fuel companies invested an infinitesimal fraction of their annual revenue in it.[1450]

Environmental engineer Mark Jacobson told *US News*: "CO_2 negative—yeah, right. It's a big sham. . . . I've looked at their published data and their own numbers."[1451]

Another analysis by Barnard pointed out that any direct capture would require a gargantuan air circulation system.

"If we wanted to just deal with 10% of our annual increase in CO_2, we'd need to filter the air out of 44 billion Houston Astrodomes or 32 million Grand Canyons," he wrote. Barnard has dubbed DAC as a "fig leaf funded by fossil fuel money."[1452]

It would cost up to $1 trillion annually for direct air capture of billions of tons of CO_2 per year, found one analysis.[1453] And that cost does not even account for the need for huge amounts of renewable energy necessary to make the industry truly carbon negative.

Using fossil fuels, DACCS would emit more CO_2 than it removed, calculated economists.[1454] They found that fossil-fuel-powered DACCS would emit from 1.46 to 3.44 metric tons of CO_2 for every ton removed. They also calculated that using the CO_2 for oil production would cause emissions of 1.42 to 4.7 metric tons of CO_2 for every ton removed. They pointed out that the analyses claiming that such capture processes would reduce CO_2 has neglected the full life cycle of the processes or contained other flaws.

Other proposed technologies to capture carbon are either in the laboratory or demonstration stage. None offers the prospect of scaling up soon enough to help capture the massive amounts of CO_2 needed to blunt climate disruption. Nor have their economic or environmental validity been established. Those technologies include:

- The CarbFix project that injects a CO_2/water solution into sub-terranean basalt to mineralize it[1455]
- Dumping gargantuan amounts of lime into the ocean to induce ocean waters to absorb more CO_2[1456][1457]
- The FuelCell Energy company's effort to use fuel cells to both generate electricity and concentrate CO_2 for storage for industrial use[1458][1459]
- The NET Power company demonstration plants that use a stream of CO_2 to drive a turbine, with the exhaust used in industrial applications.[1460][1461]

Capturing carbon in forests and soils

Growing forests to capture massive amounts of carbon seems a promising idea. One analysis found that allowing tropical forests to regrow could absorb huge amounts of carbon. Calculations showed that allowing abandoned farms and pastures in Latin America to regrow over 40 years could sequester some 31 billion tons of CO_2. This amount would be the equivalent of all the carbon emissions in Latin America and the Caribbean from 1993 to 2014.[1462]

However, this plan is unworkable, given continuing tropical deforestation and the irreversible decline in tropical forests due to climate disruption (see Ghost Forests).

Sequestering large quantities of carbon in soils by improving farming techniques has been another proposed carbon-capture technique but presents its own major obstacles (see Carbonized Farming and Respiring Soils).

Subterranean injection hazards

Most sequestration technologies involve injecting vast amounts of CO_2 into underground formations such as depleted oil fields. If the experience with fracking is any guide, such injection could cause leakage into aquifers that supply drinking water. Such CO_2 groundwater infiltration could increase metal concentrations by more than a 100-fold—including potentially hazardous uranium and barium—found laboratory experiments by environmental engineers.[1463]

CO_2 is by no means an inert gas when injected into oil reservoirs, found a study of a Louisiana injection site. The researchers discovered that a significant fraction of the injected CO_2 was transformed by bacteria into CH_4, which is less soluble and more mobile than CO_2. An even larger fraction was dissolved in the groundwater, found the researchers.[1464]

As is the case with fracking, injecting vast amounts of CO_2 could trigger earthquakes, pointed out geophysicists, who wrote:

> Because even small- to moderate-sized earthquakes threaten the seal integrity of CO_2 repositories, in this context, large-scale CCS is a risky, and likely unsuccessful, strategy for significantly reducing greenhouse gas emissions.[1465]

Another proposed sequestration plan is to inject captured CO_2 into deep-ocean sediments, where the immense pressure and low temperatures would transform it into a frozen form called a hydrate.[1466] Scientists studying the plan's potential concluded that the process appears viable. However, substantial mysteries remain about the subsea behavior of the frozen hydrates and whether changes in the marine environment might release stored deposits (see Calthrate Gun).

Deployment time crunch

Multiple independent analyses have found that the need to meet temperature limits make the time frame for massive deployment of CDR technologies unrealistically short.

A UN report concluded that keeping below the 2°C limit would require achieving net zero greenhouse gas emissions by 2070.[1467] Achieving net-zero by 2085 would require a long-term removal of carbon of at least 26 billion tons a year, climatologists have calculated.[1468] Meeting the more stringent 1.5°C increase target would require net zero emissions by 2060, and a long-term carbon removal of almost 15 billion tons a year, the study found.

The Paris Agreement's dependence on negative emissions poses a "climate risk for society," argued one group of climate policy analysts.[1469] They said that the 2°C limit is "infeasible" because of the failure of the major emitting countries to rapidly transform their energy systems.

Similarly, the European Academies' Science Advisory Council concluded that negative emissions technologies "offer only limited realistic potential to remove carbon from the atmosphere and not at the scale envisaged in some climate scenarios." The Council said that the IPCC's dependence on them "has yet to take fully into account these limitations."[1470]

The time scale for CDR technologies to be effective will stretch far into the future, found another analysis:

> Most methods are relatively slow acting and might take many decades to centuries to reduce atmospheric CO_2 to some desired level. The few methods that have the theoretical potential to rapidly remove more CO_2 remain technologically immature and would likely take decades to be fully developed and deployed at climatically relevant scales.[1471]

Research in its infancy

In fact, significant basic research on negative emissions technologies has not even begun. The US Department of Energy has launched the Carbon Negative Shot program that aims to bring all types of carbon-sequestering technologies down to less than $100 per ton.[1472] However, that goal is far from the current cost, and as of this writing, there has been no budget allocated to the effort.

A US National Academies report concluded that the US would need to spend many billions of dollars over a decade for such fundamental research. This research would be needed even before large-scale pilot plants and ultimately commercial facilities could be built, which would take even longer.[1473] Even then, the report concluded:

Negative emissions technologies are best viewed as a component of the mitigation portfolio, rather than a way to decrease atmospheric concentrations of carbon dioxide only after anthropogenic emissions have been eliminated.

One nasty wrinkle is that, even if negative emissions did work, they might not effectively reduce atmospheric CO_2 levels. For one thing, CO_2 removal would be opposed by natural outgassing from the ocean and rocks, found modeling studies. They revealed a decreasing effectiveness of removal with the amount removed.[1474] [1475]

Negative emissions might weaken or even reverse the natural CO_2 absorption by land and ocean, found another analysis of future emissions scenarios. The researchers' modeling raises the possibility that negative emissions would have to be even greater to stabilize levels, much less reduce them.[1476]

The predictable failure of negative emissions technologies is thus one more reason that humans seem doomed to suffer a rise toward a 6°C temperature increase and possible extinction.

Geoengineering Quackery

What would your gut reaction be to the following schemes?

- Launching thousands of airplane flights per day for more than a century to shower the atmosphere with millions of tons of sulfur per year to reduce sunlight.[1477]
- Using some 20,000 flights over ten days to spew a reflective mix of a million tons of sulfur dioxide and thousands of tons of carbon soot into the stratosphere. Repeating the process each year.[1478] [1479]
- Using ships to spray millions of gallons of seawater into the atmosphere to increase cloud reflectivity.[1480]
- Dispatching flotillas of tankers to dump millions of tons of iron or urea into the ocean to fertilize growth of phytoplankton to absorb carbon.[1481]

- Launching gigantic mirrors into space to reflect sunlight and cool the Earth.[1482]
- Spreading silica sand over thousands of square miles of Arctic ice to reflect sunlight and reduce melting. [1483]

If your reaction to these schemes is disbelief, you are not alone. In fact, almost all climate researchers, after careful study and analysis, have concluded that incredulity is the appropriate reaction to such geoengineering proposals.

Such "solar radiation management" schemes "introduce a widespread range of new risks to people and ecosystems, which are not well understood," concluded a landmark 2022 report of the UN Intergovernmental Panel on Climate Change (IPCC). The report cited "large uncertainties and knowledge gaps" in the approaches, and pointed out that they would "not stop atmospheric CO_2 concentrations from increasing or reduce resulting ocean acidification."[1484]

Another report by the National Academies of Sciences, Engineering, and Medicine warned that such technologies could cause "significant potential for unanticipated, unmanageable, and regrettable consequences . . . including political, social, legal, economic, and ethical dimensions . . ."[1485]

One group of scientists has called for an international non-use agreement for solar geoengineering. The agreement would ban funding, experiments, patents, deployment, or international institutional support. The group argues that solar engineering's risks are unknowable; that it will tempt government and industry to delay decarbonization; and that the "current global governance system is unfit to develop and implement" the agreements to control deployment.[1486]

"Barking mad" idea

"The idea of 'fixing' the climate by hacking the Earth's reflection of sunlight is wildly, utterly, howlingly barking mad," declared geophysicist Raymond Pierrehumbert, a co-author of the National Academies report. He wrote in an article in *Slate*:

Engineering is something you do to a system you understand very well, where you can try out new techniques thoroughly at a small scale before staking peoples' lives on them. Hacking the climate is different—we have only one planet to live on, and can't afford any big mistakes. Many of the climate "engineering" proposals are akin to turning the world's whole population into passengers on a largely untested new fleet of hypersonic airplanes.[1487]

One engineering team listed the profound unknowns of atmospheric aerosol injection.[1488] They declared that nobody knows:

- What size or distribution of aerosols to inject
- The impact on atmospheric circulation, chemistry, or clouds
- Whether the aerosols would destroy ultraviolet-protecting ozone
- How much cooling would result
- The impact on agriculture, drought, or disease
- The effect on plant photosynthesis
- Whether any observed effects could be attributable to the injection.

Nevertheless, some scientists have advocated proceeding with major research on albedo modification, despite its obvious barriers. Those scientists include the authors of a dubious National Academies report that called for a major research initiative into albedo modification.[1489]

The report does not cite any new insights into geoengineering to justify such research, but only "an urgency reinforced by the world's slow progress on climate."

And the report presents no deep analysis of research needs, but rather "*suggests* [emphasis added] that a reasonable initial investment in [solar geoengineering] research is in the range of $100–200 million total over five years."

The proposed budget is essentially fiscal hand-waving. Any budget analyst would judge as highly suspect a proposal that "suggests" such a large expenditure range, and one that is vaguely round-numbered. What's more, this investment is only an "initial" one—sure to raise red flags in a budget office.

The report concluded that only extensive research could determine whether geoengineering could be "effective, affordable, safe, and publicly acceptable" or whether it "would be ineffective, too costly, or would raise unacceptable technical or social risks."

The latter is the case, as the discussion that follows makes clear.

Insurmountable barriers

Any global geoengineering scheme would cost many billions of dollars and require the unlikely approval of every country in the world. Human rights advocates would certainly bitterly oppose any geoengineering, given that scientists would discover that some schemes would, in effect, kill people and would more heavily affect poorer countries and people.

For example, injecting particles into the atmosphere over the Northern Hemisphere would increase drought risk in the semi-arid Sahel region of Africa, imperiling the lives of millions, found one computer modeling study.[1490]

Another computer model revealed that aerosol injection would weaken storm tracks in temperate latitudes, reducing storm severity. However, such weakening would also stagnate circulation causing more intense heat waves, higher air pollution, and altered ocean circulation.[1491]

A catch-22 barrier is that only monumentally scaled geoengineering experiments could detect global-sized pitfalls. But monumentally scaled experiments are by definition global already. So the only way to study such schemes is to carry them out, thus potentially causing massive impacts on weather, agriculture, oceans, people—basically the entire Earth system.[1492]

Public fears would make any global geoengineering scheme political poison. Scientists planning geoengineering experiments are already dogged by "chemtrails" conspiracy theorists. They believe that jet airplanes are secretly spewing chemicals into the atmosphere for weather or mind control.[1493] Any global geoengineering plan would cause such fears to mushroom into a political movement that would thwart that plan.

Colossal injections

A global atmospheric geoengineering scheme would require gargantuan injections of material. For example, cutting global heating in half would initially require jets to deliver 25,000 metric tons of sulfuric acid a year into the stratosphere, estimated physicist David Keith.[1494] To compensate for rising CO_2 levels, this amount would have to increase to 250,000 metric tons by 2040.

Engineers would have to invent an entirely new tanker aircraft to carry such massive loads, calculated aviation and climate economists.[1495] The airliner-sized, four-engine plane would have double the wingspan of a conventional commercial airplane. It would cost billions of dollars to develop, and the thousands of flights a year required for an injection program would cost some $2 billion a year, they calculated.

The injections would also have to continue in perpetuity. Limiting global heating to 2°C would require 160 years of sulfur injections, beginning in 2040, found calculations by atmospheric scientists. The peak injection rate would have to be about 8 million tons a year. Calculations showed that 1°C of cooling would require 6,700 flights a day, costing $20 billion a year.[1496]

In fact, stopping such massive injections—quite likely given the fickleness of governments—would trigger rapid warming that would devastate the planet's ecosystems, found another analysis. The researchers predicted that stopping suddenly would increase ocean and land temperatures more than twice as fast as either in the past or expected future.[1497]

Of course, any sunlight-reducing scheme would reduce the output of solar panels, compromising that carbon-free energy source.

Seeding high-altitude heat-trapping cirrus clouds with sulfuric or nitric acid to thin them out has been another proposal to reduce global heating. Reducing cirrus clouds would allow the heat they trap to radiate back into space, the theory goes. But over-seeding might actually form more cirrus clouds, concluded atmospheric scientists. Thus, they declared the uncertainties mean that, "for the time being, cirrus cloud thinning should be viewed as a thought experiment."[1498]

Even a limited geoengineering scheme would be costly. For example, the sand-spreading scheme, called the Arctic Ice Project, would cost an estimated $300 million. It would involve spreading tons of silica microspheres—now used in toothpaste and milkshake mixes—over vast areas of Arctic ice.[1499] [1500]

Some advocates have argued that global geoengineering might be launched to battle a climate emergency such as melting polar ice, tropical deforestation, or a tipping point (see Climate Monsters). But, as one group of geoecologists point out, such tipping points are irreversible and tend to lag the forces that triggered them.[1501] They wrote that:

> By the time tipping is perceived, their original state may have long since lost its stability. This means that excessive climate engineering—that is, over-cooling the planet—is likely to be required to recover their original state (and even then it may not work).

Any research program that gave geoengineering the fig leaf of validity might discourage countries from reducing greenhouse emissions, charged climatologist Michael Mann.[1502] He accused geoengineering advocates as being "engaged in the kinder gentler form of denialism . . . [that] it won't be that bad, and if we stop burning carbon it's going to hurt our economy." He wrote that "When you look in detail at these schemes, in many cases they could make us much worse off than if we hadn't engaged in these interventions at all."

Nuclear Powerless

Nuclear power plants seem like a natural foundation for a carbon-free energy system. The plants emit almost no greenhouse gases in operation. And total life-cycle emissions are lower than even solar, considering all aspects from cradle to grave. Nuclear plants don't go offline when the sun doesn't shine or the wind doesn't blow. They don't require massive mining, drilling, and transport of fuel. They can produce a huge amount of electricity in a far smaller space than solar arrays or wind farms.[1503]

Manufacturers contend that the latest designs for conventional nuclear plants, such as Westinghouse's AP1000, are safer and more efficient to build.[1504] And a multitude of new reactor designs are being developed, including small modular reactors (SMRs) and those that can run on spent nuclear fuel from existing reactors.[1505]

The manufacturers claim that SMRs from such companies as Westinghouse and NuScale Power could be mass produced and installed to flexibly add as much power as needed. The companies say the plants' output could also be varied to compensate for fluctuations in solar and wind power.[1506] [1507]

However, SMRs such as the NuScale design still present the same kinds of safety and cost concerns as their much larger cousins.[1508] [1509] [1510] They also generate far more radioactive waste than conventional reactors, found one analysis.[1511] Comparing multiple SMR designs with conventional reactor designs, the researchers found that the SMRs would generate from 2 to 30 times as much volume of radioactive waste.

Nor can SMRs be as cost-efficient as claimed, concluded an analysis by nuclear engineer Arjun Makhijani and physicist M. V. Ramana.[1512] Thousands of SMRs would have to be produced before a learning curve would significantly lower costs, they wrote. And any manufacturing error would require large-scale recall, as has happened in the aircraft industry.

"But how does one recall a radioactive reactor?" they asked. "What will happen to an electricity system that relies on factory-made identical reactors that need to be recalled?"

Capital costs for SMRs have shown the same large increases as for large traditional reactors, they pointed out. They concluded that SMRs could not be deployed on a timescale needed to help reduce greenhouse gas emissions:

> The SMR contribution in the next decade will be essentially zero. The prospects for SMRs beyond that are also bleak, given that entire supply chains would need to be established after the first ones have been built, tested, and proven in the field . . . There is no realistic prospect that SMRs can make a significant dent in the need to transition rapidly to a carbon-free electricity system. The prospects of timely contributions by even the light water designs . . . are dismal.

Finally, wrote Ramana, SMRs would increase the possibility and severity of accidents because developers propose to install multiple reactors at a site to save on infrastructure costs. He wrote:

> Multiple reactors at a site increase the risk that an accident at one unit might either induce accidents at other reactors or make it harder to take preventive actions at others. This is especially the case if the underlying reason for the accident is a common one that affects all of the reactors, such as an earthquake.[1513]

In other new reactor designs, the uranium fuel is dissolved in a molten salt. Their developers claim the designs constitutes a fail-safe, proliferation-resistant technology. The fuel would be difficult to extract from the liquid to be weaponized, they contend.[1514] [1515]

However, a report on multiple such designs by the Union of Concerned Scientists (UCS) concluded otherwise. The authors found that all designs posed unacceptable risk of catastrophic accident; did not offer significant sustainability benefits; and still presented risks of nuclear proliferation and terrorism. Furthermore, the report said, no new designs could be deployed fast enough to make an impact on power generation.[1516]

Human barriers to nuclear growth

Besides facing technology barriers, the nuclear industry has failed because of human and policy shortcomings. A few examples:

- The 2011 Fukushima nuclear disaster—when a tsunami disabled generators that would have powered cooling pumps—was due to a failure of designers to allow for such a foreseeable incident.[1517]
- War or terrorism could threaten catastrophic damage to a nuclear plant; for example, the threat to the Ukrainian nuclear plants during the Russian invasion.
- Nuclear plants cannot compete economically with natural-gas-powered plants because energy policy does give credit to the carbon-free nature of nuclear plants.[1518]

- The public image of nuclear power is negative because of fear of radiation and government's failure to solve the problem of storing long-term nuclear waste.[1519]
- Mismanagement and regulatory policies have caused huge delays and cost overruns for plants under construction. Some uncompleted plants have even been abandoned.[1520]

These barriers have, indeed, thwarted nuclear power's growth, concluded an IEA report.[1521] It found that nuclear power would have to double by 2050 to meet the IEA's Net Zero Emissions by 2050 Scenario.

What's more, any increase in nuclear plant construction would have to compensate for the closure of existing plants, as is happening in the US and Germany.[1522] In the US, more than a third of nuclear plants are unprofitable or scheduled to close, found the UCS.[1523]

While China, India, Russia, and other countries have significant nuclear plant construction underway, such construction is not enough to make up for the global loss.[1524] Advanced countries could lose a quarter of their nuclear capacity by 2025 and as much as two-thirds by 2040, concluded the IEA.[1525]

Uneconomic nuclear power

"The prospects for the expansion of nuclear energy remain decidedly dim in many parts of the world," because of high cost, concluded an MIT report on the global economic future of nuclear power.[1526]

Of the US market, one research team declared that "the United States appears set to virtually lose nuclear power, and thus a wedge of reliable and low-carbon energy, over the next few decades."[1527]

Even extending the life of existing reactors is not effective climate policy, found the 2019 *World Nuclear Industry Status Report*.[1528] Nuclear plants' operating costs exceed those of investing in energy efficiency and renewable energy, said the report.

"There can be no doubt: the renewal rate of nuclear power plants is too slow to guarantee the survival of the technology," concluded the report's coordinator and publisher, Mycle Schneider. "The world is experiencing an undeclared 'organic' nuclear phaseout."

That phaseout will contine, analyses have found. The 2021 *World Nuclear Industry Status Report* documented a steady decline in the number of nuclear plants and increasing costs of new plants.[1529] The report found that since 2009, even as nuclear plant costs had increased by 33%, costs of utility-scale solar plants had dropped by 90% and wind energy by 70%. And the electricity cost from advanced nuclear plants is about double that from solar plants, found a report by the US Energy Information Administration.[1530]

Energy Inefficiency

Imagine a huge clean energy source that would need no new technology, no drilling, no refining, and no mining. If fully exploited, this source would achieve a large percentage of the carbon dioxide (CO_2) reductions needed to meet the 2°C limit on global temperature increase.

That "source" is increased energy efficiency—a reduction in the intensity of society's energy use. The impact of such reduction would be stunning. Doubling the current rate of improvement in global energy intensity to only 4% a year could avoid the equivalent of the current annual energy use of China by 2030, concluded a UN report.[1531]

Global energy efficiency improved by about 13% between 2000 and 2017, said an International Energy Agency (IEA) report. Without this improvement the global energy market would have seen an addition to final energy use the equivalent of the entire European Union.[1532]

The problem is that energy efficiency is not as sexy as carbon capture, solar cells, or nuclear power. It comprises such mundane steps as insulating buildings, using efficient lighting, recovering waste industrial heat, and making cars and appliances more efficient. It is also seen as a "negative quantity"—that is energy *not* expended. So it tends to be perceived as an intangible concept, versus "positive," tangible power generation.

Energy efficiency improvements could provide more than 40% of the abatement needed by 2040 to meet the Paris Agreement goals, found another IEA report.[1533] Investments in energy efficiency pay back on average threefold based on energy savings alone, said the report.

That said, the IEA has found that the annual rate of improvement in energy efficiency has been declining—and would need to double to meet its Net Zero Emissions by 2050 Scenario. And investment in energy efficiency would have to triple by 2030 to be consistent with the Net Zero Scenario.[1534]

With efficiency measures alone, global energy demand could be reduced by 40%, despite increases in population and income, found another study. Energy analysts charted a low-energy scenario that limited temperature rise to 1.5°C without resorting to negative emission technologies. The scenario involved electrifying transportation, increasing renewable energy, and reducing energy waste.[1535] [1536]

Despite such enormous potential, governments have badly neglected energy efficiency policies. Government policies for building energy use are inadequate, stated an IEA report.[1537] The report concluded that building emissions reductions are not on track to achieve the IEA's Net Zero Emissions by 2050 Scenario.

Vehicle fuel economy standards have also fallen far short in increasing energy efficiency. Emissions from freight trucks and buses—massive users of fossil fuels—have been growing steadily since 2000, according to the IEA.[1538]

Investment in efficiency improvements is not keeping up with the level needed to meet the 2°C limit, concluded another IEA report.[1539] Spending needs to average more than $500 billion a year for the next 20 years—well above the current level of $221 billion a year, concluded the report, declaring that, "two-thirds of potentially profitable energy efficiency investments over the next 20 years have been projected to remain untapped."

So, rather than energy *efficiency*, the global future is one of energy *inefficiency*.

Fossilized Transportation

The epic journey of a pair of sneakers I bought online vividly shows global transportation's stunning energy use. They were quite ordinary sneakers, but their route to my California home was quite extraordinary. My tracking revealed that they began their 11,000-mile journey in the industrial city of Dongguan, China. From there, they traveled to Lantau Island, Hong Kong. They were then flown to Anchorage, Alaska; and from there to Memphis, Tennessee; to Ontario, California; to Temecula, California; and finally to my house.

They likely flew aboard 100-ton cargo planes that could burn tens of thousands of gallons of aviation kerosene. If I had bought them at a local store, they would have been transported across the Pacific on fossil-fueled cargo ships—200,000-ton behemoths that can burn some 80,000 gallons per day of sludge-like bunker fuel.

Besides those cargo planes and ships, our fossil-fueled transportation comprises phalanxes of cars and trucks that stream along highways propelled by the combustion of vast quantities of gasoline and diesel fuel.

Today, our transportation system is almost totally fossil fuel-powered, and it produces about a quarter of all energy-related greenhouse gas emissions globally.[1540] In the US, about 91% of transportation energy comes from petroleum.[1541] So, a vast transition to renewable sources— electricity and biofuels—would be needed to achieve zero-emissions in transportation.

The International Energy Agency (IEA) calculated that transport emissions must fall by 20% by 2030 to meet its Net Zero Emissions by 2050 Scenario.[1542]

However, there are huge gaps in such emission scenarios regarding transportation. For example, the Paris Agreement excluded international shipping and aviation emissions from its projections. If shipping and aviation were counted as countries, they would each rank among the top ten emitters of greenhouse gases, according to a report by the International Maritime Emission Reduction Scheme (IMERS).[1543]

Meeting the 2°C goal would require a 50% to 80% reduction in transportation carbon emissions by 2050—a fantasy scenario, given that the emissions from international aviation and shipping are projected to double or even triple by 2050, according to a report by the International Council on Clean Transportation.[1544]

Foggy future for electric cars

Electric vehicles (EVS)—both electric and gas-electric hybrids—have been widely touted as a solution to lowering transportation emissions.

However, EVS now comprise only a small percentage of vehicle sales.[1545] And the future of electric cars is unclear, with predictions ranging from 10% to 70% of the global fleet by 2040. The huge differences arise because of uncertainty in oil prices, government subsidies, and battery cost and technology.[1546] Slow fleet turnover presents another significant barrier, with older, internal combustion engine (ICE) vehicles remaining on the road for up to two decades.[1547]

Net zero emission scenarios require a massive, seemingly impossible, increase in EVS. One would require 300 million EVS. But in 2020, there were only 10 million EVS on the road, which will increase to 145 million by 2030, according to the IEA.[1548]

Another would require 60% of new car sales to be zero emissions by 2030, and the last ICE vehicle to roll off the assembly line by around 2035.[1549] But by 2031, EVS will account for only 40% of European sales and 20% of US sales, according to a projection by the financial analysis firm IHS Markit.[1550]

Government policy is favoring the advent of EVS, with many countries and US states announcing plans to phase out the sale of ICE vehicles.[1551]

And major automakers and 30 national governments pledged to phase out ICE vehicle sales at the 2021 UN Climate Change Conference COP26.[1552] However, the pledge is not legally binding, illustrating the fogginess of EVS' future. There were major holdouts, including Toyota, Volkswagen, and Nissan-Renault, and abstentions by the US, China, and Japan governments.

In the US, as discussed earlier, both the 2021 US Infrastructure Investment and Jobs Act and the 2022 Inflation Reduction Act include substantial support for EVS. For example, the former features an expansion of charging stations and the latter tax credits for buying EVS.[1553] [1554] [1555]

Carmakers are also planning to increase EV production. General Motors has announced that it will only sell EVS by 2035.[1556] And Ford and other major car companies are introducing many new EV models.[1557]

New battery technology is promising faster charging times and greater range for EVS, alleviating consumer anxiety.[1558] And analyses have shown clearly that EVS do produce lower emissions and lower overall lifetime costs than for ICE vehicles.[1559]

EV barriers, consumer and economic

However, EVS constitute only a small percentage of overall near-term production by GM and Ford, according to a Reuters report.[1560]

"The plans show that Detroit's Big Two are betting their short-term futures on satisfying America's demand for bigger petroleum-fueled vehicles, which they can sell at a higher profit margin than mostly smaller, expensive-to-develop electric vehicles," said the report.

Indeed, most consumers do prefer ICE vehicles, according to a global survey by the consulting firm Deloitte.[1561] In the US, 69% of respondents preferred ICE vehicles for their next purchase. Only 5% preferred battery EVS, with 21% preferring hybrid EVS. A majority also preferred ICE vehicles in Southeast Asia, China, and India.

Another barrier has been that car dealers were reluctant to promote EVS. The dealers didn't want to spend time educating buyers, and they feared loss of service revenue, since the cars need far less maintenance.[1562] [1563] On the other hand, dealers are now being pushed to invest in selling electric cars, so future customers will be more likely to be greeted with sales pitches for them.[1564]

High EV cost and shortages of raw materials, batteries, and electronic chips also present major barriers to widespread EV adoption.[1565] And a complete switch to EVS would cause a drastic rise in electricity demand, about 25% greater than today.[1566] The increased demand would require greatly increased power generation and major renovation of transmission networks.

The wholesale replacement of ICE vehicles with EVS would eliminate the jobs of millions of people employed in car factories, repair shops, gas stations, and oil fields. EVS require far fewer parts than ICE vehicles and far fewer workers to build. And they require far less servicing and obviously do not burn fossil fuels.[1567] [1568]

EV environmental impacts, benefits

Making EVs true zero-emitters depends on a vast increase in renewable energy, which will not happen (see Renewable Energy Hype).

And EVs produce environmental impacts due to the mining of required minerals and lack of recycling. The IEA has calculated that a typical EV requires six times more minerals than a conventional car.[1569]

Currently, only a small percentage of automotive lithium-ion batteries are recycled or repurposed. The recycling need will skyrocket, as retired vehicles will result in hundreds of thousands of tons of spent batteries per year.[1570]

However, because future batteries will not use valuable cobalt, "there will be little economic incentive to invest in recycling technologies," stated public health scientist Perry Gottesfeld. "The result, if nothing is done to tip the scales, could be a massive health and environmental crisis," he wrote.[1571]

All that said, overall EVs do, indeed, produce significantly lower emissions than ICE vehicles, found a detailed "life-cycle assessment" of EVs by the International Council on Clean Transportation.[1572] The analysis not only compared direct lifetime emissions, but also the fossil-fuel intensity of electric grids, as well as emissions due to battery production.

The analysis found that even China's and India's coal-intensive electricity systems showed significantly lowered emissions from EVs. The lowered emissions were: US (60%–68%), Europe (66%–69%), China (37%–45%), and India (19%–34%).

EVs came out ahead in another analysis that also took into account indirect emissions from battery production and gasoline refining.[1573] The researchers wrote that, if electricity generation continues decarbonizing, the reduction of direct and indirect emissions from EVs "indicates a win-win situation for climate change mitigation." They dubbed a future with high numbers of EVs "a no-regrets strategy in terms of emissions."

Passenger cars, SUVs, and pickup trucks are only part of the transportation mix, however. While they use over half of the transportation energy, in the US the rest is consumed by freight trucks, ships, trains, and airplanes.[1574] These will all run almost entirely on fossil fuels for many decades to come. Economist Fatih Birol, head of the IEA, pointed out that:

> Even if there were 300 million [electric cars] with the current power generation system, the impact in terms of CO_2 emissions is less than 1%—nothing. If you can't decarbonise [the power sector], CO_2 emissions will not be going down. It may be helpful for the local pollution, but for global emissions it is not.[1575]

Airlines, ships continue to emit

Airlines will fail to significantly curb their emissions, given overwhelming technological and economic barriers.[1576] Airline emissions, largely unregulated, amounted to only about 2% of carbon emissions in 2018. However, this percentage could triple by 2045.[1577 1578]

As noted above, the airline industry has been largely excluded from climate change agreements, including the Paris Agreement. The industry is "a golden goose for politicians," in which flying is kept artificially cheap by favorable tax treatments, wrote environmental sociologist Roger Tyers. Thus, the industry will continue to grow, set to double by 2035, he wrote.[1579]

Ocean shipping will also likely fail to reduce its emissions, given that it is regulated by a group dominated by the industry it regulates: the UN's International Maritime Organization. The New York Times found that its members include "Shipbuilders, oil companies, miners, chemical manufacturers and others with huge financial stakes in commercial shipping." The Times analysis concluded that "The organization has repeatedly delayed and watered down climate regulations, even as emissions from commercial shipping continue to rise. . ."[1580]

Biofuels will not play a major role in providing a renewable transportation fuel source—not only because of the challenges of generating massive quantities. Biofuels are also more expensive than fossil fuels, making it very unlikely that cost-conscious consumers or companies would opt for them. Thus, the IEA concluded that biofuels are not on track to meet production needed for its Sustainable Development Scenario.[1581]

Carbonized Farming

To a farmer, a field of ripening wheat represents a triumph over a capricious environment. However, to a climatologist, the carbon dioxide (CO_2) generated by such farming is a dire threat to that environment.

To a rancher, a herd of cattle is an income source and a means to satisfy the world's growing appetite for meat. To a climatologist, the herd is a massive source of atmosphere-heating methane.

While the billions of acres of agricultural lands worldwide are a source of life-giving sustenance, the are also a major greenhouse gas source. Agriculture produces about 11% of global greenhouse gas emissions.[1582]

Those emissions could increase by up to 30% by 2050 if no improvements in efficiency and emissions reductions are made, found a report by the UN Food and Agriculture Organization (FAO).[1583] Another report on agriculture's climate impacts concluded:

> Even if fossil fuel emissions were immediately halted, current trends in global food systems would prevent the achievement of the 1.5°C target and, by the end of the century, threaten the achievement of the 2°C target. . . . Meeting the 1.5° and 2°C targets will likely require extensive and unprecedented changes to the global food system.[1584]

In modern times, agriculture has overtaken deforestation as a major source of greenhouse gases—due to CO_2 from crop production and methane (CH_4) from livestock and rice paddies.[1585] [1586]

A major atmospheric contributor of CH_4 is emissions by ruminants such as cattle, sheep, and goats during the digestive process. Livestock-related CO_2 is also emitted from manure, feed crop production, and deforestation for feed crops and pasture. Overall, such emissions caused a full 23% of total global heating in 2010, calculated agricultural analysts. The estimates did not include indirect emissions by livestock feed production and supply chains, they pointed out.[1587]

Governments have subsidized agriculture to the detriment of the environment just as they have subsidized the fossil fuel industry. Over two-thirds of the almost $540 billion a year in global agricultural support is price-distorting, favoring meat and dairy, found a UN report. Thus, this support is "harmful for the environment and human health." The future could be even worse, with subsidies rising to almost $1.8 trillion annually by 2030, concluded the report.[1588]

To meet the 2°C limit, global agriculture will have to cut some one billion tons of greenhouse gases a year by 2030, out of the more than five billion tons currently emitted, found an analysis by natural resource management researchers.[1589] Only 21% to 40% of the required reductions could be achieved by "plausible future mitigation pathways" involving improved crop and livestock management practices, they found.

"Vastly more effort and urgency is necessary" to bring new low-emissions technologies into agricultural practice, they warned. Those technologies would aim at reducing dairy cow emissions; and creating new cattle breeds that produce less methane; and new varieties of wheat and corn that produce less nitrous oxide (N_2O)—a powerful greenhouse gas.

The entire food system—production, processing, packaging, distribution, and waste management—could be made more sustainable, researchers have said.[1590] They wrote that "game-changing" technologies—including artificial meat, intelligent packaging, nano-drones, 3D printing and vertical agriculture—offer "a real opportunity for systemic change."

Oil-dependent industrial farming

Historically, carbon-intensive farming arose because the architects of the Green Revolution that began in 1950 emphasized adapting crop plants to industrial farming practices, wrote Rob Dunn in his book *Never Out of Season*:

"In theory, the Green Revolution could have been one in which we relied on an understanding of ecology and evolution to increase crop yields while at the same time keeping crop fields diverse," he wrote.

But instead, American scientists focused "on using pesticides, fertilizers, herbicides, and irrigation to make conditions as similar as possible everywhere and then to breed crops ideally suited to those conditions."

Thus, the Green Revolution came to depend on oil-based farm machines, chemicals, and transport.[1591]

Such agricultural practices have created a massive loss of organic soil carbon over the last 12,000 years, found a study by soil researchers.[1592] Such carbon is critical to soil fertility and structure. They calculated that the "soil carbon debt" due to soil-depleting farming and grazing is about 133 billion tons—about the same amount of loss caused by global deforestation. What's more, the rate of loss has been increasing over the last two centuries, they concluded.

Industrial farming is a major roadblock to soil-restoring "agro-ecology," charge such groups as Friends of the Earth International.[1593] Ecologically sound farming seeks to reverse the soil carbon debt using organic fertilizers, no-till farming, and composting. Its report charged that eco-friendly farming practices have been thwarted by governments that give agribusiness favorable trade and investment agreements.

Soil carbonizing barriers

Even with agroecology practices, multiple barriers will severely limit soil carbon sequestration. Such limits will likely thwart an ambitious plan called the "4 per 1000 Initiative" to increase soil organic carbon globally. It was so named because of the goal of increasing soil carbon by 0.4% a year.[1594]

For one thing, enormous amounts of nitrogen would be needed to sequester the required massive amounts of carbon in the soil as organic material—the equivalent of 75% of current nitrogen fertilizer production, calculated soil scientists.[1595] And it would have to be transported worldwide. "Practically speaking, that is just impossible," they concluded.

Also, sequestered soil carbon is by no means permanent, with organic molecules being continually broken down by microbes and emitted back into the atmosphere.[1596] It will also be extremely hard to measure and verify farmers' soil sequestration practices, pointed out climate scientists.[1597] And as with many such farming techniques, training farmers and scaling up their efforts will be a long, slow process. Finally, global heating will reduce soils' ability to retain carbon (see Respiring Soils).

Meat is climate murder

Reducing food demand is the only way to meet future food needs and limit greenhouse gases, according to one group of agricultural scientists. Increasing crop yield or the area of farmland would be inadequate, their computer models revealed.[1598]

The demand for meat is a major climate problem. Livestock production accounts for more than half of greenhouse gas emissions from the food sector, found one report.[1599] This, even though livestock contribute only 18% of calories and 37% of global human protein supply. Livestock production accounts for about 70% of all agricultural land, found the report.

"Intensive meat production is on an unstoppable trajectory comprising the single greatest contributor to climate change," declared an editorial in the journal *The Lancet*. "Humanity's dominant diets are not good for us, and they are not good for the planet."[1600]

Indeed, greenhouse emissions from animal-based foods are twice those of plant-based foods, found another analysis.[1601]

Reducing meat and dairy intake by 75% annually by 2050 could reduce emissions by an amount greater than the emissions from the entire transportation sector in 2010, concluded another analysis.[1602] However, "if global trends in meat and dairy intake continue, global mean temperature rise will more than likely exceed 2°C, even with dramatic emissions reductions across nonagricultural sectors," wrote the researchers.

Artificial meat on the rise

One promising development has been the advance of plant-based meat replacements and cultured meat from animal cells grown in bioreactors. Such products are gaining consumer acceptance, and they will grow to 60% of the market for meat by 2040, predicted the consulting firm A.T. Kearny.[1603] The same culture techniques can be used to produce artificial milk, egg white, and fish, their report noted.

Plant-based and cultured meat are far more efficient at converting input materials and water to meat, said the report. While traditional meat production has a 23% efficiency, plant-based meat has a conversion efficiency of 75%, and cultured meat an efficiency of 70%.

Advocates tout multiple benefits of artificial meat—including reducing land and water demand, animal diseases, food-borne illnesses, antibiotic resistance, and animal waste pollution. Opponents, however, warn that manufacturing processes could create allergens, unwanted by-products, and possibly hazardous wastes.[1604]

Shifting to a lower-meat diet could yield health as well as climate benefits, concluded food policy analysts.[1605] Rather than a purely vegan diet, they suggested "healthy global diets" that required an average 25% increase in fruits and vegetables, a 56% reduction in red meat, and 15% fewer calories. They concluded that such a diet would reduce global mortality by 6% to 10% and reduce food-related greenhouse gases by 29% to 70%.

Food waste is another massive problem, constituting loss of about a third of food production, according to an FAO report.[1606] This loss permeates the food chain—including food processing—and waste of food in homes, stores, and restaurants. To reduce waste, the report said that food system changes across the board were feasible to improve the efficiency of food harvesting, processing, transport, and storage.

VII
Climate Pandemic Endpoint?

This section marks the completion of an image of our looming fate as a species. This image, just as a digital image comprises an array of picture elements, is composed of hundreds of scientific papers, reports, and books.

Some of these elements will change, since science is by its nature tentative. Some findings may be revised or proved wrong. But taken together, the insights and discoveries this book details form a stark portrait of a catastrophic endpoint to the climate pandemic.

This portrait is not a Rorschach test subject to interpretation. The findings compose an unequivocal image of decline that threatens our species with extinction. Climate disruption is a nightmare from which we would not awaken.

We would be the victims of the relentless, human-caused rise, and centuries-long persistence, of atmospheric greenhouse gases.

We would have been a brilliant, failed experiment in evolution—living, or rather dying, proof that intelligence is not a survival trait.

We would have compromised our own survival because we are a profoundly paradoxical species. We are warlike pacifists, destructive builders, and adherents to both myth *and* science.

Our road to extinction would be straight and downhill. It would be:

- *Insidious*: A death of a thousand climatic cuts marked not by sudden, major disruptions, but by a relentless scourge of disasters and deterioration.
- *Intangible*: Not a particular concrete object, but a diffuse, multifarious phenomenon.
- *Inevitable*: An unavoidable accumulation of greenhouse gases irresistible in its momentum, with neither the global political

structure nor the political will to prevent extraction of most fossil fuel reserves.

- *Irreversible*: An ecological overshoot of Earth's carrying capacity that cannot be undone. None of its drivers—including CO_2 emissions, polar melting, and ocean warming and acidification—are reversible.
- *Inescapable*: Not sparing even society's privileged, including our leaders—although they might feel a false sense of security.

A key question is *when* the current trajectory of climate disruption would reach extinction-level. Any precise timeline would be pure speculation. However, the evidence presented in this book indicates that over the next decades the environment will continue to worsen until—without massive political and economic change—humanity will begin "circling the drain." This sardonic phrase is used by physicians to describe a patient whose death is inevitable, but whose demise is forestalled only by continual desperate measures.

We would resort to desperate measures to maintain society against the relentless onslaught of the carbon contagion—including environmental tipping points, lethal temperatures, megadroughts, failing agriculture, dying oceans, and rising sea levels.

Many of those desperate measures would trigger feedback cycles that would make things even worse. Some cycles would be as mundane as an increase in air conditioning to battle heat waves, which would produce more CO_2 and thus even higher temperatures. Other cycles would be as precipitous as conflicts over water sources that explode into wars that create even worse societal collapse.

Although we are unique as a species, we are not unique in the environmental mechanism of the extinctions we would cause. Mass extinctions in the past have been caused by global heating, found researchers who analyzed the paleontological record.[1607] The difference is that many such past extinctions were due to volcanism.

We would go down in paleo-history as the biological equivalent of supervolcanoes—producing up to 100 times the CO_2 emitted by the planet's volcanoes.[1608] But unlike extinctions from volcanic eruptions, our end would not be with a bang, but a whimper. After we were dethroned as the Earth's dominant species, remnant human populations might well survive for some time at the ragged edge of survival on a ruined Earth. But they would ultimately succumb to famine, disease, and a lethally hot, toxic environment spawned by the 6°C-plus temperature rise.

While the whimper of our extinction might last for a century, it could occur within a single lifetime. As a National Academies report on abrupt climate change impacts concluded:

> The history of climate on the planet—as read in archives such as tree rings, ocean sediments, and ice cores—is punctuated with large changes that occurred rapidly, over the course of decades to as little as a few years. . . . The current rate of carbon emissions is changing the climate system at an accelerating pace, making the chances of crossing tipping points all the more likely. . . . Surprises are indeed inevitable.[1609]

Alarm of the Anthropocene

To fully grasp the stark reality of our potential future, we must grasp the profound impact we have had upon the Earth. We humans have produced an imprint on the planet that will last for many millennia. That imprint does not consist of our sprawling cities, web of highways, or soaring monuments. These will erode and disappear over geological time. Our imprint is on the environment.

It can be hard to believe we have had a global impact if one stands on an ocean shore and scans the waters that stretch to the horizon; or scales a mountain peak and peers across a vast, uninhabited mountain range; or speeds across a hundred miles of trackless desert.

But our imprint has been profound, so much so that scientists have proposed defining a new epoch called the Anthropocene, as distinctive as the Pleistocene during which modern humans evolved.

One hallmark of the Anthropocene is what scientists have dubbed The Great Acceleration—a sudden, explosive growth after 1950 in multiple measures of human activity.[1610] These include growth in population and the use of energy, water, fertilizers, and transportation. And they include trends such as an increase in carbon dioxide, methane, ocean acidification, tropical forest loss, and marine fish capture.

The skyrocketing graphs of rising greenhouse gases and global temperature are incontrovertible proof that humans abruptly drove the Earth into a new epoch.

Analysts Owen Gaffney and Will Steffen crystallized these changes into what they call the Anthropocene equation, which revealed that the effects of human industrial society have swamped natural influences. They found that, while over the last 7,000 years global temperature gradually decreased, just over the last 45 years, this reduction reversed course, and the rate of increase is 170 times this baseline.[1611] [1612]

"Taken together, human actions are challenging the biosphere foundation for a prosperous development of civilizations," they and their colleagues wrote in an overview of the impacts of the Anthropocene.[1613] Humans have caused Earth to cross "planetary boundaries," they wrote, which they define as a "safe-operating space for humanity."

As discussed earlier, climate disruption is triggering self-sustaining feedback loops (see Climate Monsters). The unraveling of ecosystems is triggering irreversible extinctions (see Mass Extinctions). And heating and CO_2 are altering ocean chemistry (see Sea Change).

If any intelligent beings evolve after we go extinct, they will readily detect the planetary alterations we have wrought. As they excavate geological strata laid down during the Anthropocene, they will detect the clear signature of our civilization, not in our cultural artifacts, but in our detritus. Their excavations will reveal a band of sediment high in concrete, ash from fossil fuel combustion, radionuclides from nuclear fallout, pesticides, reactive nitrogen compounds, and aluminum and other refined metals.[1614] They will also find the strata rich in plastics, notably rock-like conglomerates of plastic, sand, and pebbles.[1615] [1616]

Future scientists—perhaps rational reptiles or cerebral cockroaches—will also detect evidence that the Anthropocene saw almost instant glacial melting, sea-level rise, ocean acidification, disappearance of forests, and spread of deserts.

Their excavations of fossils will reveal a sudden, catastrophic disappearance of huge numbers of species, and the appearance of invasive species in areas where they had not lived before. Anthropocene strata will be particularly rich in fossils of an awkwardly constructed creature with a large skull balanced precariously on top of a vertical spine.

The deposits such future beings detect will portray a global transformation as drastic as the impact of the meteor and the planet-shrouding volcanic eruptions implicated in wiping out the dinosaurs.

The abrupt temporal blip of the Anthropocene—measured in centuries over the billions of years of the Earth's history—will no doubt flabbergast any intelligent denizens of future Earth. It may even aid their survival, serving as a cautionary lesson.

Our fatal problem is that we who created the Anthropocene are not flabbergasted. We tend to minimize, even ignore its consequences, due to our relatively brief lifespans, limited perspective, and the distractions of everyday life.

Our Comfortable Extinction

Even given our profound impact on the global environment, it may seem patently absurd to contend that we are rushing headlong toward extinction. After all, we citizens of developed countries live an incredibly material-rich existence. Food and water are plentiful, and our stores display a stunning wealth of consumer goods. In fact, we don't even have to visit a store to buy those goods. We can order just about anything we desire online to be delivered to our door. When we don't wish to cook, we can order food from any of a multitude of restaurants.

Our technological achievements such as our transport system are nothing short of stunning. To be whisked to whatever local destination we wish, we only need to get into our car and speed away on paved roads. Or we can summon a ride-hailing service; or if we have access to a mass transit system, walk to the nearest station and be carried to our destination.

Our transportation system also readily takes us to far-flung destinations. On a trip to Japan, my plane departed from Los Angeles' LAX, which before the COVID-19 pandemic handled some 88 million passengers a year. Hours later, it landed at Tokyo's Narita International Airport, which accommodated more than 40 million.

My trip took me through Shinjuku Station in Tokyo—a transport hub where a web of rail and subway lines easily handled more than three million commuters a day. From there, we boarded the fabled Japanese bullet train, which sped smoothly at some 150 miles an hour over a countryside green with rice paddies.

Our utilities serve us just as well. We bring light with the flick of a switch, obtain water with the twist of a tap, and make our waste disappear with the flush of a toilet or a pitch into a trash bin, which is emptied weekly from in front of our homes and carted away to become "not our problem."

With the internet, information flows into our lives just as any other utility. We can call up facts, documents, or videos with the tap of a few keys or a voiced question to an artificially intelligent computer.

We enjoy a vast array of easily summoned entertainment. We are seduced and distracted by blockbuster special-effects movies and computer games that immerse us in rich fantasy realms; by sporting events that excite and engage us; and by amusement parks that offer beguiling refuge from the real world. This entertainment has become the opiate of the people, amusing us toward extinction.

Even our news is infotainment, feeding us a neatly packaged flow of information that is heavy on crimes, scandals, and celebrity peccadilloes. The dramatic news of wars and other violence attracts far more coverage than the slow violence of climate disruption.

Amid this flood of information, news of climate disruption constitutes a mere trickle that attracts our attention only fleetingly before disappearing into the vast historical archive.

This media-spawned "false sensory security" is one reason climate disruption has not made the impact on our conscience that could have enabled our survival.

Embedded in the cascade of news are legions of alluring commercials "aimed to keep [people] in a perpetual state of infantile self-gratification as dependable and dependent consumers rather than as informed, active, engaged, and thoughtful citizens," wrote environmentalist and political scientist David Orr in his book *Down to the Wire: Confronting Climate Collapse*.[1617] "People distracted by consumption, which is to say the thoroughly infantilized, seldom disturb the public order or become zealous revolutionaries," he wrote.

Nature documentaries are a form of enviro-ads, portraying the artfully edited beauty of the natural world, while ignoring the ugly reality of humans' degradation of that world. Few give even passing mention to the large-scale extinction of species.

Sir David Attenborough has been among the most prominent producers of such rose-colored documentaries. Over the decades, his documentaries have celebrated the wonders of nature without featuring the threats to their continued existence. One could argue that he thereby abdicated his responsibility to the very creatures he covered and benefited from. In a 2002 interview for CBS's *60 Minutes*, Attenborough rationalized his approach in terms of the need to hold an audience:

"The most important job is persuading people that the natural world is complex and wonderful and one of the most precious things we have," he said. "And if you're going to do that, then every time you do it, you show the facts, you end up by saying, 'And it's all disappearing and it's all your fault,' people will stop viewing." [1618]

Only late in his career did Attenborough begin to highlight the dangers of climate disruption, in TV interviews and his documentary *Extinction: The Facts*.[1619]

We also discount the possibility of our extinction because of our perception of calamities such as floods, hurricanes, tornadoes, and wildfires. We tend to see them as unavoidable "natural" disasters. We take comfort in the belief that we are not to blame for that tornado, that wildfire, or that flood. So, we accept their damage, grieve over the human loss, and work to recover.

"Benign" pollutant

Even as fossil fuel combustion, the basis of our economy, overburdens our atmosphere with heat-trapping carbon dioxide (CO_2), we do not perceive the gas as an extinction-level threat. Colorless, odorless, and non-toxic, it seems perfectly benign.

But what if it wasn't? What if CO_2 were brown-colored and with a foul odor? Then we would see and smell it spewing from the tailpipe of every petroleum-powered car and truck. It would waft from the stack of every fossil fuel power plant, transforming blue sky into brown. The effect would be horrendous.

Now, in our thought experiment let's make things even worse. What if every object exuded the CO_2 created in its production? All plastics, in fact all human-made materials, would emit the brown, effluvia-smelling stuff because of the energy required to produce them.

Even the fresh, "natural" fruits and vegetables in the supermarket cooler would give off the disgusting gas because fuel was burned in its planting, cultivation, harvest, and transport.

Within a short time, our air would be thoroughly stained. That is, except for the near certainty that the world's governments would likely have acted instantly to pass laws banning emission of this disgusting vapor. However, that banning has not been the case, and we and our governments have relegated reducing CO_2 pollution to a low priority.

In reality, our comfortable existence is but an instant in the time of human evolution that is sliding toward extinction.

We wrongly believe we are insulated from the vicissitudes of nature—that we can even recover from its catastrophes—because we are comfortably enfolded in our technology.

But in the end, we will be entombed in that technology.

Our Industrial Age has created what philosopher Gunther Anders termed a "Promethean gap"—named for the Greek god who gave humans fire. It is a gap between our success in creating machines and our failure to understand the social consequences of that creation.

We suffer "apocalyptic blindness," Anders proposed. Such blindness "renders human beings incapable of facing the possibility of a bad end to their history," explained sustainability researchers Ulrike Ehgartner, Patrick Gould, and Marc Hudson. "The belief in progress, persistently ingrained since the Industrial Revolution . . . causes the incapability of humans to understand that their existence is threatened, and that this could lead to the end of their history," they wrote.[1620]

Palliate the Planet

Given the devastating future scenario this book reveals, a central, even consuming, question is: How could we cope with the prospect of human extinction? Although extinction is less personal, more abstract, than our own death, perhaps the best way to process our reaction would be in terms of the five stages of grief first described by psychiatrist Elisabeth Kübler-Ross.[1621]

She proposed that dying people go through denial, anger, bargaining, depression, and acceptance. She did not regard those stages as a linear progression. Indeed, we would find ourselves randomly cycling from one to another, depending on our personality, our mood, and any number of other circumstances. Anger would give way to acceptance; depression to anger; acceptance to denial. We might also find ourselves experiencing any combination of those emotions simultaneously.[1622]

Our society has been largely in a stage of denial of "environmental black elephants"—a term attributed to environmentalist Adam Sweidan. The term is a cross between "black swan"—an unexpected event with enormous consequences—and the "elephant in the room," a highly visible problem that no one wishes to address. Sweidan warned against "a herd of environmental black elephants," most notably climate catastrophes.

"When they hit, we'll claim they were black swans no one could have predicted, but, in fact, they are black elephants, very visible right now," he told *The New York Times*.[1623]

Our black-elephant denial has changed to some extent because of the punishing onslaught of climate catastrophes and the psychological impact of a world becoming increasingly alien. David Orr described that effect in *Down to the Wire: Confronting Climate Collapse*:

> As the once familiar trees, birds, and animals of a region die out, the sense of loss will be impossible to calculate. People, attached to the sights, sounds, and smells of familiar landscapes and regions will go through a process of grieving similar to that of refugees forced to flee their homes and cherished places.[1624]

Taking climate action

Some of us are suffering a spiritually corrosive "climate despair"—understandable, given the evidence presented in his book. Instead, sustainability researcher Max Goodman advocates a resolute "climate stoicism," which means "accepting the reality of a tragic future, and committing to help soften the blow." He wrote:

> A good stoic journeys into darkness and emerges able to cope with the real world, grateful for their opportunities and intensely practical about cultivating them. Climate Stoicism extends this mental resilience to the collective, calling us to get over our apocalyptic dread by learning to mentally project ourselves into the future's landscape of loss.[1625]

Perhaps the pithiest expression of such stoicism is the motto of the Extinction Rebellion activist group: "Hope dies—action begins."[1626]

Some might see the dark future of climate disruption as an excuse to indulge in our most selfish, destructive impulses—continuing to plunder the Earth for our own benefit. However, one hopes that our better angels would prevail; that in the twilight of our species we would instead seek solace in environmental good works—in essence, palliating our planet.

As we cycle among the stages of grief, we could give our lives meaning by offering our time, money, and effort to the organizations and causes that work toward mitigating climate disruption.

Climatologist Katharine Hayhoe offers a valuable guide to persuading and motivating people to action in her book, *Saving Us: A Climate Scientist's Case for Hope and Healing in a Divided World.*[1627] Her attitude is in contrast to those who would promulgate blind false hope. She writes:

> Pretending we can defy physics by putting our heads in the sand or cultivating a positive attitude will merely keep us slightly happier until (and more surprised when) the axe falls. Rational hope accepts that success is not inevitable, or even entirely probable. It takes courage to do that, but when we are doubtful, when the odds are

low and success is possible rather than probable, it's that courage and hope that carry us forward.

Author Sarah Jaquette Ray advises how to cope with climate grief in her deeply insightful book *A Field Guide to Climate Anxiety: How to Keep Your Cool on a Warming Planet*.[1628] She writes:

> Grief is the opposite of hope, but, perhaps counterintuitively, it's a more important affect for doing the existential work of facing climate disruption. . . . Embracing grief and decline is not a morose, fatalistic orientation. Facing death—the planet's and ours—opens us up to the love that is necessary in order to sustain the work of climate action. . . .We are of no use to the cause if we are burned out by apocalypse fatigue or so overwhelmed by fear, shame, and sadness that we simply opt out to save ourselves from pain.

Nor should we allow climate guilt to hinder climate action, she counsels:

> Framing our environmental crisis in simplistic "humans are bad for the planet" terms undermines our efforts to live better with each other and with nature. People are profoundly disturbed by climate change, and being told that it is the fault of our own moral failings is not only demoralizing but factually wrong. It does not help us muster the stamina to stay involved in environmental work for the long haul. Instead, it can lead to various forms of self-erasure, or cause people to give up in despair, choosing short-term avoidance and apathy over long-term climate justice. I want to suggest that if climate justice is your goal, you should ditch the green guilt and eco-fragility, learn to appreciate the nuances of hope, and take time to love, laugh about, and delight in the world and in your work.

Besides Hayhoe's and Ray's books, other excellent sources of information and inspiration include:

- The book *Drawdown: The Most Comprehensive Plan Ever Proposed to Reverse Global Warming* is a good guide to advocacy.[1629]

- The book *How to Prepare for Climate Change: A Practical Guide to Surviving the Chaos* is a comprehensive guide to coping with climate disruption.[1630]
- The Climate Psychology Alliance is a useful resource on psychological issues of climate disruption.[1631]
- Project InsideOut by clinical psychologists offers techniques for coping with climate disruption and effecting change.[1632]
- The Climate Emotions Conversation comprises small groups that share and listen about the climate emergency.[1633]
- The EAT-Lancet Commission on Food, Planet, Health has produced a guide to a healthy, sustainable diet.[1634]
- The website Conceivable Future is a helpful resource for addressing the personal issue of whether to have children.[1635]

Planetary palliation means taking steps that benefit society besides yourself—just as the COVID-19 pandemic prompted (most) people to take steps such as being vaccinated, quarantining, social distancing, and wearing masks.

You might prefer to become involved in traditional environmental organizations, such as those on the list compiled by Bill Moyers Reports.[1636] Or, you might join or support a more focused group such as the Extinction Rebellion, 350.org, the Climate Reality Project, the Climate Mobilization, and/or the Climate Emergency Fund.[1637][1638][1639][1640][1641]

Calling out journalists for inaccurate media reports or failure to cover climate disruption is also effective—and again, soul-satisfying. Journalists do heed their readers and viewers.

To aid climate coverage, you can support such groups as the Society of Environmental Journalists.[1642] You can support climate news outlets and journalism initiatives, including *Anthropocene* magazine, Climate Central, Climatewire, Covering Climate Now, DeSmog, Inside Climate News, and Floodlight.[1643][1644][1645][1646][1647][1648][1649] You can support environmental journalists' efforts, such as Emily Atkin's HEATED newsletter.[1650]

You can also act individually. The most effective actions to mitigate climate disruption are having smaller families, living car-free, avoiding air travel, and eating a plant-based diet, according to sustainability researchers Seth Wynes and Kimberly Nicholas.[1651]

Actively advocating with local, state, and national politicians is both effective and soul-satisfying. Legislators do heed voters, not just donors and lobbyists.

Even though you're eventually going to die, you still try to live a virtuous life. By the same token, just because our species may be headed for extinction doesn't mean we can't try to be a virtuous species. So, strive for environmental virtue. If you are an oil company executive, work for the end of fossil fuels. If you are a de-nihilist, face the truth of climate disruption and advocate for your planet. If you are a legislator, campaign for climate-saving laws.

Poet Dylan Thomas perhaps expressed most eloquently how to cope with the prospect of an ending:[1652]

> Though wise men at their end know dark is right,
> Because their words had forked no lightning they
> Do not go gentle into that good night.
>
> Good men, the last wave by, crying how bright
> Their frail deeds might have danced in a green bay,
> Rage, rage against the dying of the light.

Appendix 1
A history of neglected climate coverage

The mainstream media's historical neglectful attitude toward climate coverage is exemplified by a comment in 2014 by then-CNN president Jeff Zucker:

> Climate change is one of those stories that deserves more attention . . . but we haven't figured out how to engage the audience in that story in a meaningful way. When we do do those stories, there does tend to be a tremendous amount of lack of interest on the audience's part.[1653]

Zucker's opinion has almost certainly changed since then, but his attitude reflected CNN's coverage priorities at the time. They also reflected a lack of interest in climate coverage and a lack of understanding of climate disruption's potential impact.

Over past years, even in covering major climate-related disasters, climate disruption was mentioned only sporadically. For example, a, 2017 analysis by the Public Citizen advocacy group of climate change mentions in US newspaper articles found that climate change was mentioned by only

- 33% of pieces on record heat
- 24% of pieces on record drought
- 10% of pieces on record rainfall
- 9% of pieces on historic wildfires or floods
- 4% of pieces on hurricanes.[1654]

Beginning in 2017, more mainstream media outlets did begin to cover the link between hurricanes and global heating, but the coverage remained spotty and with little explanatory depth.[1655 1656 1657 1658 1659] Also, the media tended not to give scientists major roles in such coverage. For example, climate coverage on the Sunday talk shows in 2017 did not include any scientists.[1660]

Regarding 2017's coverage, Lisa Hymas, climate and energy program director at Media Matters, commented:

> Even in a year when we've had [a] string of hurricanes, heat waves, and wildfires worthy of the Book of Revelation . . . the effect of climate change on extreme weather has been dramatically undercovered. Some of Trump's tweets generate more national coverage than devastating disasters.[1661]

Climate coverage fell short in subsequent years, as well. In 2018, the *Columbia Journalism Review* declared, "When it comes to burying the reality of climate change, the news media is still complicit." Reporter Jon Allsop pointed out that coverage of the California wildfires that year "has not asserted a strong enough link to climate change," and that Sunday TV talk shows continued to give platforms to de-nihilists.[1662] Other US examples of coverage in past years:

- During Hurricane Florence (2018), less than 8% of stories about the storm in the 50 largest newspapers mentioned climate disruption, found a Public Citizen analysis. Only 4% of segments on major television outlets mentioned climate disruption.[1663]
- Climate disruption coverage in 2020 by ABC, CBS, NBC, and Fox plummeted by 53% over the previous year, found a Media Matters analysis of nightly news and Sunday shows. The analysis found that the shows devoted only 112 total minutes to covering climate disruption—the lowest amount since 2016.[1664]
- During Hurricane Ida (2021) only 4% of the segments on the hurricane by the major commercial TV networks—ABC, CBS, CNN, Fox, NBC, and MSNBC—mentioned climate disruption in their coverage.[1665]
- During a week of wildfires in 2021, broadcast and cable TV news shows mentioned climate change in only 36% of their segments.[1666]

Historical lack of media coverage meant that Americans just did not get much news about global heating's consequences. Even in 2022—with its record droughts, heat waves and wildfires—just over half of respondents to a national US survey said they see media coverage of global heating once a month or more often; and 33% say they see coverage several times a year or less often.[1667]

Timid meteorologists

Mainstream media meteorologists were also timid about linking climate-related events to climate disruption. Historically, broadcast meteorologists were reluctant to talk about climate disruption, even though they had an on-air bully pulpit, according to a 2016 survey by the Center for Climate Change Communication. Only a small minority in the survey said they felt comfortable presenting information on-air about climate projections or impacts. They feared upsetting viewers or station management.[1668]

A classic example of such avoidance is the Weather Channel's 2017 coverage of hurricanes Harvey and Irma. *The New York Times* reporter David Gelles wrote about the journalistic discussions in the Weather Channel's newsroom:

> In all the nonstop coverage there was no mention of climate change and its role in creating extreme weather. . . . the omission reflects the network's delicate balancing act. Though there is no debate among Weather Channel executives and meteorologists about man-made global warming, they are wary of alienating their core audience, which leans right. But the words "climate change" don't appear in any promotional materials or show titles, and the phrase is only occasionally uttered on the air.

Dave Shull, The Weather Channel's chief executive, rationalized the decision, saying that, "I believe in climate change, and I believe it's man-made. But I'm not a big fan of the term. It's been politicized."[1669]

To be fair, however, The Weather Channel has begun to cover climate disruption more recently.[1670] But the fact remains that historically one of the most important outlets for climate disruption coverage failed in its responsibility.

Weather coverage had failed to cover climate disruption in part because, historically, few broadcast meteorologists accepted its reality. Even as late as 2017, only about half believed climate disruption to be mainly human-caused. One assumes the percentage has grown since then, given the considerable increase in climate disruption coverage in weathercasts.[1671]

Boring climate disruption

Climate disruption's perceived banality also reduced the media's appetite for covering it. For example, wrote political reporter Tom Engelhardt in 2014:

> In news terms, much of global warming is boring and repetitive. I mean, drip, drip, drip. How many times can you write about the melting Arctic sea ice or shrinking glaciers and call it news? . . . climate change and its potential devastations exist on a timescale not congenial either to media time or to the individual lifetimes of our short-lived species.[1672]

In reporting on that long timescale, journalists were just following the lead of the environmental movement, wrote journalist Krista Langlois in 2015:

> More and more, environmental organizations are dedicating their efforts to . . . seemingly distant threats. Environmental journalists often follow suit, which means we're losing touch with our audience.[1673]

Unfair unbalance

Too often, newspaper opinion pages aimed to achieve false balance by pairing a legitimate climate science article with a de-nihilist piece. For example, two USA *Today* essays cited by Media Matters paired a climate disruption editorial with an op-ed by a de-nihilist representative of the Hoover Institution. In the editorial, the newspaper criticized the nomination of de-nihilist Scott Pruitt as head of the Environmental Protection Agency, but the Hoover Institution op-ed declared that he was "the right choice."[1674] Pruitt ultimately resigned amid charges of ethics transgressions.[1675]

Indeed, media mentions of de-nihilist think tanks rose over the five years ending in 2017, leveling out in 2018, found the Public Citizen advocacy group.[1676]

The television networks were guilty of such false balance when they covered the 2017 March for Science, pointed out Media Matters. The group detailed how CNN, CBS, and C-SPAN all featured de-nihilists in their coverage of the event.[1677]

Inviting such de-nihilists to comment on climate disruption was akin to inviting a flat-Earther to comment on the launch of an Earth-orbiting satellite.

This unbalance was rife during a period in history when accurate media coverage could have had a timely influence on climate policy. One analysis of more than three thousand newspaper articles published between 1988 and 2002 in *The New York Times*, *The Washington Post*, *Los Angeles Times*, and *Wall Street Journal* found that just over half gave "roughly equal attention" to the opposing views that global heating was human-caused versus that it was due to natural fluctuations.[1678]

"The media have to let go of the addiction to 'balance'. . ., which affords mendacious extremists as much credibility as reasonable and truthful people," declared cognitive scientist Stephan Lewandowsky.[1679] While such false balance has since waned, it remains a low-level, chronic infection in the media.

Appendix 2
Major print media published de-nihilist opinion

While many national newspapers have published misleading opinion pieces on climate disruption, *The Wall Street Journal* has led the pack. For example, an analysis of opinion pieces in major newspapers in 2015–2016 by Media Matters for America found that the *Journal* published 55 inaccurate pieces.[1680]

A more recent example of *The Wall Street Journal*'s biased coverage was a 2018 opinion piece by de-nihilist Fred Singer entitled "The Sea Is Rising, but Not Because of Climate Change." Singer, who is not a climate scientist, asserted that data revealed no effect on sea levels between 1915 and 1945, as global temperature rose. He said that "the temperature of sea water has no direct effect on sea-level rise. That means neither does the atmospheric content of carbon dioxide."[1681] Singer's article was a classic case of cherry-picking data, citing only short-term measurements and ignoring the long-term effects of temperature on sea level.

Mother Jones journalist Kevin Drum criticized *The Wall Street Journal* editorial page as being "dedicated as always to telling its readers what they want to hear." He declared that "virtually every piece is a deliberate attempt to misstate the truth in some way."[1682]

The Boston Globe—whose coverage area includes some of the world's most prominent research institutions—has also published inaccurate articles. One was a column by Jeff Jacoby entitled "Why are Climate-Change Models So Flawed? Because Climate Science Is So Incomplete." In the column, Jacoby asserted that climate models are flawed because:

> Earth's climate system is unfathomably complex. . . . The
> science is far from settled. That is why calls to radically

reduce carbon emissions are so irresponsible—and why dire warnings of what will happen if we don't are little better than reckless fearmongering.[1683]

In a critique of Jacoby's piece, climatologist James Screen wrote: "This is a highly inaccurate article . . . The discussion of complexity is intended to mislead: the fact that the climate system is incredibly complex does not mean we don't understand key aspects of how it functions."[1684] Jacoby has no credentials as a climate scientist or environmental journalist. His degree is in law.

In 2018, USA *Today* ran a highly misleading opinion piece by de-nihilist Roy Spencer declaring that "Hurricane Florence is Not Climate Change or Global Warming. It's Just the Weather." The piece prompted climatologist Michael Mann to comment: "There is not a single sentence in that piece, near as I can tell, that is factually defensible."[1685]

In a *New York Post* opinion article on the 2021 IPCC report, de-nihilist Bjørn Lomborg inveighed against "climate change alarmism." He cited the irrelevant comparison that more people die from cold than from heat.[1686]

In reviewing Lomborg's book, *False Alarm: How Climate Change Panic Costs Us Trillions, Hurts the Poor, and Fails to Fix the Planet*, Nobel Laureate economist Joseph E. Stiglitz calls out numerous errors, writing:

> Written with an aim to convert anyone worried about the dangers of climate change, Lomborg's work would be downright dangerous were it to succeed in persuading anyone that there was merit in its arguments. This book proves the aphorism that a little knowledge is dangerous. It's nominally about air pollution. It's really about mind pollution.[1687]

Even *The New York Times*—among the nation's most influential newspapers—has published misleading articles. An example is columnist Bret Stephens' opinion piece about his 2022 trip to Greenland to observe the melting glaciers.[1688] Stephens had been a long-time de-nihilist, in his previous *The Wall Street Journal* columns calling climate disruption "hysteria" and an example of "imaginary enemies."[1689]

However, his Greenland trip "changed my mind about climate change." But it did not change his faith that "that markets, not government, provide the cure."

He emphasized the benefits of natural gas and minimized climate disruption's challenge, wondering if it was "akin to cancer—manageable or curable in its earlier stages, disastrous in its later ones."

He advocated "partial solutions that work with the grain of human nature, not big ones that work against it."

Environmental journalist Emily Atkin charged that Stephens' article was "a collection of discredited talking points from the fossil fuel industry, and a prime example of delay discourse"—accepting climate disruption but justifying inaction or inadequate efforts.[1690] She wrote that "it is the fossil fuel industry's favorite way to pretend they care about climate change while continuing to pollute as long as possible."

Stephens has no experience as a climate scientist or environmental journalist. His academic training is in political philosophy and comparative politics.

Media have all too often accepted misleading de-nihilist opinion pieces without making any apparent effort to apply the same journalistic vetting they would with other topics. For example, *Forbes* published a misleading opinion piece whose headline was "As the Consensus among Scientists Crumbles, Global Warming Alarmists Attack Their Integrity." The author, James Taylor, cited a survey which found that "only 36% of geoscientists and engineers agree that humans are causing a serious global warming problem."[1691]

However, the survey published in the journal *Organizational Studies* was not of climate scientists, but of scientists and engineers working in the petroleum industry. And the paper emphatically did not claim that the survey was a valid indicator of scientific opinion. Rather the paper aimed to answer the psychological question of how such industry professionals legitimize themselves as experts "while engaging in defensive institutional work against others."[1692]

Of course, de-nihilist news sites such as Breitbart News have no compunction about propagating unbalanced, even false information. The site engages in personal attacks on climate scientists and environmental advocates, variously terming them "talentless low-lives," "abject liars," and "global warming Nazis."[1693]

Appendix 3
As if that weren't enough . . .

Each of these global hazards could contribute to, or even cause, human extinction. They are certainly important enough to be the topic of whole libraries of books, and this brief summary is certainly not meant to minimize them. But they should be acknowledged. Here are quotes from the *Global Catastrophic Risks* report on key potential threats:[1694]

- *Nuclear war (politically triggered).* "Although the tension between nuclear states has diminished since the end of the Cold War and disarmament efforts have reduced arsenals, the prospect of a nuclear war remains present, and might be closer today than it was a decade ago."
- *Biological and chemical warfare.* "New technological developments give cause for concern. In particular, developments in synthetic biology and genetic engineering make it possible to modify the characteristics of micro-organisms. New genetically engineered pathogens—released intentionally or inadvertently— might cause a pandemic of unprecedented proportions."
- *Asteroid impact.* "The largest near-Earth asteroids (> 1 km diameter) have the potential to cause geologic and climate effects on a global scale, disrupting human civilization, and perhaps even resulting in extinction of the species."
- *Supervolcanic eruption.* "Supervolcanic eruptions are events in which at least 400 [cubic kilometers] of bulk material is expelled. Eruptions of such magnitude may happen at any time in the future, with catastrophic consequences."
- *Artificial intelligence.* "AI systems that were deployed with the best of intentions . . . have instead inadvertently reinforced

institutional racism, put jobs at risk, and exacerbated inequality. It's not hard to imagine how much worse these problems could get with advanced AI systems functioning across many platforms or falling into the hands of terrorists or despots."

And, of course, there are global pandemics, as exemplified by the COVID-19 outbreak. There are certainly many more such virulent microbes out there. And there is absolutely nothing preventing an outbreak of a new influenza pandemic on top of a pandemic of an emerging virus such as the SARS-COV-2 virus.[1695] There is also a microbial menagerie of other infectious diseases whose local outbreaks could spread globally. These include dengue virus, West Nile virus, Ebola virus, methicillin-resistant *Staphylococcus aureus* (MRSA), Middle East Respiratory Syndrome (MERS), severe acute respiratory syndrome (SARS), and drug-resistant tuberculosis.[1696]

Rising antibiotic resistance also threatens to devastate global populations, according to the *Review on Antimicrobial Resistance* report. Unless antimicrobial resistance is solved, global death rates from infections will amount to 10 million people a year between now and 2050, with a total economic loss of $100 trillion. Wrote economist Jim O'Neill in the report:

> It is of course possible that our estimates may turn out to be too large, but we believe it is even more likely that they could be too small. This is because we did not even consider the secondary effects of antibiotics losing their effectiveness, such as the risks in carrying out caesarean sections, hip replacements, or gut surgery.[1697]

Polluting chemicals

Industrial chemicals are manufactured in vast quantities without adequate testing of health effects. They are endangering global health and reducing fertility, according to scientific reports.

Prominent among these chemicals are "endocrine disruptors," which mimic natural hormones enough to interfere with their function. These chemicals include organochlorinated pesticides, plastics, and plasticizers, according to the Endocrine Society. In its scientific assessment of endocrine disruptors, the society cited evidence that the chemicals cause obesity and diabetes, female and male infertility, hormone-sensitive cancers in females, prostate and thyroid disruption, and neurological development disorders.[1698]

The International Federation of Gynecology and Obstetrics issued a report detailing the impact of such chemicals on pregnancy and breast-feeding.[1699] It concluded that such exposure "is ubiquitous and is a threat to healthy human reproduction. There are tens of thousands of chemicals in global commerce, and even small exposures to toxic chemicals during pregnancy can trigger adverse health consequences."

The report declared that "the global health and economic burden related to toxic environmental chemicals is in excess of millions of deaths and billions of dollars every year."

The report charged that "the industrialized food system is a major contributor to the introduction of toxic chemicals—from pesticides to plastics—into the environment," and that research has "documented that virtually every pregnant woman in the USA has at least 43 different environmental chemicals in her body."

In fact, an analysis of samples from pregnant women and their newborns' umbilical cord blood found more than 55 previously unre-ported environmental chemicals. Most of these chemicals had little or no information about their sources or uses.[1700] [1701]

Chemical contamination is so ubiquitous, that "to a disturbing extent babies are born 'pre-polluted,'" stated a report by the President's Cancer Panel.[1702]

Plasticized planet

Vast quantities of plastics are finding their way into the oceans, con-stituting a danger to the ocean's ecology. Unlike the threats discussed above, plastic pollution is not likely an extinction threat. However, it is another form of carbon pollution which, like greenhouse gas emissions, is proceeding largely unchecked.

This plastic ranges from large chunks, such as those found in the stomachs of dead sperm whales on shores of the North Sea, to "microplastic" particles from clothing and other sources that are ingested by seabirds, fish, and filter feeders such as clams.[1703] [1704] [1705]

The plastic is also draping coral reefs, stressing them and triggering disease, found a survey of 159 coral reefs by marine disease ecologists. The researchers estimated that more than 11 billion pieces of plastic are entangled in Asia-Pacific reefs.[1706]

Overall, there are currently more than 5 trillion plastic pieces floating in the world's oceans, constituting over 250,000 tons, according to one estimate.[1707] And plastic fibers are being detected in tap water around the world, making it almost certain they are in food as well, found an investigation by Orb media.[1708] Microplastics have also been detected in human blood.[1709]

It has been calculated that some 8.3 billion metric tons of plastic had been produced as of 2017 worldwide. About 80% of this production has accumulated in landfills or the natural environment.[1710] If current production continues, the mass of plastic waste has been estimated to more than triple by 2060.[1711]

The lifespan of plastic is so long that plastic-containing rocks will be among the scant surviving evidence of human existence far in the future (see Alarm of the Anthropocene).

Researchers don't know the health and environmental impacts of such ubiquitous plastic pollution. But effects could include disruption of the food web by accumulation of plastic in organisms, and toxicity in humans and other organisms from the plasticizing chemicals and pollutants carried by plastic particles.[1712]

References

(Hyperlinked references may be accessed and
downloaded from ClimatePandemic.com)

1   Mann, Michael E. *The New Climate War: The Fight to Take Back Our Climate.* PublicAffairs, 2021.
2   Watts, Jonathan. "Climatologist Michael E Mann: 'Good People Fall Victim to Doomism. I Do Too Sometimes'." *The Guardian* (February 21, 2021).
3   Pester, Patrick. "Could Climate Change Make Humans Go Extinct?" Live Science (August 30, 2021).
4   Yuval Noah Harari. "Why Fiction Trumps Truth." *The New York Times* (May 24, 2019).
5   Meredith, Dennis. *Explaining Research; How to Reach Key Audiences to Advance Your Work, Second Edition.* Oxford University Press, 2021.
6   Higginbotham, Adam. *Midnight in Chernobyl: The Untold Story of the World's Greatest Nuclear Disaster.* Simon & Schuster, 2020.
7   Levin, Kelly, Benjamin Cashore, Steven Bernstein, and Graeme Auld. "Overcoming the Tragedy of Super Wicked Problems: Constraining Our Future Selves to Ameliorate Global Climate Change," *Policy Sciences* 45, no. 2 (June 2012).
8   Marshall, George. *Don't Even Think About It: Why Our Brains are Wired to Ignore Climate Change.* Bloomsbury, 2014.
9   Hill, Alice C. *The Fight for Climate after COVID-19.* Oxford University Press, 2021.
10   Hess, Amanda. "Apocalypse When? Global Warming's Endless Scroll." *The New York Times* (February 3, 2022).
11   Bentz, Barbara. "Bark Beetles and Climate Change in the United States." US Department of Agriculture, Forest Service. Climate Change Resource Center (2014).
12   Box, Jason E., William T. Colgan, Torben Røjle Christensen, Niels Martin Schmidt, Magnus Lund, Frans-Jan W. Parmentier, and Ross Brown et al. "Key Indicators of Arctic Climate Change: 1971–2017." *Environmental Research Letters* 14, no. 4 (April 8, 2019).
13   Rocha, Juan C., Garry Peterson, Örjan Bodin, and Simon Levin. "Cascading Regime Shifts Within and Across Scales," *Science* 362, no. 6421 (December 21, 2018).

14   Ricke, Katharine L. and Ken Caldeira." Maximum Warming Occurs About One Decade after a Carbon Dioxide Emission." *Environmental Research Letters* 9 (2014).

15   Roberts, David. "The Scariest Thing about Global Warming (and Covid-19)." *Vox* (July 7, 2020).

16   US Fish and Wildlife Service, *Polar Bear Conservation Management Plan* (2017).

17   Union of Concerned Scientists. Climate Hot Map: Republic of Maldives (2022).

18   Leiserowitz, Anthony, Edward Maibach, Seth Rosenthal, John Kotcher, Jennifer Carman, Liz Neyens, Jennifer Marlon, Karine Lacroix, and Matthew Goldberg. *Climate Change in the American Mind, April 2022.* Yale Program on Climate Change Communication and George Mason University Center for Climate Change Communication (April 2022).

19   Yale School of Forestry and Environmental Studies. "Local Consumption, Global Consequences: Examining the Impacts of an Increasingly Connected World." *Journal of Industrial Ecology*, 20, no., 3 (July 6, 2016).

20   Gilbert, Daniel. "If Only Gay Sex Caused Global Warming." *Los Angeles Times* (July 2, 2006).

21   Schelling, Thomas. "Foreword," in Wohlstetter, Roberta, *Pearl Harbor: Warning and Decision.* Stanford University Press, 1962.

22   Knowlton, Kim. "Zika Goes Viral in the U.S." Natural Resources Defense Council (August 3, 2016).

23   Ginty, Molly M. "Climate Change Bites," Natural Resources Defense Council (February 1, 2018).

24   Centers for Disease Control and Prevention. "Vibrio Species Causing Vibriosis." (May 13, 2016).

25   Baker-Austin, Craig, Joaquin A. Trinanes, Nick G. H. Taylor, Rachel Hartnell, Anja Siitonen, and Jaime Martinez-Urtaza. "Emerging Vibrio Risk at High Latitudes in Response to Ocean Warming." *Nature Climate Change*, 3 (July 22, 2012).

26   Jefferson, R.D., R.E. Goans, and S.H. Thomas. "Diagnosis and Treatment of Polonium Poisoning." *Clinical Toxicology* (July 2009).

27   Kaufman, Alexander C. "A Star Psychiatrist Swerves From Nuclear Armageddon to Climate Change." *Huffington Post* (November 26, 2017).

28   Moore, Frances C., Nick Obradovich, Flavio Lehner, and Patrick Baylis."Rapidly Declining Remarkability of Temperature Anomalies May Obscure Public Perception of Climate Change." *Proceedings of the National Academy of Sciences* 116 no. 11 (February 25, 2019).

29   DeSilver, Drew. "How Americans Are—And Aren't—Making Eco-Friendly Lifestyle Changes." Pew Research Center (November 17, 2015).

30   Tomer, Adie. "America's Commuting Choices: 5 Major Takeaways from 2016 Census Data," Brookings Institution (October 3, 2017).

31   International Energy Agency. *Global EV Outlook 2022.* (May 2022).

32 US Energy Information Administration. "Motor Gasoline Remains the Most Prevalent Transportation Fuel Despite Electric Vehicles Gaining Market Share." From: *Annual Energy Outlook 2022* (2022).

33 Poushter, Jacob, and Moira Faga. "Americans See Spread of Disease as Top International Threat, Along With Terrorism, Nuclear Weapons, Cyberattacks." Pew Research Center (April 13, 2020).

34 Pew Research Center. "Public's Top Priority for 2022: Strengthening the Nation's Economy." (February 16, 2022).

35 IPCC. *Climate Change 2021: The Physical Science Basis, Summary for Policymakers* From: *Climate Change 2021: The Physical Science Basis* (August 7, 2021).

36 Li, Guancheng, Lijing Cheng, Jiang Zhu, Kevin E. Trenberth, Michael E. Mann, and John P. Abraham. "Increasing Ocean Stratification over the Past Half-Century." *Nature Climate Change* 3 (September 28, 2020).

37 Archer, David, Michael Eby, Victor Brovkin, Andy Ridgwell, Long Cao, Uwe Mikolajewicz, Ken Caldeira, Katsumi Matsumoto, Guy Munhoven, Alvaro Montenegro, and Kathy Tokos. "Atmospheric Lifetime of Fossil Fuel Carbon Dioxide," *Annual Review of Earth and Planetary Sciences* 37 (January 26, 2009).

38 Inman, Mason. "Carbon is Forever." *Nature Climate Change* (November 20, 2008).

39 Emile-Geay, Julian. "What Is 'Committed Warming'? A Climate Scientist Explains Why Global Warming Can Continue after Emissions End." *The Conversation* (June 9, 2022).

40 World Meteorological Organization. Greenhouse Gas Bulletins.

41 NOAA, Earth System Research Laboratory Global Monitoring Division. Global Greenhouse Gas Reference Network.

42 Willeit, M., A. Ganopolskir, Calov, and V. Brovkin. "Mid-Pleistocene Transition in Glacial Cycles Explained by Declining CO_2 and Regolith Removal." *Science Advances* 5, no. 4 (April 3, 2019).

43 Carrington, Damien. "Last Time CO_2 Levels Were This High, There Were Trees at the South Pole." *The Guardian* (April 3, 2019).

44 Royal Meteorological Society. "The Pliocene: The Last Time Earth had >400 ppm of Atmospheric CO_2." (April 3, 2019).

45 Climate Central, Surging Seas Risk Zone Map.

46 Blunden, J. and T. Boyer, eds. *State of the Climate in 2021*. American Meteorological Society (August 2022).

47 Christensen, P., K. Gillingham, and W. Nordhaus. "Uncertainty in Forecasts of Long-Run Economic Growth." *Proceedings of the National Academy of Sciences* 15, no. 21 (May 22, 2018).

48 Liu, Zhu, Zhu Deng, Steven J. Davis, Clement Giron, and Philippe Ciais. "Monitoring Global Carbon Emissions in 2021." *Nature Reviews: Earth & Environment* (March 21, 2022).

49 Environmental Protection Agency. "Overview of Greenhouse Gases, Methane Emissions."

50 Environmental Protection Agency. "Overview of Greenhouse Gases, Nitrous Oxide Emissions."

51 Global Carbon Project. *Global Carbon Budget.*

52 Wong, Edward. "China Wants to Be a Climate Change Watchdog, but Can It Lead by Example?" *The New York Times*, January 10, 2017.

53 Liu, Zhu et al., "Climate Policy: Steps to China's Carbon Peak," *Nature* June 17, 2015.

54 Reuters, "China Greenhouse Gas Emissions Soar 50% during 2005–2014: Government Data," July 14, 2019.

55 Houston Museum of Natural Science Weiss Energy Hall

56 The Houston Museum of Natural Science Weiss Energy Hall Catalog.

57 US Energy Information Administration, "Table 5. Refiners' Total Operable Atmospheric Crude Oil Distillation Capacity as of January 1, 2020." (2020).

58 US Energy Information Administration. Rankings: Total Carbon Dioxide Emissions (2018).

59 ExxonMobil. Our Houston Campus.

60 McLaughlin, Tim. "Three Exxon Refineries Top the List of US Polluters." Reuters (June 1, 2021).

61 Environmental Integrity Project. *Environmental Justics and Refinery Pollution* (April 28, 2021).

62 Environmental Integrity Project. *Formaldehyde Air Pollution in Houston* (July 1, 2021).

63 City of Houston. Houston Climate Action Plan.

64 Watkins, Kate and Jen Rice. "5 Things You Should Know About Houston's Climate Action Plan." Houston Public Media (June 17, 2020).

65 Climate Central. Surging Seas Risk Zone Map.

66 Blackburn, Jim. "Texas Is Running Out of Near Misses." *The New York Times* (August 28, 2020).

67 Baurick, Tristan. "Gathering Storm: The Industrial Infrastructure Catastrophe Looming over America's Gulf Coast." *Bulletin of the Atomic Scientists* (December 9, 2021).

68 Bender, Eric. "A $26-Billion Plan to Save the Houston Area from Rising Seas." *Undark* (June 14, 2021).

69 Dart, Tom. "Houston Fears Climate Change Will Cause Catastrophic Flooding: 'It's Not If, It's When'." *The Guardian* (June 16, 2017).

70 Texas Living Waters Project. "Understanding Subsidence in the Houston-Galveston Region."

71 Lakritz, Talia, "These 11 Sinking Cities Could Disappear by 2100." World Economic Forum (September 10, 2019).

72 Nielsen-Gammon, John W., Jay L. Banner, Benjamin I. Cook, Darrel M. Tremaine, Corinne I. Wong, Robert E. Mace, Huilin Gao, Zong-Liang Yang, Marisa Flores Gonzalez, Richard Hoffpauir, Tom Gooch, and Kevin Kloesel. "Unprecedented Drought Challenges for Texas Water Resources in a Changing Climate: What Do Researchers and Stakeholders Need to Know?" *Earth's Future* (June 29, 2020).

73 Palalexiou, Simon Michael, Amir AghaKouchak, Kevin E. Trenberth, and Efi Foufoula-Georgiou. "Global, Regional, and Megacity Trends in the Highest Temperature of the Year: Diagnostics and Evidence for Accelerating Trends." *Earth's Future* 6, no. 1 (January 22, 2018).

74 Dahl, Kristina, Erika Spanger-Siegfried, Rachel Licker, Astrid Caldas, Rachel Cleetus, Shana Udvardy, Juan Declet-Barreto, and Pamela Worth. *Killer Heat in the United States.* Union of Concerned Scientists (July 2019).

75 Crowley, Kevin, and Rathi, Akshat. "Exxon's Plan for Surging Carbon Emissions Revealed in Leaked Documents." Bloomberg Green (October 5, 2020).

76 International Energy Agency. *The Oil and Gas Industry in Energy Transitions* (January 2020).

77 Krauss, Clifford. "US and European Oil Giants Go Different Ways on Climate Change." *The New York Times* (December 11, 2020).

78 BP. BP *Statistical Review of World Energy 70th Edition.* (July 2021).

79 International Energy Agency. *World Energy Outlook 2022* (October 2022).

80 Krauss, Clifford. "Flood of Oil Is Coming, Complicating Efforts to Fight Global Warming." *The New York Times* (April 13, 2020).

81 US Energy Information Administration. *International Energy Outlook 2021* (October 6, 2021).

82 International Energy Agency. *World Energy Outlook 2016* (2016).

83 International Energy Agency. "Key World Energy Statistics 2021, Supply" (September 2021).

84 International Energy Agency. Coal 2021 (December 2021).

85 International Energy Agency. *World Energy Outlook 2022* (October 2022).

86 International Energy Agency. "Tracking Clean Energy Progress: Coal-Fired Power." (November 2021).

87 Littlecott, Chris, Leo Roberts, Oyku Senlen, Jesse Burton, Madhura Joshi, Christine Shearer, and Matt Ewen. *No New Coal by 2021: The Collapse of the Global Coal Pipeline.* E3G (September 2021).

88 UN Environment Programme. *The Emissions Gap Report 2020* (2020).

89 Urgewald. "NGOs Release the 2020 Global Coal Exit List: 935 Companies that Banks, Investors and Insurers Need to Avoid." (November 12, 2020).

90 Cave, Damien. "In Australia, It's 'Long Live King Coal'." *The New York Times* (October 21, 2021).

91 Zaremba, Haley. "India Won't Be Giving up on Fossil Fuels Any Time Soon," OilPrice.com (August 24, 2021).

92 Shearer, Christine. *Boom and Bust 2020: Tracking the Global Coal Pipeline* (2020).

93 Global Energy Monitor, Global Coal Plant Tracker, 2021.

94 Paybarah, Azi. "China Says It Won't Build New Coal Plants Abroad. What Does That Mean?" *The New York Times* (September 22, 2021).

95 TransitionZero. Turning the Supertanker (April 15, 2021).

96 Harvey, Fiona. "China 'Must Shut 600 Coal-Fired Plants' to Hit Climate Target." *The Guardian* (April 14, 2021).

97 NASEO and EFI. *The 2019 US Energy and Employment Report* (2019).

98 Gladstone, Rick. "Oil Collapse and Covid-19 Create Toxic Geopolitical Stew." *The New York Times* (April 22, 2020).

99 Troianovski, Anton. "On a Pacific Island, Russia Tests Its Battle Plan on Climate Change." *The New York Times* (October 19, 2021).

100 Kramer, Andrew E. "How Russia Is Cashing In on Climate Change." *The New York Times* (October 22, 2021).

101 Lustgarten, Abrahm. "How Russia Wins the Climate Crisis." *The New York Times* (December 16, 2020).

102 Parfenova, Elena, Nadezhda Tchebakova, and Amber Soja. "Assessing Landscape Potential for Human Sustainability and 'Attractiveness' Across Asian Russia in a Warmer 21st Century." *Environmental Research Letters*" (June 7, 2019).

103 Climate Action Tracker. "Russian Federation" (September 20, 2020).

104 CGTN. "China Discovers 900m-Tonne Oil and Gas Field in Xinjiang" (June 18, 2021).

105 Paris Equity Check. Pledged Warming Map (2021).

106 UN Environment Programme et al. *Production Gap Report*, October 2021.

107 Kühne, Kjell, NilsBartsch, Ryan DriskellTated, Julia Higson, and André Habet. "'Carbon Bombs'—Mapping Key Fossil Fuel Projects." *Energy Policy* (May 12, 2022).

108 Oil Change International. *Drilling toward Disaster: Why Oil and Gas Expansion is Incompatible with Climate Limits*, January 2019.

109 Climate TRACE. "More Than 70,000 of the Highest Emitting Greenhouse Gas Sources Identified in Largest Available Global Emissions Inventory." (November 9, 2022).

110 ExxonMobil Corporation. "ExxonMobil to Prioritize Capital Investments on High-Value Assets." (November 30, 2020).

111   Union of Concerned Scientists. What are Tar Sands?

112   Alberta Energy. Oil sands Facts and Statistics.

113   McGlade, Christophe, and Paul Ekins. "The Geographical Distribution of Fossil Fuels Unused When Limiting Global Warming to 2°C." *Nature* 517, no. 7533 (January 7, 2015).

114   Mikulka, Justin. "Analysis: How Exxon Is Being Forced To Accept the Reality Of Bad Fossil Fuel Investments." DeSmog (February 26, 2021).

115   Trans Mountain. Expansion Project.

116   Fountain, Henry. "One Site, 95 Tons of Methane an Hour." *The New York Times* (June 14, 2022).

117   Saunois, Marielle, Ann R. Stavert, Ben Poulter, Philippe Bousquet, Josep G. Canadell, Robert B. Jackson, Peter A. Raymond, Edward J. Dlugokencky, Sander Houweling, Prabir K. Patra et al. "The Global Methane Budget 2000–2017." *Earth Syst. Sci. Data*, 12, no. 3 (July 15, 2020).

118   Global Carbon Project. "Global Methane Budget." (2020).

119   Nisbet, E.G., M. R. Manning, E. J. Dlugokencky, R. E. Fisher, D. Lowry, S. E. Michel, C. Lund Myhre et al. "Very Strong Atmospheric Methane Growth in the Four Years 2014–2017: Implications for the Paris Agreement." *Global Biogeochemical Cycles* (February 5, 2019).

120   NOAA Earth System Monitoring Laboratory. Trends in CH_4. Global Greenhouse Reference Network.

121   Fletcher, Sara Mikaloff and Hinrich Schaefe. "Rising Methane: A New Climate Challenge." *Science* 364, no. 6444 (June 7, 2019).

122   NOAA Global Monitoring Laboratory. Trends in Atmospheric Methane.

123   Cheng, Chin-Hsien and Simon A. T. Redfern. "Impact of Interannual and Multidecadal Trends on Methane-Climate Feedbacks and Sensitivity." *Nature Communications* 13 (June 23, 2022).

124   Ravilious, Kate. "Methane Much More Sensitive to Global Heating than Previously Thought—Study." *The Guardian* (July 5, 2022).

125   Jackson, R. B., M. Saunois, P. Bousquet, J. G. Canadell, B. Poulter, A. R. Stavert, P. Bergamaschi, Y. Niwa, A. Segers, and A. Tsuruta. "Increasing Anthropogenic Methane Emissions Arise Equally From Agricultural and Fossil Fuel Sources." *Environmental Research Letters* (July 15, 2020).

126   Larson, Eric D. *Natural Gas & Climate Change.* Climate Central (May 2013).

127   Brandt, A. R., G. A. Heath, E. A. Kort, F. O'Sullivan, G. Pétron, S. M. Jordaan, P. Tans, J. Wilcox, A. M. Gopstein, D. Arent, S. Wofsy, N. J. Brown, R. Bradley, G. D. Stucky, D. Eardley, and R. Harriss. "Methane Leaks from North American Natural Gas Systems," *Science* 343 (February 14, 2014).

128   Alvarez, Ramón A., Daniel Zavala-Araiza, David R. Lyon, David T. Allen, Zachary R. Barkley, Adam R. Brandt Kenneth J. Davis Scott C. Herndon et al.

"Assessment of Methane Emissions from the U.S. Oil and Gas Supply Chain." *Science* (June 21, 2018).

129 International Energy Agency. "Tracking Clean Energy Progress: Methane Emissions from Oil and Gas." (November 2021).

130 Environmental Defense Fund. Methane Research Series: 16 Studies.

131 Maasakkers, Joannes D., Daniel J. Jacob, Melissa P. Sulprizio, Tia R. Scarpelli, Hannah Nesser, Jianxiong Sheng, Yuzhong Zhang et al. "2010–2015 North American Methane Emissions, Sectoral Contributions, and Trends: A High-Resolution Inversion of GOSAT Observations of Atmospheric Methane," *Atmospheric Chemistry and Physics* 21, no. 6 (March 22, 2021).

132 Tate, Ryan Driskell. *Bigger than Oil or Gas: Sizing up Coal Mine Methane*, Global Energy Monitor (March 2022).

133 Schneising, Oliver, John P. Burrows, Russell R. Dickerson, Michael Buchwitz, Maximilian Reuter, and Heinrich Bovensmann. "Remote Sensing of Fugitive Methane Emissions from Oil and Gas Production in North American Tight Geologic Formations." *Earth's Future* 2 (October 6, 2014).

134 Frazier, Mya. "Gas Companies Are Abandoning Their Wells, Leaving Them to Leak Methane Forever." Bloomberg Green (September 17, 2020).

135 Groom, Nichola. "Special Report: Millions of Abandoned Oil Wells Are Leaking Methane, a Climate Menace," Reuters, June 16, 2020.

136 Seo, Hannah, "Unplugged: Abandoned Oil and Gas Wells Leave the Ocean Floor Spewing Methane." *Environmental Health News* (December 8, 2020).

137 Howarth, Robert W. "Ideas and Perspectives: Is Shale Gas a Major Driver of Recent Increase in Global Atmospheric Methane?" *Biogeosciences* 16, no. 15 (August 14, 2019).

138 EPA. "Assessment of the Potential Impacts of Hydraulic Fracturing for Oil and Gas on Drinking Water Resources." (June 2015).

139 Earthworks. "Hydraulic Fracturing 101."

140 US Geological Survey. "Does the production of oil and gas from shales cause earthquakes? If so, how are the earthquakes related to these operations?"

141 Gas Drilling Awareness Coalition. "Light Your Water On Fire from Gas Drilling, Fracking." (December 10, 2011).

142 Buckingham, Jerry, "A RIVER ON FIRE! Gas explodes from Australian river near fracking site" (April 22, 2016).

143 Concerned Health Professionals of New York, Physicians for Social Responsibility, *Compendium of Scientific, Medical, and Media Findings Demonstrating Risks and Harms of Fracking (Unconventional Gas and Oil Extraction) Sixth Edition* (June 19, 2019).

144 Hausfather, Zeke. "Bounding the Climate Viability of Natural Gas as a Bridge Fuel to Displace Coal." *Energy Policy* 86 (November 2015).

145 Ingraffea, Anthony R. "Gangplank to a Warm Future." *The New York Times* (July 28, 2013).

146 Newell, Richard G. and Daniel Raimi. "Implications of Shale Gas Development for Climate Change." *Environmental Science and Technology* 48, no. 15 (April 22, 2014).

147 Eaton, Collin. "Oil Frackers Brace for End of the U.S. Shale Boom." *The Wall Street Journal* (February 3, 2022).

148 Deemer, Bridget, John A. Harrison, Siyue Li, Jake J. Beaulieu, Tonya DelSontro, Nathan Barros, José F. Bezerra-Neto, Stephen M. Powers, Marco A. dos Santos, and J. Arie Vonk. "Greenhouse Gas Emissions from Reservoir Water Surfaces: A New Global Synthesis." *BioScience* 66, no. 11 (October 5, 2016).

149 Zarfl, Christiane, Alexander E. Lumsdon, Jürgen Berlekamp, Laura Tydecks, and Klement Tockner. "A Global Boom in Hydropower Dam Construction." *Aquatic Sciences"* 77, no. 1 (October 25, 2014).

150 Columbia Center on Global Energy Policy. "Power of the River: Introducing the Global Dam Tracker (GDAT)," November 19, 2018.

151 Latrubesse, Edgardo et al., "Damming the Rivers of the Amazon Basin." *Nature* 546 (June 14, 2017).

152 Griesse, Rachel. "Hydroelectric Dams May Jeopardize the Amazon's Future." University of Texas news (June 14, 2017).

153 Fearnside, Philip. "How a Dam Building Boom Is Transforming the Brazilian Amazon." Yale Environment 360 (September 26, 2017).

154 Yvon-Durocher, Gabriel, Chris J. Hulatt, Guy Woodward, and Mark Trimmer. "Long-Term Warming Amplifies Shifts in the Carbon Cycle of Experimental Ponds." *Nature Climate Change* 7 (February 20, 2017).

155 US Department of State. "European Union, and Partners Formally Launch Global Methane Pledge to Keep 1.5C Within Reach." (November 2, 2021).

156 Rainforest Action Network et al. *Banking on Climate Change: Fossil Fuel Finance Report 2020* (March 18, 2020).

157 International Energy Agency. Fossil-Fuel Subsidies.

158 BloombergNEF. *Climate Policy Factbook* (July 20, 2021).

159 Parry, Ian, Simon Black, and Nate Vernon. "Still Not Getting Energy Prices Right: A Global and Country Update of Fossil Fuel Subsidies." International Monetary Fund Working Paper (September 24, 2021).

160 Environmental and Energy Study Institute. Fact Sheet: Fossil Fuel Subsidies: A Closer Look at Tax Breaks and Societal Costs (July 29, 2019).

161 Krauss, Clifford. "Global Governments, Loath to Change, are Wasting Oil with Subsidies." *The New York Times* (October 18, 2016).

162 Oil Change International. "Dirty Energy Dominance: Dependent on Denial—How the US Fossil Fuel Industry Depends on Subsidies and Climate Denial." (October 2017).

163 Oil Change International. "Subsidies: Propping up Oil Profits & Polluting the Climate." (January 2017).

164 Overseas Development Institute. *Statement: Implementation of G20 Commitment to Phase-Out Fossil Fuel Subsidies.*

165 Overseas Development Institute. "MEDIA NOTE: Major insurers urge G20 leaders to commit to 2020 fossil fuel subsidy phase out." (August 29, 2016).

166 Jewell, Jessica, David McCollum, Johannes Emmerling, Christoph Bertram, David E. H. J. Gernaat, Volker Krey, Leonidas Paroussos et al. "Limited Emission Reductions From Fuel Subsidy Removal Except In Energy-Exporting Regions." *Nature* 554 (February 8, 2018).

167 Jenkins, McKay. "The Road to Fossil Fuel Dependence." *Undark* (January 30, 2017).

168 Bolton, Patrick, Morgan Despres, Luiz Awazu Pereira Da Silva, Frédéric Samama, and Romain Svartzman. "The Green Swan: Central Banking and Financial Stability in the Age of Climate Change." Bank for International Settlements (January 2020).

169 International Energy Agency. *Energy Technology Perspectives 2020: Special Report on Clean Energy Innovation* (2020).

170 International Energy Agency. "The Challenge of Reaching Zero Emissions in Heavy Industry." (September 19, 2020).

171 Victor, David G., Frank W. Geels, and Simon Sharpe. *Accelerating the Low Carbon Transition.* Energy Transitions Commission (2019).

172 IPCC. *Climate Change 2022: Mitigation of Climate Change, Summary for Policymakers.* From *Climate Change 2022: Mitigation of Climate Change* (April 4, 2022).

173 Welsby, Dan, James Price, Steve Pye, and Paul Ekins. "Unextractable Fossil Fuels in a 1.5 °C World." *Nature* 497 (September 8, 2021).

174 Trout, Kelly, Greg Muttitt, Dimitri Lafleur, Thijs Van de Graaf, Roman Mendelevitch, Lan Mei and Malte Meinshausen. "Existing Fossil Fuel Extraction Would Warm the World beyond 1.5 °C." *Environmental Research Letters* 16, no. 6 (May 17, 2022).

175 McGlade, Christophe, and Paul Ekins. "The Geographical Distribution of Fossil Fuels Unused When Limiting Global Warming to 2°C." *Nature* 517, no. 7533 (January 7, 2015).

176 Semieniuk, Gregor, Philip B. Holden, Jean-Francois Mercure, Pablo Salas, Hector Pollitt, Katharine Jobson, Pim Vercoulen, Unnada Chewpreecha, Neil R. Edwards,

and Jorge E. Viñuales. "Stranded Fossil-Fuel Assets Translate to Major Losses for Investors in Advanced Economies." *Nature Climate Change* (May 26, 2022).

177 Tooze, Adam. "Why Central Banks Need to Step up on Global Warming." *Foreign Policy* (July 20, 2019).

178 Tienhaara, Kyla, Rachel Thrasherb, Alexander Simmons, and Kevin P. Gallagher. "Investor-State Disputes Threaten the Global Green Energy Transition." *Science* 376, no. 6594 (May 5, 2022).

179 Walsh, Brian, Philippe Ciais, Ivan A. Janssens, Josep Peñuelas, Keywan Riahi, Felicjan Rydzak, Detlef P. van Vuuren, and Michael Obersteiner. "Pathways for Balancing CO_2 Emissions and Sinks." *Nature Communications* 8 (April 13, 2017).

180 Rockström, Johan, Hans Joachim Schellnhuber, Brian Hoskins, Veerabhadran Ramanathan, Peter Schlosser, Guy Pierre Brasseur, Owen Gaffney, Carlos Nobre, Malte Meinshausen, Joeri Rogelj, and Wolfgang Lucht. "The World's Biggest Gamble." *Earth's Future* 4, no. 10 (October 27, 2016).

181 Jones, Nicola. "How the World Passed a Carbon Threshold and Why It Matters." Yale Environment 360 (January 26, 2017).

182 University of Hamburg Climate. *Hamburg Climate Futures Outlook.* (June 10, 2021).

183 Hedemann, Christopher, Eduardo Gresse, and Jan Petzold. "Global Warming Below 1.7°C Is 'Not Plausible', Reveals Our Study of the Social Drivers of Decarbonization." *The Conversation* (June 24, 2021).

184 International Energy Agency. "Achieving Net-Zero Emissions by 2050." *World Energy Outlook 2020* (October 2020).

185 Princeton University. *Net-Zero America: Potential Pathways, Infrastructure, and Impacts* (December 15, 2020).

186 Sustainable Development Solutions Network. *America's Zero Carbon Action Plan* (2020).

187 International Renewable Energy Agency. *Global Renewables Outlook: Energy Transformation 2050* (April 2020).

188 Tong, Dan, Qiang Zhang, Yixuan Zheng, Ken Caldeira, Christine Shearer, Chaopeng Hong, Yue Qin, and Steven J. Davis. "Committed Emissions from Existing Energy Infrastructure Jeopardize 1.5°C Climate Target." *Nature* 572 (July 1, 2019).

189 UC Irvine. "'Committed' CO_2 Emissions Jeopardize International Climate Goals, UCI-Led Study Finds." news release (July 1, 2019).

190 Pfeiffer, Alexander, Cameron Hepburn, Adrien Vogt-Schilb, and Ben Caldecott. "Committed Emissions from Existing and Planned Power Plants and Asset Stranding Required to Meet the Paris Agreement." *Environmental Research Letters* 13 (May 4, 2018).

191 MIT Joint Program on the Science and Policy of Global Change. *2018 Food, Water, Energy & Climate Outlook* (2018).

192 Drouet, Laurent, Valentina Bosetti, Simone A. Padoan, Lara Aleluia Reis, Christoph Bertram, Francesco Dalla Longa, Jacques Després et al. "Net Zero-Emission Pathways Reduce the Physical and Economic Risks of Climate Change." *Nature Climate Change* 11 (November 29, 2021).

193 Rahi, Keywan, Christoph Bertram, Daniel Huppmann, Joeri Rogelj, Valentina Bosetti, Anique-Marie Cabardos, Andre Deppermann et al. "Cost and Attainability of Meeting Stringent Climate Targets without Overshoot." *Nature Climate Change* 11 (November 29, 2021).

194 IPCC, *Climate Change 2022: Impacts, Adaptation and Vulnerability: Summary for Policymakers*. From: IPCC Sixth Assessment Report: Impacts, Adaptation and Vulnerability. (February 27, 2022).

195 BloombergNEF. *Hydrogen Economy Outlook, Key Messages* (March 30, 2020).

196 Office of Energy Efficiency & Renewable Energy. Hydrogen Pipelines.

197 Elberry, Ahmed M., Jagruti Thakur, Annukka Santasalo-Aarnio, and Martti Larmia. "Large-Scale Compressed Hydrogen Storage as Part of Renewable Electricity Storage System." *International Journal of Hydrogen Energy* 46, no. 29 (April26, 2021).

198 Livermore, Stephen. "Exploring the Potential for Domestic Hydrogen Appliances." *The Engineer* (May 2018).

199 World Nuclear Association. Transport and the Hydrogen Economy (October 2018,).

200 Friedmann, Julio, Zhiyuan Fan, and Ke Tang. "Low-Carbon Heat Solutions for Heavy Industry: Sources, Options, and Costs Today." Columbia University Center on Global Energy Policy (October 7, 2019.)

201 International Energy Agency. *Global Hydrogen Review 2021* (October 2021).

202 International Renewable Energy Agency. *Global Renewables Outlook: Energy Transformation 2050* (April 2020).

203 International Renewable Energy Agency. *Global Renewables Outlook: Energy Transformation 2050* (April 2020).

204 Webber, Michael, E., "The Water Intensity of the Transitional Hydrogen Economy," *Environmental Research Letters* (September 6, 2007).

205 Slav, Irina. "The Green Hydrogen Problem That No One Is Talking About." OilPrice.com (October 28, 2020).

206 US Department of Energy. *Department of Energy Hydrogen Program Plan* (November 2020).

207 Loftus, Peter J., Armond M. Cohen, Jane C. S. Long, and Jesse D. Jenkins. "A Critical Review of Global Decarbonization Scenarios: What do they Tell us About Feasibility?" *WIREs Climate Change* 6 (January/February 2015).

208   Sinn, Hans-Werner. "The Green Paradox: A Supply-side View of the Climate Problem." *Review of Environmental Economics and Policy* 9, no. 2 (July 2015).

209   Samset, B. H., J. S Fuglestvedt, and M. T. Lund. "Delayed Emergence of a Global Temperature Response after Emission Mitigation." *Nature Communications* 11 (July 7, 2020).

210   Dreyfus, Gabrielle B., Yangyang Xu, Drew T. Shindell, Durwood Zaelke, and Veerabhadran Ramanathan. "Mitigating Climate Disruption in Time: A Self-Consistent Approach for Avoiding both Near-Term and Long-Term Global Warming." *Proceedings of the National Academy of Sciences* 119, no 22 (May 23, 2022).

211   Frölicher, Thomas Lukas, Michael Winton, and Jorge Louis Sarmiento. "Continued Global Warming After CO_2 Emissions Stoppage." *Nature Climate Change* 4 (November 24, 2013).

212   Radford, Tim. "Global Warming 'Hard to Reverse' Say Scientists." Climate News Network (November 28, 2013).

213   Samset, B. H., M. Sand, C. J. Smith, S. E. Bauer, P. M. Forster, J. S. Fuglestvedt, S. Osprey, C.-F. Schleussner. "Climate Impacts from a Removal of Anthropogenic Aerosol Emissions." *Geophysical Research Letters* 45, no. 2 (January 8, 2018).

214   Samset, Bjørn Hallvard. "How Cleaner Air Changes the Climate," *Science* 360, no. 6385 (April 13, 2018).

215   Takemura, Toshihiko. "Return To Different Climate States by Reducing Sulphate Aerosols under Future CO_2 Concentrations." *Scientific Reports* 10 (December 10, 2020).

216   Schiffman, Richard. "How Air Pollution Has Put a Brake on Global Warming." Yale Environment 360 (March 8, 2018).

217   NOAA. The NOAA Annual Greenhouse Gas Index (2020).

218   Readfearn, Graham. "Earth's Climate Monsters Could be Unleashed as Temperatures Rise." *The Guardian* (October 5, 2018.)

219   IPCC. *Climate Change 2021: The Physical Science Basis. Chapter 4: Future Global Climate: Scenario-Based Projections and Near-Term Information* From: *Climate Change 2021: The Physical Science Basis* (August 9, 2021).

220   McKay, David I. Armstrong, Arie Staal, Jesse F. Abrams, Ricarda Winkelmann, Boris Sakschewski, Sina Loriani, Xingo Fetzer, Sarah E. Cornell, Johan Rockström, and Timothy M. Lenton. "Exceeding 1.5°C Global Warming Could Trigger Multiple Climate Tipping Points." *Science* 377, no 6611 (September 9, 2022).

221   Stockholm University. "Risk of Multiple Climate Tipping Points Escalates above 1.5°C Global Warming." EurekAlert! (September 8, 2022).

222   Wunderling, Nico, Jonathan F. Donges, Jürgen Kurths, and Ricarda Winkelmann. "Interacting Tipping Elements Increase Risk of Climate Domino Effects under Global Warming." *Earth System Dynamics* 12 (June 3, 2021).

223 Carrington, Damian. "Climate Tipping Points Could Topple Like Dominoes, Warn Scientists" *The Guardian* (June 3, 2021).

224 Tobie, Gabriel, Jonathan I. Lunine, and Christophe Sotin. "Episodic Outgassing as the Origin of Atmospheric Methane on Titan." *Nature* 440 (March 2, 2006).

225 Anderson, Richard. "Methane Hydrate: Dirty Fuel or Energy Saviour?" BBC News (April 17, 2014).

226 World Ocean Review. "Climate Change Impacts on Methane Hydrates."

227 Johnson, Paul H., Una K. Miller, Marie S. Salmi, and Evan A. Solomon. "Analysis of Bubble Plume Distributions to Evaluate Methane Hydrate Decomposition on the Continental Slope." *Geochemistry, Geophysics, Geosystems* 16 no. 11 (November 15, 2015.)

228 American Geophysical Union. "Bubble Plumes off Washington, Oregon Suggest Warmer Ocean May be Releasing Frozen Methane." (October 14, 2015).

229 Hautala, Susan, Evan A. Solomon, H. Paul Johnson, Robert N. Harris, and Una K. Miller. "Dissociation of Cascadia Margin Gas Hydrates in Response to Contemporary Ocean Warming." *Geophysical Research Letters* 41, no. 23 (December 16, 2014).

230 Skarke, A., C. Ruppel, M. Kodis, D. Brothers, and E. Lobecker. "Widespread Methane Leakage from the Sea Floor on the Northern US Atlantic Margin." *Nature Geoscience* 7 August 24, 2014).

231 Ruppel, Carolyn, and John Kessler. "The Interaction of Climate Change and Methane Hydrates." *Reviews of Geophysics* 55, no. 1 (December 14, 2016).

232 Robock, Alan. "Could Subsea Methane Hydrates Be a Warming 'Tipping Point'?" *EOS* (April 13, 2017).

233 NASA Earth Observatory. "Batagaika Crater Expands." (June 7, 2016).

234 Stone, Richard. "Siberia's 'Gateway to the Underworld' Grows as Record Heat Wave Thaws Permafrost." *Science* (July 28, 2020).

235 Tesi, T., F. Muschitiello, R. H. Smittenberg, M. Jakobsson, J. E. Vonk, P. Hill, A. Andersson et al. "Massive Remobilization Of Permafrost Carbon during Post-Glacial Warming." *Nature Communications* (November 26, 2016).

236 Tarnocai, C., J. G. Canadell, E. A. G. Schuur, P. Kuhry, G. Mazhitova, and S. Zimov. "Soil Organic Pools in the Northern Circumpolar Permafrost Region." *Global Biogeochemical Cycles* 23, no. 2 (June 2009).

237 Farquharson, Louise M., Vladimir E. Romanovsky, William L. Cable, Donald A. Walker, Steven V. Kokelj, and Dmitry Nicolsky. "Climate Change Drives Widespread and Rapid Thermokarst Development in Very Cold Permafrost in the Canadian High Arctic." *Geophysical Research Letters* (June 10, 2019).

238 Liljedahl, Anna K., Julia Boike, Ronald P. Daanen, Alexander N. Fedorov, Gerald V. Frost, Guido Grosse, Larry D. Hinzman et al. "Pan-Arctic Ice-Wedge

Degradation in Warming Permafrost and its Influence on Tundra Hydrology." *Nature GeoScience* 9 (March 14, 2016).

239 Mooney, Chris. "The Arctic is Thawing Much Faster than Expected, Scientists Warn." *The Washington Post* (March 23, 2016).

240 Pastick, Neal J., M. Torre, Jorgenson, Bruce K. Wylie, Shawn J. Niel, Kristofer D. Johnson, and Andrew O.Finley. "Distribution of Near-Surface Permafrost in Alaska: Estimates of Present and Future Conditions." *Remote Sensing of Environment* 168 (October 2015).

241 AFP. "Russia May Lose 30 Percent of Permafrost by 2050: Official" (July 29, 2011).

242 Schaefer, Kevin, Tingjun Zhang, Lori Bruhwiler, and Andrew P. Barrett. "Amount and Timing of Permafrost Carbon Release in Response to Climate Warming." *Tellus B* 63 no. 2 (February 15, 2011).

243 Commane, Róisín. "Carbon Dioxide Sources from Alaska Driven By Increasing Early Winter Respiration from Arctic Tundra." *Proceedings of the National Academy of Sciences* 114, no. 2 (May 23, 2017).

244 Turetsky, Merritt R., Benjamin W. Abbott, Miriam C. Jones, Katey Walter Anthony, David Olefeldt, Edward A. G. Schuur, Charles Koven et al. "Permafrost Collapse is Accelerating Carbon Release." *Nature* (April 30, 2019).

245 Anthony, Katey Walter, Thomas Schneider von Deimling, Ingmar Nitze, Steve Frolking, Abraham Emond, Ronald Daanen, Peter Anthony, Prajna Lindgren, Benjamin Jones, and Guido Grosse. "21st-Century Modeled Permafrost Carbon Emissions Accelerated by Abrupt Thaw beneath Lakes." *Nature Communications* (August 15, 2018).

246 Anthony, Katey Walter, Ronald Daanen, Peter Anthony, Thomas Schneider von Deimling, Chien-Lu Ping, Jeffrey P. Chanton, and Guido Grosse. "Methane Emissions Proportional to Permafrost Carbon Thawed in Arctic Lakes since the 1950s." *Nature Geoscience* 9 (August 22, 2016).

247 Chadburn, S. E., E. J. Burke, P. M. Cox, P. Friedlingstein, G. Hugelius, and S. Westermann. "An Observation-Based Constraint on Permafrost Loss as a Function of Global Warming." *Nature Climate Change* 7 (April 10, 2017).

248 Shakhova, Natalia, Igor Semiletov, Anatoly Salyuk, Vladimir Yusupov, Denis Kosmach, and Örjan Gustafsson. "Extensive Methane Venting to the Atmosphere from Sediments of the East Siberian Arctic Shelf." *Science* 327, no. 5970 (March 5, 2010).

249 Shakhova, Natalia, Igor Semiletov, Orjan Gustafsson, Valentin Sergienko, Leopold Lobkovsky, Oleg Dudarev, Vladimir Tumskoy et al. "Current Rates and Mechanisms of Subsea Permafrost Degradation in the East Siberian Arctic Shelf." *Nature Communications* 8 (June 22, 2017).

250 Tomsk Polytechnic University. "Russian Scientists Deny Climate Model of IPCC." EurekAlert! (August 15, 2017).

251 Breeze, Nick. "Interview by Nick Breeze with Dr Natalia Shakhova and Dr Igor Semiletov." EnvisioNation (April 2017).

252 Romm, Joseph. *Climate Change: What Everyone Needs to Know? Second edition*, Oxford University Press (2018).

253 Weber, Bob. "Ancient Carbon Seeping from Permafrost Could Set off Climate Change Bomb." *The Canadian Press* (August 24, 2016).

254 Page, Susan E., Florian Siegert, John O. Rieley, Hans-Dieter V. Boehm, Adi Jaya, and Suwido Limin. "The Amount of Carbon Released From Peat and Forest Fires in Indonesia during 1997." *Nature* 420 (November 7, 2002).

255 Koplitz, Shannon N., Loretta J Mickley, Miriam E Marlier, Jonathan J Buonocore, Patrick S Kim, Tianjia Liu, Melissa P Sulprizio et al. "Public Health Impacts of the Severe Haze In Equatorial Asia In September–October 2015: Demonstration of a New Framework for Informing Fire Management Strategies to Reduce Downwind Smoke Exposure." *Environmental Research Letters* 11, no. 9 (September 19, 2016).

256 Turetsky, Merritt R., Brian Benscoter, Susan Page, Guillermo Rein, Guido R. van der Werf, and Adam Watts. "Global Vulnerability of Peatlands to Fire and Carbon Loss," *Nature Geoscience* 8 (December 23, 2014).

257 Dargie, Greta C., Simon L. Lewis, Ian T. Lawson, Edward T. A. Mitchard, Susan E. Page, Yannick E. Bocko, and Suspense A. Ifo. "Age, Extent and Carbon Storage of the Central Congo Basin Peatland Complex." *Nature* 542 (January 11, 2017).

258 Lewis, Simon, and Greta Dargie. "How We Discovered the World's Largest Tropical Peatland, Deep in the Jungles of Congo." *The Conversation* (January 11, 2017).

259 Yin, Yi, Philippe Ciais, Frederic Chevallier, Guido R. van der Werf, Thierry Fanin, Gregoire Broquet, Hartmut Boesch et al. "Variability of Fire Carbon Emissions in Equatorial Asia and Its Nonlinear Sensitivity to El Niño." *Geophysical Research Letters* 43, no. 9 (October 9, 2016).

260 Higuera, Philip, Melissa L. Chipman, Jennifer L. Barnes, Michael A. Urban, and Feng Sheng Hu. "Variability of Tundra Fire Regimes in Arctic Alaska; Millennial-Scale Patterns and Ecological Implications." *Ecological Applications* 21, no. 8 (December 2011).

261 Young, Adam M., Philip E. Higuera, Paul A. Duffy, and Feng Sheng Hu. "Climatic Thresholds Shape Northern High-Latitude Fire Regimes and Imply Vulnerability to Future Climate Change." *Ecography* (April 9, 2016).

262 Cormier, Zoe. "The Arctic Will Burn." New Internationalist blog (December 21, 2011).

263 Crowther, T.W., K. E. O. Todd-Brown, C. W. Rowe, W. R. Wieder, J. C. Carey, M. B. Machmuller, B. L. Snoek et al. "Quantifying Global Soil Carbon Losses in Response to Warming." *Nature* 540, no. 7631 (November 30, 2016).

264 Mooney, Chris. "Scientists Have Long Feared This 'Feedback' to the Climate System. Now They Say It's Happening." *The Washington Post* (November 30, 2016).

265 Dennehy, Kevin. "Losses of Soil Carbon under Global Warming Might Equal US Emissions." *Yale News* (November 30, 2016).

266 Melillo, J. M., S. D. Frey, M. Deangelis, W. J. Werner, M. J. Bernard, F. P. Bowles, G. Pold, M. A. Knorr, and A. S. Grandy. "Long-Term Pattern and Magnitude of Soil Carbon Feedback to the Climate System in a Warming World." *Science* 358 (October 6, 2017).

267 Mooney, Chris. "One of the Oldest Climate Change Experiments Has Led to a Troubling Conclusion." *The Washington Post* (October 5, 2017).

268 Hicks Pries, Caitlin E., C. Castanha, R. C. Porras, and M. S. Torn. "The Whole-Soil Carbon Flux in Response to Warming." *Science* 355, no. 6332 (March 31, 2017).

269 Carey, Johanna C., Jianwu Tang, Pamela H. Templer, Kevin D. Kroeger, Thomas W. Crowther, Andrew J. Burton, Jeffrey S. Dukes et al. "Temperature Response of Soil Respiration Largely Unaltered With Experimental Warming." *Proceedings of the National Academy of Sciences* 113, no. 48 (November 29, 2016).

270 Kergo, Denise. "MBL Study Finds Limited Sign of Soil Adaptation to Climate Warming." University of Chicago Marine Biological Laboratory (November 14, 2016).

271 Cavicchioli, Ricardo, William J. Ripple, Kenneth N. Timmis, Farooq Azam, Lars R. Bakken, Matthew Baylis, Michael J. Behrenfeld et al. "Scientists' Warning to Humanity: Microorganisms and Climate Change." *Nature Reviews* (June 18, 2019).

272 World Meteorological Organization. *State of the Global Climate 2021* (2022).

273 IPCC. *Climate Change 2021: The Physical Science Basis, Summary for Policymakers* From: *Climate Change 2021: The Physical Science Basis* (August 7, 2021).

274 Hood, Marlowe. "Earth Warming More Quickly Than Thought, New Climate Models Show." Phys.org (September 17, 2019).

275 Raftery, Adrian E., Alec Zimmer, Dargan M. W. Frierson, Richard Startz, and Peiran Liu. "Less Than 2 °C Warming By 2100 Unlikely." *Nature Climate Change* 7 (July 31, 2017).

276 Brown, Patrick T. and Ken Caldeira. "Greater Future Global Warming Inferred from Earth's Recent Energy Budget." *Nature* 552 (December 6, 2017).

277 Universal Ecological Fund. *The Truth about Climate Change* (September 2016).

278 MIT Joint Program on the Science and Policy of Global Change. *2018 Food, Water, Energy & Climate Outlook* (2018).

279 Sims, Andrew. "'A Cat in Hell's Chance'—Why We're Losing the Battle to Keep Global Warming Below 2C." *The Guardian* (January 19, 2017).

280 Sanderson, Benjamin et al. "What Would It Take To Achieve The Paris Temperature Targets?" *Geophysical Research Letters* 43, no. 13 (January 28, 2017).

281 Friedrich, Tobias, Axel Timmermann, Michelle Tigchelaar, Oliver Elison Timm, and Andrey Ganopolski. "Nonlinear Climate Sensitivity and Its Implications for Future Greenhouse Warming." *Science Advances* 2, no. 11 (November 9, 2016).

282 University of Hawaii at Manoa. "A Warm Climate is More Sensitive to Changes in Atmospheric CO_2." Phys.org (November 9, 2016).

283 Schneider, Tapio, Colleen M. Kaul, and Kyle G. Pressel. "Possible Climate Transitions from Breakup of Stratocumulus Decks under Greenhouse Warming." *Nature Geoscience* 12 (February 25, 2019).

284 Loeb, Norman G., Gregory C. Johnson, Tyler J. Thorsen, John M. Lyman, Fred G. Rose, and Seiji Kato. "Satellite and Ocean Data Reveal Marked Increase in Earth's Heating Rate." *Geophysical Research Letters* (June 15, 2021).

285 NASA. "Joint NASA, NOAA Study Finds Earth's Energy Imbalance Has Doubled" (June 15, 2021).

286 Parag Khanna. The World 4 Degrees Warmer (February 1, 2016).

287 GreenFacts. "Impacts of a 4°C Global Warming." (2012).

288 National Research Council. *Climate Stabilization Targets: Emissions Concentrations and Impacts over Decades to Millennia* (2011).

289 Warren, Rachel. "The Role of Interactions in a World Implementing Adaptation and Mitigation Solutions to Climate Change," *Philosophical Transactions of the Royal Society A* 369, no. 1934 (January 13, 2011).

290 Tokarska, Katarzyna, Nathan P. Gillett, Andrew J. Weaver, Vivek K. Arora, and Michael Eby. "The Climate Response to Five Trillion Tonnes of Carbon." *Nature Climate Change* 6 (May 23, 2016).

291 Jardine, Phil. "Patterns in Palaeontology: The Paleocene–Eocene Thermal Maximum." *Palaeontology* 1 (January 1, 2011).

292 Cui, Ying, Lee R. Kump, Andy J. Ridgwell, Adam J. Charles, Christopher K. Junium, Aaron F. Diefendorf, Katherine H. Freeman, Nathan M. Urban, and Ian C. Harding. "Slow Release of Fossil Carbon during the Palaeocene–Eocene Thermal Maximum." *Nature Geoscience* 4 (June 5, 2011).

293 Gingerich, Philip D. "Temporal Scaling of Carbon Emission and Accumulation Rates: Modern Anthropogenic Emissions Compared to Estimates of PETM-Onset Accumulation." *Paleoceanography and Paleoclimatology* (January 30, 2019).

294 American Geophysical Union. "Earth May Be 140 Years Away from Reaching Carbon Levels Not Seen in 56 Million Years." (February 20, 2019).

295 Zeebe, Richard E., Andy Ridgwell, and James C. Zachos. "Anthropogenic Carbon Release Rate Unprecedented During the Past 66 Million Years." *Nature Geoscience* 9 (March 21, 2016).

296 Zeebe, Richard E., James C. Zachos, and Gerald R. Dickens. "Carbon Dioxide Forcing Alone Insufficient to Explain Palaeocene–Eocene Thermal Maximum Warming." *Nature Geoscience* 2 (July 13, 2009).

297 Naafs, B. D. A., M. Rohrssen, G. N. Inglis, O. Lähteenoja, S. J. Feakins, M. E. Collinson, E. M. Kennedy, P. K. Singh, M. P. Singh, D. J. Lunt, and R. D. Pancost. "High Temperatures in the Terrestrial Mid-Latitudes during the Early Palaeogene." *Nature Geoscience* 11 (July 30, 2018).

298 US Global Change Research Program. *Fourth National Climate Assessment* (2018).

299 World Bank. *Turn down the Heat: Why a 4°c Warmer World Must be Avoided* (2012).

300 EPA. *Climate Change Indicators in the United States 2016, Fourth Edition* (2016)

301 Taillant, Jorge Daniel. *Meltdown: The Earth Without Glaciers.* Oxford University Press, 2021.

302 Hugonnet, Romain, Robert McNabb, Etienne Berthier, Brian Menounos, Christopher Nuth, Luc Girod, Daniel Farinotti et al. "Accelerated Global Glacier Mass Loss in the Early Twenty-First Century." *Nature* 592 (April 28, 2021).

303 IPCC. *Climate Change 2021: The Physical Science Basis, Summary for Policymakers* From: *Climate Change 2021: The Physical Science Basis* (August 7, 2021).

304 Lee, Ethan, Jonathan L. Carrivick, Duncan J. Quincey, Simon J. Cook, William H. M. James, and Lee E. Brown. "Accelerated Mass Loss of Himalayan Glaciers since the Little Ice Age." *Scientific Reports* 11 (December 20, 2021).

305 Maurer, J.M., J. M. Schaefer, S. Rupper, and A. Corley. "Acceleration of Ice Loss across the Himalayas over the Past 40 Years." *Science Advances* 5, no. 6 (June 19, 2019).

306 Krajick, Kevin. "Melting of Himalayan Glaciers Has Doubled in Recent Years." Columbia Climate School (June 19, 2019).

307 Kraaijenbrink, P. D. A., M. F. P. Bierkens, A. F. Lutz, and W. W. Immerzeel. "Impact of a Global Temperature Rise of 1.5 Degrees Celsius on Asia's Glaciers." *Nature* 549 (September 13, 2017).

308 Lutz, Stefanie. "The Biogeography of Red Snow Microbiomes and Their Role in Melting Arctic Glaciers." *Nature* 7 (June 22, 2016).

309 Khan, Alia L., Heidi Dierssen, Joshua P. Schwarz, Carl Schmitt, Adam Chlus, Mark Hermanson, Thomas H. Painter, and Diane M. McKnight. "Impacts of Coal Dust From an Active Mine on the Spectral Reflectance of Arctic Surface Snow

in Svalbard, Norway." *Journal of Geophysical Research: Atmospheres* 122, no. 3 (February 3, 2017).

310 Arctic Mapping and Assessment Programme. *Snow, Water, Ice and Permafrost. Summary for Policy-makers* (2017).

311 Slater, Thomas, Isobel R. Lawrence1, Inès N. Otosaka1, Andrew Shepherd, Noel Gourmelen, Livia Jakob, Paul Tepes, Lin Gilbert, and Peter Nienow. "Review Article: Earth's Ice Imbalance." *The Cryosphere* 15 (January 25, 2021).

312 European Space Agency. "Greenland and Antarctica Losing Ice Six Times Faster Than Expected" (March 3, 2020).

313 The IMBIE Team. "Mass Balance of the Greenland Ice Sheet from 1992 to 2017." *Nature* 579 (June 13, 2018).

314 The IMBIE Team. "Mass Balance of the Greenland Ice Sheet from 1992 to 2018." *Nature* 558 (December 10, 2019).

315 European Space Agency. "Our World Is Losing Ice at Record Rate"(January 25, 2021).

316 ICCI. *State of the Cryosphere Report 2022* (November 2022).

317 IPCC. *Climate Change 2021: The Physical Science Basis, Summary for Policymakers* From: *Climate Change 2021: The Physical Science Basis* (August 7, 2021).

318 Rahmstorf, Stefan, Jason E. Box, Georg Feulner, Michael E. Mann, Alexander Robinson, Scott Rutherford, and Erik J. Schaffernicht. "Exceptional Twentieth-Century Slowdown in Atlantic Ocean Overturning Circulation." *Nature Climate Change* 5 (March 23, 2015).

319 Lindsey, Rebecca. Understanding the Polar Vortex. NOAA (March 5, 2021).

320 Stockholm Environment Institute. *Arctic Resilience Report* (November 25, 2016).

321 NOAA Arctic Program. *Arctic Report Card.*

322 National Snow & Ice Data Center. Quick Facts on Arctic Sea Ice.

323 Notz, Dirk, and Julienne Stroeve. "Observed Arctic Sea-Ice Loss Directly Follows Anthropogenic CO_2 Emission." *Science* 354, no. 6313 (November 11, 2016).

324 Screen, J.A. and C. Deser. "Pacific Ocean Variability Influences the Time of Emergence of a Seasonally Ice-Free Arctic Ocean." *Geophysical Research Letters* (February 5, 2019).

325 Landrum, Laura, and Marika M. Holland. "Extremes Become Routine in an Emerging New Arctic." *Nature Climate Change* 10 (September 14, 2020).

326 National Snow & Ice Data Center. Arctic vs. Antarctic.

327 Lai, Ching-Yao, Jonathan Kingslake, Martin G. Wearing, Po-Hsuan Cameron Chen, Pierre Gentine, Harold Li, Julian J. Spergel, and J. Melchior van Wessem. "Vulnerability of Antarctica's Ice Shelves to Meltwater-Driven Fracture." *Nature* 584 (August 26, 2020).

328 NASA. Massive Iceberg Breaks off From Antarctica (July 12, 2017).

329 Turner, Ben. "World's Largest Iceberg Breaks off of Antarctica." Live Science (May 19, 2021).

330 Khazendar, Ala, Eric Rignot, Dustin M. Schroeder, Helene Seroussi, Michael P. Schodlok, Bernd Scheuchl, Jeremie Mouginot, Tyler C. Sutterley, and Isabella Velicogna. "Rapid Submarine Ice Melting In the Grounding Zones of Ice Shelves in West Antarctica." *Nature Communications* 7 (October 25, 2016).

331 Silvano, Alessandro, Stephen Rich Rintoul, Beatriz Peña-Molino, William Richard Hobbs, Esmee Van Wijk, Shigeru Aoki, Takeshi Tamura, and Guy Darvall Williams. "Freshening by Glacial Meltwater Enhances Melting of Ice Shelves and Reduces Formation of Antarctic Bottom Water." *Science Advances* 4, no. 4 (April 18, 2018).

332 Gilbert, E. and C. Kittel. "Surface Melt and Runoff on Antarctic Ice Shelves at 1.5°C, 2°C and 4°C of Future Warming." *Geophysical Research Letters* (April 8, 2021).

333 Gudmundsson, G. Hilmar, Fernando S. Paolo, Susheel Adusumilli, and Helen A. Fricker. "Instantaneous Antarctic Ice Sheet Mass Loss Driven by Thinning Ice Shelves," *Geophysical Research Letters* 46 (December 11, 2019).

334 Rintoul, Stephen Rich, Alessandro Silvano, Beatriz Pena-Molino, Esmee Van Wijk, Mark Rosenberg, Jamin Stevens Greenbaum, and Donald D. Blankenship. "Ocean Heat Drives Rapid Basal Melt of the Totten Ice Shelf." *Science Advances* 2, no. 12 (December 16, 2016).

335 Scambos, T. A., R. E. Bell, R. B. Alley, S. Anandakrishnan, D. H. Bromwich, K. Brunt, K. Christianson et al. "How Much, How Fast?: A Science Review and Outlook for Research on the Instability of Antarctica's Thwaites Glacier in the 21st Century." *Global and Planetary Change* 153 (June 2017).

336 Rowlatt, Justin. "Antarctica Melting: Climate Change and the Journey to the 'Doomsday Glacier'." BBC (January 28, 2020).

337 Wåhlin, A. K, A. G. C. Graham, K. A. Hogan, B. Y. Queste, L. Boehme, R. D Larter, E. C. Pettit, J. Wellner, and K. J. Heywood. "Pathways and Modification of Warm Water Flowing beneath Thwaites Ice Shelf, West Antarctica." *Science Advances* 7, no. 15 (April 9, 2021).

338 Rignot, Eric, Jérémie Mouginot, Bernd Scheuchl, Michiel van den Broeke, Melchior J. van Wessem, and Mathieu Morlighem. "Four Decades of Antarctic Ice Sheet Mass Balance From 1979–2017." *Proceedings of the National Academy of Sciences* 116 no. 4 (January 22, 2019).

339 IMBIE team. "Mass Balance of the Antarctic Ice Sheet from 1992 to 2017." *Nature* 558 (June 13, 2018).

340 Smith, Ben, Helen A. Fricker, Alex S. Gardner, Brooke Medley, Johan Nilsson, Fernando S. Paolo, Nicholas Holschuh et al. "Pervasive Ice Sheet Mass Loss Reflects

Competing Ocean and Atmosphere Processes." *Science* 368 no. 6496 (April 30, 2020).

341 Lhermitte, Stef, Sainan Sun, Christopher Shuman, Bert Wouters, Frank Pattyn, Jan Wuite, Etienne Berthier, and Thomas Nagler. "Damage Accelerates Ice Shelf Instability and Mass Loss in Amundsen Sea Embayment." *Proceedings of the National Academy of Sciences* 117 (September 14, 2020).

342 Joughin, Ian, Daniel Shapero, Ben Smith, Pierre Dutrieux, and Mark Barham. "*Ice-Shelf Retreat Drives Recent Pine Island Glacier Speedup.*" *Science Advances* 7, no. 24 (June 11, 2021).

343 Shepherd, Andrew, Lin Gilbert, Alan S. Muir,Hannes Konrad, Malcolm McMillan, Thomas Slater, Kate H. Briggs, Aud V. Sundal, Anna E. Hogg, and Marcus E. Engdahl. "Trends in Antarctic Ice Sheet Elevation and Mass." *Geophysical Research Letters* 46 no. 14 (May 16, 2019).

344 Carrington, Damian. "'Extraordinary Thinning' of Ice Sheets Revealed Deep Inside Antarctica." *The Guardian* (May 16, 2019).

345 Voosen, Paul. "Antarctic Ice Melt 125,000 Years Ago Offers Warning." *Science* 362, no. 6421 (December 21, 2018).

346 University of Reading. "One-Third of Antarctic Ice Shelf Area at Risk of Collapse as Planet Warms." *ScienceDaily* (April 8, 2021).

347 Garbe, Julius, Torsten Albrecht, Anders Levermann, Jonathan F. Donges, and Ricarda Winkelmann. "The Hysteresis of the Antarctic Ice Sheet." *Nature* 585 (September 23, 2020).

348 National Snow & Ice Data Center. Quick Facts on Ice Sheets.

349 Ignéczi, Ádám, Andrew J. Sole, Stephen J. Livingstone, Amber A. Leeson, Xavier Fettweis, Nick Selmes, Noel Gourmelen, and Kate Briggs. "Northeast Sector of the Greenland Ice Sheet to Undergo the Greatest Inland Expansion of Supraglacial Lakes during the 21st Century." *Geophysical Research Letters* 43, no. 18 (September 23, 2016).

350 Carroll, D., D. A. Sutherland, B. Hudson, T. Moon, G. A. Catania, E. L. Shroyer, J. D. Nash et al. "The Impact of Glacier Geometry on Meltwater Plume Structure and Submarine Melt in Greenland Fjords." *Geophysical Research Letters* 43 no. 18 (September 28, 2016).

351 Fraser, Neil J., Mark E. Inall, Marcello G. Magaldi, Thomas W. N. Haine, and Sam C. Jones. "Wintertime Fjord-Shelf Interaction and Ice Sheet Melting in Southeast Greenland," *Journal of Geophysical Research* 124 no. 12 (December 5, 2018).

352 King, Michalea D., Ian M. Howat, Salvatore G. Candela, Myoung J. Noh, Seongsu Jeong, Brice P. Y. Noël, Michiel R. van den Broeke, Bert Wouters, and Adelaide Negrete. "Dynamic Ice Loss from the Greenland Ice Sheet Driven by

Sustained Glacier Retreat." *Communications Earth & Environment* 1 (August 13, 2020).

353 Shankman, Sabrina. "Greenland's Melting: Heat Waves Are Changing the Landscape before Their Eyes." Inside Climate News (August 1, 2019).

354 Mouginot, Jérémie, Eric Rignot, Anders A. Bjørk, Michiel van den Broeke, Romain Millan, Mathieu Morlighem, Brice Noël, Bernd Scheuchl, and Michael Wood. "Forty-Six Years of Greenland Ice Sheet Mass Balance from 1972 to 2018." *Proceedings of the National Academy of Sciences* 116 no. 19 (April 22, 2019).

355 Bevis, Michael, Christopher Harig, Shfaqat A. Khan, Abel Brown, Frederik J. Simons, Michael Willis, Xavier Fettweis et al. "Accelerating Changes in Ice Mass within Greenland, and the Ice Sheet's Sensitivity to Atmospheric Forcing." *Proceedings of the National Academy of Sciences* 116 no. 6 (January 22, 2019).

356 Trusel, Luke D., Sarah B. Das, Matthew B. Osman, Matthew J. Evans, Ben E. Smith, Xavier Fettweis, Joseph R. McConnell, Brice P. Y. Noël, and Michiel R. van den Broeke. "Nonlinear Rise in Greenland Runoff in Response to Post-Industrial Arctic Warming." *Nature* 564 (December 5, 2018).

357 Rice, Doyle. "Greenland's Ice Sheet Melt Has 'Gone into Overdrive' and is Now 'Off the Charts.'" *USA Today* (December 5, 2018).

358 Box, Jason E., Alun Hubbard, David B. Bahr, William T. Colgan, Xavier Fettweis, Kenneth D. Mankoff, Adrien Wehrlé et al. "Greenland Ice Sheet Climate Disequilibrium and Committed Sea-Level Rise." *Nature Climate Change* (August 29, 2022).

359 National Snow & Ice Data Center. Quick Facts on Ice Sheets.

360 National Wildlife Federation. Ecosystem Services.

361 Dasgupta, Partha. *Final report—The Economics of Biodiversity* (February 2, 2021).

362 Tennesen, Michael. *The Next Species*. Simon & Schuster, 2015.

363 World Wildlife Fund. *Living Planet Report 2018: Aiming Higher* (2018).

364 World Wildlife Fund. *Living Planet Report 2016* (2016).

365 IPBES. *Global Assessment Report on Biodiversity and Ecosystem Services* (2021).

366 Warren R., J. Price, J. VanDerWal, S. Cornelius, and H. Sohl. "The Implications of the United Nations Paris Agreement on Climate Change for Globally Significant Biodiversity Areas." *Climatic Change* 147, no. 3–4 (March 14, 2018).

367 Penn, Justin L. and Curtis Deutsch. "Avoiding Ocean Mass Extinction from Climate Warming." *Science* 376, no. 6592 (April 28, 2022).

368 Pimm, Stuart. "Climate Disruption and Biodiversity." *Current Biology* 19, no. 14 (July 28, 2008).

369 World Wildlife Fund. *Living Planet Report: Building a Nature-Positive Society* (2022).

370 Pacifici, Michaela, Piero Visconti, Stuart H. M. Butchart, James E. M. Watson, Francesca M. Cassola,and Carlo Rondinini. "Species' Traits Influenced Their Response to Recent Climate Change." *Nature Climate Change* 7 (February 13, 2017).

371 Lister, Bradford C. and Andres Garcia. "Climate-Driven Declines in Arthropod Abundance Restructure a Rainforest Food Web." *Proceedings of the National Academy of Sciences* 115 no. 44 (October 15, 2018).

372 Hallmann, Caspar A., Martin Sorg, Eelke Jongejans, Henk Siepel, Nick Hofland, Heinz Schwan, Werner Stenmans, Andreas Müller, Hubert Sumser, Thomas Hörren, Dave Goulson, and Hans de Kroon. "More Than 75 Percent Decline Over 27 Years in Total Flying Insect Biomass in Protected Areas." *PLOS ONE* (October 18, 2017).

373 Embury-Dennis, Tom. "Scientists Warn of 'Ecological Armageddon' After Study Shows Flying Insect Numbers Plummeting 75%." *The Independent* (October 19, 2017).

374 Warren, R., J. Price, E. Graham, N. Forstenhaeusler, and J. Vanderwal. "The Projected Effect on Insects, Vertebrates, and Plants of Limiting Global Warming to 1.5°C rather than 2°C." *Science* 360, no. 6390 (May 18, 2018).

375 Sales, Kris, Ramakrishnan Vasudeva, Matthew E. Dickinson, Joanne L. Godwin, Alyson J. Lumley, Łukasz Michalczyk, Laura Hebberecht, Paul Thomas, Aldina Franco, and Matthew J. G. Gage. "Experimental Heatwaves Compromise Sperm Function and Cause Transgenerational Damage in a Model Insect." *Nature Communications* 9 (November 13, 2018).

376 Carlson, Colin J., Kevin R. Burgio, Eric R. Dougherty, Anna J. Phillips, Veronica M. Bueno, Christopher F. Clements, and Giovanni Castaldo. "Parasite Biodiversity Faces Extinction and Redistribution in a Changing Climate." *Science Advances* 3, no. 9 (September 6, 2017).

377 Strona, Giovanni, and Corey J. A. Bradshaw. "Co-Extinctions Annihilate Planetary Life during Extreme Environmental Change." *Scientific Reports* 8 (November 13, 2018).

378 Trisos, Christopher H., Cory Merow, and Alex L. Pigot. "The Projected Timing of Abrupt Ecological Disruption from Climate Change." *Nature* 580 (April 8, 2020).

379 Diffenbaugh, Noah H. and Christopher B. Field. "Changes in Ecologically Critical Terrestrial Climate Conditions." *Science* 341, no. 6145 (August 2, 2013).

380 Jezkova, Tereza, and John Wiens. "Rates of Change in Climatic Niches in Plant and Animal Populations are Much Slower than Projected Climate Change." *Proceedings of the Royal Society B* 283, no. 1843 (November 13, 2016).

381 Carleton, Tamma, and Solomon Hsiang. "Social and Economic Impacts of Climate." *Science* 353, no. 6304 (September 21, 2016).

382 NOAA. "Northern Hemisphere Just Had Its Hottest Summer on Record." (September 14, 2020).

383 European Environmental Agency. "Global and European Temperature" (June 14, 2019).

384 Bova, Samantha, Yair Rosenthal, Zhengyu Liu, Shital P. Godad, and Mi Yan. "Seasonal Origin of the Thermal Maxima at the Holocene and the Last Interglacial." *Nature* 589 (January 27, 2021).

385 Earth Observatory. "Heatwaves and Fires Scorch Europe, Africa, and Asia." (July 13, 2022).

386 Fischer, E. M., S. Sippel, and R. Knutti. "Increasing Probability of Record-Shattering Climate Extremes." *Nature Climate Change* 11 (July 26, 2021).

387 Zeppetello, Lucas R. Vargas, Adrian E. Raftery, and David S. Battisti. "Probabilistic Projections of Increased Heat Stress Driven by Climate Change." *Communications Earth & Environment* 3 (August 25, 2022).

388 Xu, Chi, Timothy A. Kohler, Timothy M. Lenton, Jens-Christian Svenning, and Marten Scheffer. "Future of the Human Climate Niche." *Proceedings of the National Academy of Sciences* 117 no. 21 (May 4, 2020).

389 Mora, Camilo, Bénédicte Dousset, Iain R. Caldwell, Farrah E. Powell, Rollan C. Geronimo, Coral R. Bielecki, Chelsie W. W. Counsell et al. "Global Risk of Deadly Heat." *Nature Climate Change* 7 (June 19, 2017).

390 Mora, Camilo et al. Heat Waves: Number of Deadly Heat Days.

391 Milman, Oliver. "A Third of the World Now Faces Deadly Heat Waves as Result of Climate Change," *The Guardian*, June 19, 2017.

392 Meehl, Gerald A., Claudia Tebaldi, and Dennis Adams-Smith. "US Daily Temperature Records Past, Present, and Future." *Proceedings of the National Academy of Sciences* 113, no. 49 (December 6, 2016).

393 First Street Foundation. The 6th National Climate Risk Assessment: Hazardous Heat. (August 15, 2022)

394 Im, Eun-Soon, Jeremy Pal, and Elfatih Eltahir. "Deadly Heat waves Projected in the Densely Populated Agricultural Regions of South Asia." *Science Advances* 3 (August 2, 2017).

395 Chandler, David. "Deadly Heat Waves Could Hit South Asia This Century." MIT News Office (August 2, 2017).

396 Russo, Simone, Andrea F Marchese, J Sillmann, and Giuseppina Immé. "When Will Unusual Heat Waves Become Normal in a Warming Africa?" *Environmental Research Letters* 11, no. 5 (May 12, 2016).

397 Harrington, Luke, David J Frame, Erich M Fischer, Ed Hawkins, Manoj Joshi, and Chris D Jones. "Poorest Countries Experience Earlier Anthropogenic Emergence of Daily Temperature Extremes." *Environmental Research Letters* 11 (May 17, 2016).

398 Lehner, Flavio, Clara Deser, and Benjamin M. Sanderson. "Future Risk of Record-Breaking Summer Temperatures and Its Mitigation." *Climatic Change* 146 (February 16, 2016).

399 NSF. "Future Summers Could be Hotter than any on Record" (June 13, 2016).

400 Li, Dawei, Jiacan Yuan, and Robert E. Kopp. "Escalating Global Exposure to Compound Heat-Humidity Extremes with Warming." *Environmental Research Letters* 15, no.6 (May 19, 2020).

401 Raymond, Colin, Tom Matthews, and Radley M. Horton. "The Emergence of Heat and Humidity Too Severe for Human Tolerance." *Science Advances* 6, no. 19 (May 8, 2020).

402 Vicedo-Cabrera, A. M., N. Scovronick, F. Sera, D. Royé, R. Schneider, A. Tobias, C. Astrom et al. "The Burden of Heat-Related Mortality Attributable to Recent Human-Induced Climate Change." *Nature Climate Change* 11 (May 31, 2021).

403 Im, Eun-Soon, Jeremy Pal, and Elfatih Eltahir. "Deadly Heat Waves Projected in the Densely Populated Agricultural Regions of South Asia." *Science Advances* 3 no.8 (August 2, 2017).

404 Russo, Simone, Jana Sillmann, and Andreas Sterl. "Humid Heat Waves at Different Warming Levels." *Scientific Reports* 7 (August 7, 2017).

405 Sherwood, Steven C. and Matthew Huber. "An Adaptability Limit to Climate Change Due to Heat Stress." *Proceedings of the National Academy of Sciences* 107, no. 21 (May 25, 2010).

406 US Global Change Research Program. *The Impacts of Climate Change on Human Health in the United States* (April 2016).

407 Herring, Stephanie C., Nikolaos Christidis, Andrew Hoell, James P. Kossin, Carl J. Schreck III, and Peter A. Stott. *Explaining Extreme Events of 2016 from a Climate Perspective. Bulletin of the American Meteorological Society* 99, no. 1 (January 1, 2018).

408 Fischer, E.M. and R. Knutti. "Anthropogenic Contribution to Global Occurrence of Heavy-Precipitation and High-Temperature Extremes." *Nature Climate Change* 5 (April 27, 2015).

409 Gillis, Justin. "New Study Links Weather Extremes to Global Warming." *The New York Times* (April 27, 2015).

410 Diffenbaugh, Noah S., Deepti Singh, Justin S. Mankin, Daniel E. Horton, Daniel L. Swain, Danielle Touma, Allison Charland, Yunjie Liu, Matz Haugen, Michael Tsiang, and Bala Rajaratnam. "Quantifying the Influence of Global Warming on Unprecedented Extreme Climate Events." *Proceedings of the National Academy of Sciences* 114, no. 9 (May 19, 2017).

411 Harvey, Chelsea. "Record-Breaking Climate Events All Over the World Are Being Shaped by Global Warming, Scientists Find." *The Washington Post* (April 24, 2017).

412 Palalexiou, Simon Michael, Amir AghaKouchak, Kevin E. Trenberth, and Efi Foufoula-Georgiou. "Global, Regional, and Megacity Trends in the Highest Temperature of the Year: Diagnostics and Evidence for Accelerating Trends." *Earth's Future*, 6, no. 1 (January 22, 2018).

413 Tuholske, Cascade, Kelly Caylor, Chris Funk, Andrew Verdin, Stuart Sweeney, Kathryn Grace, Pete Peterson, and Tom Evans. "Global Urban Population Exposure to Extreme Heat." *Proceedings of the National Academy of Sciences* 118, no. 41 (October 12, 2021).

414 Wilby, Robert. "Climate Change: What Would 4°C of Global Warming Feel Like?" *The Conversation* (January 15, 2021).

415 Dahl, Kristina, Rachel Licker, John T Abatzoglou, and Juan Declet-Barreto. "Increased Frequency of and Population Exposure to Extreme Heat Index Days in the United States during the 21st Century." *Environmental Research Communications* 1, no. 7 (July 16, 2019).

416 Dahl, Kristina, Erika Spanger-Siegfried, Rachel Licker, Astrid Caldas, Rachel Cleetus, Shana Udvardy, Juan Declet-Barreto, and Pamela Worth. *Killer Heat in the United States*, Union of Concerned Scientists (July 2019).

417 Bastin, Jean-Francois, Emily Clark, Thomas Elliott, Simon Hart, Johan van den Hoogen, Iris Hordijk et al. "Understanding Climate Change from a Global Analysis of City Analogues." *PLOS ONE* (July 10, 2019).

418 Jones, Bryan, Brian C. O'Neill, Larry McDaniel, Seth McGinnis, Linda O. Mearns, and Claudia Tebaldi. "Future Population Exposure to US Heat Extremes." *Nature Climate Change* 5 (May 18, 2015).

419 Dunne, John P. Ronald J. Stouffer, and Jasmin G., John. "Reductions in Labour Capacity from Heat Stress under Climate Warming." *Nature Climate Change* 3 (February 24, 2013).

420 NOAA. "New NOAA Study Estimates Future Loss of Labor Capacity as Climate Warms." (February 25, 2013).

421 UN Development Programme. *Climate Change and Labour: Impacts of Heat in the Workplace* (April 28, 2016).

422 Kjellstrom, Tord, David Briggs, Chris Freyberg, Bruno Lemke, Matthias Otto, and Olivia Hyatt. "Heat, Human Performance, and Occupational Health: A Key Issue for the Assessment of Global Climate Change Impacts." *Annual Review of Public Health* 37 (January 21, 2016).

423 Burke, Marshall, Solomon M Hsiang, and Edward Miguel. "Global Non-Linear Effect of Temperature on Economic Production." *Nature* 527 (October 21, 2015).

424 Hsiang, Solomon, Robert Kopp, Amir Jina, James Rising, Michael Delgado, Shashank Mohan, D. J. Rasmussen et al. "Estimating Economic Damage from Climate Change in the United States." *Science* 356, no. 6345 (June 30, 2017).

425 American Psychiatric Association. "Extreme Heat Contributes to Worsening Mental Health, Especially among Vulnerable Populations" (June 30, 2021).

426 Burke, Marshall, Felipe González, Patrick Baylis, Sam Heft-Neal, Ceren Baysan, Sanjay Basu, and Solomon Hsiang. "Higher Temperatures Increase Suicide Rates in the United States and Mexico." *Nature Climate Change* 8 (July 23, 2018).

427 Dixon, P. Grady, Mark Sinyor, Ayal Schaffer, Anthony Levitt, Christa R. Haney, Kelsey N. Ellis, and Scott C. Sheridan. "Association of Weekly Suicide Rates with Temperature Anomalies in Two Different Climate Types." *International Journal of Environmental Research and Public Health* 11, no. 11 (November 13, 2014).

428 Mares, Dennis M. and Kenneth W. Moffett. "Climate Change and Interpersonal Violence: A 'Global' Estimate and Regional Inequities." *Climatic Change* 135, no. 2 (March 2016.)

429 Ranson, Matthew. "Crime, Weather, and Climate Change." *Journal of Environmental Economics and Management* 67, no. 3 (May 2014).

430 Sivak, Michael. "Will AC Put a Chill on the Global Energy Supply?" *American Scientist* 101, no. 4 (September–October 2013).

431 Sherman, Peter, Haiyang Lin, and Michael McElroy. "Projected Global Demand for Air Conditioning Associated With Extreme Heat and Implications for Electricity Grids in Poorer Countries." *Energy and Buildings* 268 (August 2022).

432 International Energy Agency. *The Future of Cooling* (May 15, 2018).

433 Auffhammer, Maximillian, Patrick Baylis, and Catherine H. Hausman. "Climate Change Is Projected To Have Severe Impacts on the Frequency and Intensity of Peak Electricity Demand across the United States." *Proceedings of the National Academy of Sciences* 114, no. 8 (February 21, 2017).

434 van Ruijven, Bas J., Enrica De Cian, and Ian Sue Wing. "Amplification of Future Energy Demand Growth Due to Climate Change." *Nature Communications* 10 (June 24, 2019).

435 Fountain, Henry. "The Western Drought Is Bad. Here's What You Should Know about It," *The New York Times* (September 13, 2021).

436 NOAA. *NOAA Drought Task Force Report on the 2020–2021 Southwestern US Drought* (September 21, 2021).

437 National Drought Mitigation Center, University of Nebraska-Lincoln US Drought Monitor.

438 Williams, A. Park, Benjamin I. Cook, and Jason E. Smerdon. "Rapid Intensification of the Emerging Southwestern North American Megadrought in 2020–2021." *Nature Climate Change* 3 (February 14, 2022).

439 Nield, David. "Parts of North America are Currently Heading for a Megadrought, Study Finds." ScienceAlert (April 20, 2020).

440 Büntgen, Ulf, Otmar Urban, Paul J. Krusic, Michal Rybníček, Tomáš Kolář, Tomáš Kyncl, Alexander Ač et al. "Recent European Drought Extremes beyond Common Era Background Variability." *Nature Geoscience* 14 (March 15, 2021).

441 Swain, Daniel L., Baird Langenbrunner, J. David Neelin, and Alex Hall. "Increasing Precipitation Volatility in Twenty-First-Century California." *Nature Climate Change* 8 (April 23, 2018).

442 US Global Change Research Program. Extreme Weather. Third National Climate Assessment.

443 Martin, E. R. "Future Projections of Global Pluvial and Drought Event Characteristics." *Geophysical Research Letters* 45, no. 21 (October 19, 2018).

444 Totz, Sonja, Stefan Petri, Jascha Lehmann, and Dim Coumou. "Regional Changes in the Mean Position and Variability of the Tropical Edge." *Geophysical Research Letters* 45, no. 21 (October 31, 2018).

445 Lehmann, J., F. Mempel, and D. Coumou. "Increased Occurrence of Record-Wet and Record-Dry Months Reflect Changes in Mean Rainfall." *Geophysical Research Letters* 45, no. 24 (December 13, 2018).

446 Potsdam Institute for Climate Impact Research. "Record-Wet and Record-Dry Months Increased in Regions Worldwide." EurekAlert! (December 12, 2018).

447 Thomas, Natalie and Sumant Nigam. "Twentieth-Century Climate Change over Africa: Seasonal Hydroclimate Trends and Sahara Desert Expansion." *Journal of Climate* 31, no. 10 (May 2018).

448 Krajik, Kevin. "The 100th Meridian, Where the Great Plains Begin, May Be Shifting." State of the Planet (April 11, 2018).

449 Dai, Aguo. "Drought under Global Warming: A Review." *Wiley Interdisciplinary Reviews: Climate Change* 2, no. 1 (January/February 2011).

450 Dai, Aiguo. "Increasing Drought under Global Warming In Observations and Models." *Nature Climate Change* 3 (August 5, 2012).

451 Hofste, Rutger Willem, Paul Reig, and Leah Schleife. "17 Countries, Home to One-Quarter of the World's Population, Face Extremely High Water Stress." World Resources Institute (August 6, 2019).

452 Park, Chang-Eui, Su-Jong Jeong, Manoj Joshi, Timothy J. Osborn, Chang-Hoi Ho, Shilong Piao, Deliang Chen et al. "Keeping Global Warming within 1.5°C Constrains Emergence of Aridification." *Nature Climate Change* 8 (January 1, 2018).

453 IPCC. *Climate Change 2022: Impacts, Adaptation and Vulnerability: Summary for Policymakers*. From: IPCC Sixth Assessment Report: Impacts, Adaptation and Vulnerability (February 27, 2022).

454 UNESCO World Water Assessment Programme. *The United Nations World Water Development Report, Nature-based Solutions for Water* (2018).

455 Schwalm, Christopher R., William R. L. Anderegg, Anna M. Michalak, Joshua B. Fisher, Franco Biondi, George Koch, Marcy Litvak et al. "Global Patterns of Drought Recovery." *Nature* 548 (August 9, 2017).

456 Guiot, Joel, and Wolfgang Cramer. "Climate Change: The 2015 Paris Agreement Thresholds and Mediterranean Basin Ecosystems." *Science* 354, no. 6311 (October 28, 2016).

457 Bathiany, Sebastian, Vasilis Dakos, Marten Scheffer, and Timothy M. Lenton. "Climate Models Predict Increasing Temperature Variability in Poor Countries." *Science Advances* 4, no. 5 (May 2, 2018).

458 Feldpausch, T. R., O. L. Phillips, R. J. W. Brienen, E. Gloor, J. Lloyd, G. Lopez-Gonzalez, A. Monteagudo-Mendoza et al. "Amazon Forest Response to Repeated Droughts." *Global Biochemical Cycles* 30 no. 7 (August 10, 2016).

459 Baker, J. C. A., L. Garcia-Carreras, W. Buermann, D. Castilho de Souza, J. H. Marsham, P. Y. Kubota, M. Gloor, C. A. S. Coelho, and D. V. Spracklen. "Robust Amazon Precipitation Projections in Climate Models That Capture Realistic Land–Atmosphere Interactions." *Environmental Research Letters* 16, no. 7 (June 22, 2021).

460 Iglesias, Virginia, Jennifer K. Balch, and William R. Travis. "US Fires Became Larger, More Frequent, and More Widespread in the 2000s." *Science Advances* 8, no. 11 (March 16, 2022).

461 UN Environment Programme, GRID-Arendal. *Spreading like Wildfire: The Rising Threat of Extraordinary Landscape Fires* (February 23, 2022).

462 National Park Service. Wildfire Causes and Evaluations.

463 Howard, Peter. *Flammable Planet: Wildfires and the Social Cost of Carbon.* Environmental Defense Fund, Institute for Policy Integrity, and Natural Resource Defense Council (September 2014).

464 NOAA. Wildfires Reports. National Centers for Environmental Information.

465 Yue, Siyao, Jialei Zhu, Shuang Chen, Qiaorong Xie, Wei Li, Linjie Li, Hong Ren et al. "Brown Carbon from Biomass Burning Imposes Strong Circum-Arctic Warming." *One Earth* 5, no.3 (March 18, 2022).

466 World Meteorological Organization. "Australia Suffers Devastating Fires after Hottest, Driest Year on Record" (January 7, 2020.)

467 World Weather Attribution. Attribution of the Australian Bushfire Risk to Anthropogenic Climate Change (January 10, 2020).

468 Abatzoglou, John, and Park Williams. "Impact of Anthropogenic Climate Change on Wildfire across Western US Forests." *Proceedings of the National Academy of Sciences* 113, no. 42 (October 18, 2016).

469 Cho, Renee. "What Do Wildfires Have to Do with Climate Change?" State of the Planet (October 13, 2014).

470 Westerling, Anthony LeRoy. "Increasing Western US Forest Wildfire Activity: Sensitivity to Changes in the Timing of Spring." *Philosophical Transactions of the Royal Society B* 371 (May 23, 2016).

471 Westerling, Anthony LeRoy. "Wildfires in West Have Gotten Bigger, More Frequent and Longer since the 1980s." *The Conversation* (May 23, 2016).

472 Keyser, Alisa, and Anthony LeRoy Westerling. "Climate Drives Inter-Annual Variability in Probability of High Severity Fire Occurrence in the Western United States." *Environmental Research Letters* 12 (May 26, 2017).

473 Zhuang, Yizhou, Rong Fu, Benjamin D. Santer, Robert E. Dickinson, and Alex Hall. "Quantifying Contributions of Natural Variability and Anthropogenic Forcings on Increased Fire Weather Risk over the Western United States" *Proceedings of the National Academy of Sciences* 118 no. 45 (November 9, 2021).

474 Cal Fire. Top 20 Largest California Wildfires.

475 Higuera, Philip E., Bryan N. Shuman, and Kyra D. Wolf. "Rocky Mountain Subalpine Forests Now Burning More Than Any Time In Recent Millennia." *Proceedings of the National Academy of Sciences* 118, no. 25 (June 22, 2021).

476 US Department of Agriculture. *Effects of Climatic Variability and Change on Forest Ecosystems* (December 2012).

477 Borealforest.org. World Boreal Forests: An Introduction.

478 EUMETSAT. "Unprecedented Wildfires Devastate Siberia and Spread Smoke over the Arctic." (August 17, 2021).

479 Kelly, Ryan, Melissa L. Chipman, Philip E. Higuera, Ivanka Stefanova, Linda B. Brubaker, and Feng Sheng Hu. "Recent Burning of Boreal Forests Exceeds Fire Regime Limits of the Past 10,000 Years." *Proceedings of the National Academy of Sciences* 10, no. 32 (August 6, 2013).

480 Kelly, Ryan, "Palaeodata-Informed Modelling of Large Carbon Losses from Recent Burning of Boreal Forests," *Nature Climate Change* 6 (October 19, 2015).

481 Castro, Joseph. "Subarctic Wildfire Activity Is Heating up." *LiveScience* (July 22, 2013).

482 Flannigan, Mike, Brian Stocks, Merritt Turetsky, and Mike Wotton. "Impacts of Climate Change on Fire Activity and Fire Management in the Circumboreal Forest," *Global Change Biology* 15, no. 3 (March 2009).

483 NASA. "Fires Raged in the Amazon Again in 2020" Earth Observatory (2020).

484 Mooney, Chris. "Why We Should All Worry About the Amazon Catching on Fire this Year." *The Washington Post* (July 12, 2016).

485 Stevens-Rumann, Camille S., Kerry B. Kemp, Philip E. Higuera, Brian J. Harvey, Monica T. Rother, Daniel C. Donato, Penelope Morgan, and Thomas T. Veblen. "Evidence for Declining Forest Resilience to Wildfires under Climate Change." *Ecology Letters* 21, no. 2 (December 12, 2017).

486 Guiden, Mary. "Forest Resilience Declines In Face Of Wildfires, Climate Change." Colorado State University (December 12, 2017).

487 Davis, Kimberley T., Solomon Z. Dobrowski, Philip E. Higuera, Zachary A. Holden, Thomas T. Veblen, Monica T. Rother, Sean A. Parks, Anna Sala, and Marco P. Maneta. "Wildfires and Climate Change Push Low-Elevation Forests across a Critical Climate Threshold for Tree Regeneration." *Proceedings of the National Academy of Sciences* 116 no. 13 (March 11, 2019).

488 Williams, A. Park, Craig D. Allen, Alison K. Macalady, Daniel Griffin, Connie A. Woodhouse, David M. Meko, Thomas W. Swetnam et al. "Temperature as a Potent Driver of Regional Forest Drought Stress and Tree Mortality." *Nature Climate Change* 3 (September 30, 2012).

489 Adams, Henry D., Greg A Barron-Gafford, Rebecca L Minor, Alfonso A Gardea, Lisa Patrick Bentley, Darin J Law, David D Breshears, Nate G McDowell, and Travis E Huxman. "Temperature Response Surfaces for Mortality Risk of Tree Species with Future Drought." *Environmental Research Letters* 12, no. 11 (November 17, 2017).

490 Robbins, Jim. "With Climate Change, Tree Die-Offs May Spread in the West." *The New York Times* (December 11, 2017).

491 Reinmann, Andrew B. and Lucy R. Hutyra. "Edge Effects Enhance Carbon Uptake and Its Vulnerability to Climate Change in Temperate Broadleaf Forests." *Proceedings of the National Academy of Sciences* 114, no. 1 (January 3, 2017).

492 Robbins, Jim. "The Rapid and Startling Decline of World's Vast Boreal Forests," Yale Environment 360 (October 12, 2015).

493 IIASA. "Boreal Forests Challenged by Global Change." (August 21, 2015).

494 Gauthier, S., P. Bernier, T. Kuuluvainen, A. Z. Shvidenko, and D. G. Schepaschenko. "Boreal Forest Health and Global Change." *Science* 349, no. 6250 (August 21, 2015).

495 Garcia, Elizabeth S., Abigail L. S. Swann, Juan C. Villegas, David D. Breshears, Darin J. Law, Scott R. Saleska, and Scott C. Stark. "Synergistic Ecoclimate Teleconnections from Forest Loss in Different Regions Structure Global Ecological Responses." *PLOS ONE* 11, no. 11 (November 16, 2016).

496 Hickey, Hannah. "Large Forest Die-Offs Can Have Effects That Ricochet to Distant Ecosystems." University of Washington (November 16, 2016).

497 Feldpausch, T., O. L. Phillips, R. J. W. Brienen, E. Gloor, J. Lloyd, G. Lopez-Gonzalez, A. Monteagudo-Mendoza et al. "Amazon Forest Response to Repeated Droughts," *Global Biogeochemical Cycles* 30, no. 7 (August 10, 2016).

498 Maddern, Kerra. "Drought Stalls Tree Growth and Shuts down Amazon Carbon Sink, Researchers Find." University of Leeds (July 6, 2016).

499 Bauman, David, Claire Fortunel, Guillaume Delhaye, Yadvinder Malhi, Lucas A. Cernusak, Lisa Patrick Bentley, Sami W. Rifai, Jesús Aguirre-Gutiérrez et al.

"Tropical Tree Mortality Has Increased With Rising Atmospheric Water Stress." *Nature* (May 18, 2022).

500 Brienen, R. J. W., O. L. Phillips, T. R. Feldpausch, E. Gloor, T. R. Baker, J. Lloyd, G. Lopez-Gonzalez et al. "Long-Term Decline of the Amazon Carbon Sink," *Nature* 519, no. 7543 (March 18, 2015).

501 Weisse, Mikaela, and Liz Goldman. "We Lost a Football Pitch of Primary Rainforest Every 6 Seconds in 2019." World Resources Institute (June 2, 2020).

502 Arnold, Chris Feliciano. "In the Amazon, a Catastrophic Gold Rush Looms" *The New York Times* (September 18, 2017).

503 Casado, Leticia, and Ernesto Londoño. "Under Brazil's Far Right Leader, Amazon Protections Slashed and Forests Fall." *The New York Times* (July 28, 2019).

504 Spring, Jake and Gloria Dickie. "Explainer: Causes and Consequences of Amazon Fires and Deforestation." (August 11, 2022).

505 Lovejoy, Thomas E. and Carlos Nobre. "Amazon Tipping Point." *Science Advances* 4, no. 2 (February 21, 2018).

506 Boulton, Chris A., Timothy M. Lenton, and Niklas Boers. "Pronounced Loss of Amazon Rainforest Resilience since the Early 2000s." *Nature Climate Change* 12 (March 7, 2022).

507 Zemp, Delphine Clara, Carl-Friedrich Schleussner, Henrique M. J. Barbosa, Marina Hirota, Vincent Montade, Gilvan Sampaio, Arie Staal, Lan Wang-Erlandsson, and Anja Rammig. "Self-Amplified Amazon Forest Loss Due to Vegetation-Atmosphere Feedbacks." *Nature Communications* 8 (March 13, 2017).

508 Global Forest Watch. Global Primary Forest Loss.

509 World Resources Institute. Global Forest Review.

510 Baccini, A., W. Walker, L. Carvalho, M. Farina, D. Sulla-Menashe, and R. A. Houghton. "Tropical Forests Are a Net Carbon Source Based On Aboveground Measurements of Gain and Loss." *Science* 358, no. 6360 (September 28, 2017).

511 Feng, Yu, Zhenzhong Zeng, Timothy D. Searchinger, Alan D. Ziegler, Jie Wu, Dashan Wang, Xinyue He et al. "Doubling Of Annual Forest Carbon Loss over the Tropics during the Early Twenty-First Century." *Nature Sustainability* (February 22, 2022).

512 Gatti, Luciana, V., Luana S. Basso, John B. Miller, Manuel Gloor, Lucas Gatti Domingues, Henrique L. G. Cassol, Graciela Tejada et al. "Amazonia as a Carbon Source Linked to Deforestation and Climate Change." *Nature* 595 (July 14, 2021).

513 Qin, Yuanwei, Xiangming Xiao, Jean-Pierre Wigneron, Philippe Ciais, Martin Brandt, Lei Fan, Xiaojun Li et al. "Carbon Loss from Forest Degradation Exceeds That from Deforestation in the Brazilian Amazon." *Nature Climate Change* 11 (April 29, 2021).

514 Covey, Kristofer, Fiona Soper, Sunitha Pangala, Angelo Bernardino, Zoe Pagliaro, Luana Basso, Henrique Casso et al. "Carbon and Beyond: The

Biogeochemistry of Climate in a Rapidly Changing Amazon." *Frontiers in Forests and Global Change* (March 11, 2021).

515 UN Climate Change Conference. "Glasgow Leaders' Declaration on Forests and Land Use" (November 11, 2021).

516 Einhorn, Catrin, and Chris Buckley. "Global Leaders Pledge to End Deforestation by 2030." *The New York Times* (November 5, 2021).

517 Welz, Adam. "Are Huge Tree Planting Projects More Hype than Solution?" Yale Environment 360 (April 8, 2021).

518 Hoek van Dijke, Anne J., Martin Herold, Kaniska Mallick, Imme Benedict, Miriam Machwitz, Martin Schlerf, Agnes Pranindita, Jolanda J. E. Theeuwen, Jean-François Bastin, and Adriaan J. Teuling. "Shifts in Regional Water Availability Due to Global Tree Restoration." *Nature Geoscience* 15 (May 11, 2022).

519 Pan, Yefeng, Liming Li, Xun Jiang, Gan Li, Wentao Zhang, Xinyue Wang, and Andrew P. Ingersoll. "Earth's Changing Global Atmospheric Energy Cycle in Response to Climate Change." *Nature Communications* 8 (January 24, 2017).

520 Trenberth, Kevin E., Lijing Cheng, Peter Jacobs, Yongxin Zhang, and John Fasullo. "Hurricane Harvey Links to Ocean Heat Content and Climate Change Adaptation." *Earth's Future* 6, no. 5 (May 9, 2018).

521 Reed, Kevin, Alyssa M. Stansfield, Michael F. Wehner, and Colin M. Zarzycki. "Estimating The Potential Impact of Climate Change on Hurricane Florence." Climate Extremes Modeling Group (September 12, 2018).

522 National Weather Service. Hurricane Florence: September 14, 2018, website.

523 Wikipedia. Hurricane Ida website.

524 Barnard, Anne, Jonah E. Bromwich, Maria Cramer, Isabella Grullón Paz, Matthew Haag, Jesus Jiménez, Michael Levenson et al. "At Least 43 Are Dead After Ida Causes Flooding in Four States," *The New York Times* (September 8, 2021).

525 Committee on Extreme Weather Events and Climate Change Attribution; Board on Atmospheric Sciences and Climate; Division on Earth and Life Studies; National Academies of Sciences, Engineering, and Medicine, *Attribution of Extreme Weather Events in the Context of Climate Change* (2016).

526 US Global Change Research Program. *Climate Science Special Report, Chapter 7* (2018).

527 Fischer, E. M. and R. Knutti. "Anthropogenic Contribution to Global Occurrence of Heavy-Precipitation and High-Temperature Extremes." *Nature Climate Change* 5 (April 27, 2015).

528 Ye, Hengchun, Eric J. Fetzer, Sun Wong, and Bjorn H. Lambrigtsen. "Rapid Decadal Convective Precipitation Increase over Eurasia during the Last Three Decades of the 20th Century." *Science Advances* 3, no. 1 (January 25, 2017).

529 Prein, Andreas F., Roy M. Rasmussen, Kyoko Ikeda, Changhai Liu, Martyn P. Clark & Greg J. Holland. "The Future Intensification of Hourly Precipitation Extremes." *Nature Climate Change* 7 (December 5, 2016).

530 National Science Foundation. "Extreme Downpours Could Increase 400 Percent across Parts of US" (December 5, 2016).

531 Prein, Andreas F., Changhai Liu, Kyoko Ikeda, Stanley B. Trier, Roy M. Rasmussen, Greg J. Holland, and Martyn P. Clark. "Increased Rainfall Volume from Future Convective Storms in the US." *Nature Climate Change* 7 (November 30, 2017).

532 Diffenbaugh, Noah S., Martin Scherer, and Robert J Trapp. "Robust Increases in Severe Thunderstorm Environments in Response to Greenhouse Forcing." *Proceedings of the National Academy of Sciences* 110, no. 41 (October 8, 2013).

533 Corringham, Thomas W., F. Martin Ralph, Alexander Gershunov, Daniel R. Cayan, and Cary A. Talbot. "Atmospheric Rivers Drive Flood Damages in the Western United States." *Science Advances* 5, no. 12 (December 4, 2019).

534 NOAA. What are Atmospheric Rivers? website.

535 Waliser, Duane, and Bin Guan. "Extreme Winds and Precipitation during Landfall of Atmospheric Rivers." *Nature GeoScience* 10 (February 20, 2017).

536 Lavers, David A., Richard P Allan, Gabriele Villarini, Benjamin Lloyd-Hughes, David J Brayshaw, and Andrew J Wade. "Future Changes in Atmospheric Rivers and Their Implications for Winter Flooding In Britain." *Environment Research Letters* 8, no. 3 (July 23, 2013).

537 Ramos, Alexandre M., Ricardo Tomé, Ricardo M. Trigo, Margarida L. R. Liberato, Joaquim G. Pinto. "Projected Changes in Atmospheric Rivers Affecting Europe in CMIP5 Models." *Geophysical Research Letters* 43, no. 17 (August 22, 2016).

538 Massoud, E. C., V. Espinoza, B. Guan, and D. E. Waliser. "Global Climate Model Ensemble Approaches for Future Projections of Atmospheric Rivers." *Earth's Future* 7, no. 10 (October 12, 2019).

539 Huang, Xingying and Daniel L. Swain. "Climate Change Is Increasing the Risk of a California Megaflood." *Science Advances* 8, no. 32 (August 12, 2022).

540 Zhong, Raymond, Mira Rojanasakul and Erin Chaff. "The Coming California Megastorm." *The New York Times* (August 12, 2022).

541 Wasko, Conrad, and Ashish Sharma. "Reduced Spatial Extent of Extreme Storms at Higher Temperatures." *Geophysical Research Letters* 43, no. 8 (April 28, 2016).

542 University of New South Wales. "In Cities, Flooding and Rainfall Extremes to Rise as Climate Changes." ScienceDaily (May 9, 2016). (May 9, 2016).

543 National Weather Service. "Hurricane Irma 2017 website.

544 Wikipedia. Hurricane Ian website.

545 Saba, Vincent, Stephen M. Griffies, Whit G. Anderson, Michael Winton, Michael A. Alexander, Thomas L. Delworth, Jonathan A. Hare et al. "Enhanced Warming of the Northwest Atlantic Ocean under Climate Change." *Journal of Geophysical Research* 121, no. 1 (January 2016).

546 Rahmstorf, Stefan, Jason E. Box, Georg Feulner, Michael E. Mann, Alexander Robinson, Scott Rutherford, and Erik J. Schaffernicht. "Exceptional Twentieth-Century Slowdown in Atlantic Ocean Overturning Circulation." *Nature Climate Change* 5 (March 23, 2015).

547 Geophysical Fluid Dynamics Laboratory. "Global Warming and Hurricanes." (June 12, 2020).

548 Holland, Greg, and Cindy Bruyere. "Recent Intense Hurricane Response to Global Climate Change." *Climate Dynamics* 42, no. 3 (March 15, 2013).

549 Holland, Greg. "Will Climate Change Cause More Large, Destructive Hurricanes?" *Tremblor* (September 11, 2017).

550 Geiger, Tobias, Katja Frieler, and Anders Levermann. "High-Income Does Not Protect against Hurricane Losses." *Environmental Research Letters* 11, no. 8 (August 16, 2016).

551 Potsdam Institute for Climate Impact Research. "Can We Economically Outgrow Climate Change Damages? Not For Hurricanes We Can't" (August 16, 2016).

552 Hansen, James, Makiko Sato, Paul Hearty, Reto Ruedy, Maxwell Kelley, Valerie Masson-Delmotte, Gary Russell et al. "Ice Melt, Sea Level Rise and Superstorms: Evidence from Paleoclimate Data, Climate Modeling, and Modern Observations That 2 Degree C Global Warming Could be Dangerous." *Atmospheric Chemistry and Physics* 16 no. 6 (March 22, 2016).

553 NOAA Fisheries. "Gray Whale Numbers Continue Decline; NOAA Fisheries Will Continue Monitoring." (October 7, 2022).

554 IPCC. *Climate Change 2021: The Physical Science Basis, Summary for Policymakers.* From: *Climate Change 2021: The Physical Science Basis* (August 7, 2021).

555 IPCC. *Climate Change 2022: Impacts, Adaptation and Vulnerability: Summary for Policymakers.* From: IPCC Sixth Assessment Report: Impacts, Adaptation and Vulnerability (February 27, 2022).

556 Gruber, Nicholas. "Warming up, Turning Sour, Losing Breath: Ocean Biogeochemistry under Global Change." *Philosophical Transactions of the Royal Society A* (May 28, 2011).

557 Henson, Stephanie A., Claudie Beaulieu, Tatiana Ilyina, Jasmin G. John, Matthew Long, Roland Séférian, Jerry Tjiputra, and Jorge L. Sarmiento. "Rapid

Emergence of Climate Change in Environmental Drivers of Marine Ecosystems." *Nature Communications* 8 (March 7, 2017).

558 Gattuso, J.-P., A. Magnan, R. Billé, W. W. L. Cheung, E. L. Howes, F. Joos, D. Allemand, L. Bopp et al. "Contrasting Futures for Ocean and Society from Different Anthropogenic CO_2 Emissions Scenarios." *Science* 349, no. 6243 (July 3, 2015).

559 Moffitt, Sarah E., Tessa M. Hill, Peter D. Roopnarine, and James P. Kennett. "Response of Seafloor Ecosystems to Abrupt Global Climate Change," *Proceedings of the National Academy of Sciences* 112, no. 5 (April 14, 2015).

560 Kerlin, Kat. "Sea Change: What Took Decades To Destroy in Oceans Took Millennia To Recover." UC Davis (March 30, 2015).

561 Global Ocean Commission. *From Decline to Recovery: A Rescue Package for the Global Ocean* (2014).

562 EPA. *Climate Change Indicators in the United States 2016, Fourth Edition* (2016).

563 Johnson, G. C. and R. Lumpkin, eds. *State of the Climate in 2021: Global Oceans*. From: Blunden, J. and T. Boyer, eds. *State of the Climate in 2021*. American Meteorological Society (August 2022).

564 Cheng, Lijing, Kevin E. Trenberth, John Fasullo, Tim Boyer, John Abraham, and Jiang Zhu. "Improved Estimates of Ocean Heat Content from 1960 to 2015." *Science Advances* 3, no. 3 (March 10, 2017).

565 Cheng, Lijing, John Abraham, Kevin E. Trenberth, John Fasullo, Tim Boyer, Ricardo Locarnini, Bin Zhang et al. "Upper Ocean Temperatures Hit Record High in 2020." *Advances in Atmospheric Science* 38 (January 13, 2021).

566 Carrington, Damian. "Climate Crisis: Record Ocean Heat in 2020 Supercharged Extreme Weather." *The Guardian* (January 13, 2021).

567 Chaudhary, Chhaya, Anthony J. Richardson, David S. Schoeman, and Mark J. Costello. "Global Warming Is Causing a More Pronounced Dip in Marine Species Richness around the Equator." *Proceedings of the National Academy of Sciences* 118 no. 15 (April 13, 2021).

568 Richardson, Anthony, Chhaya Chaudhary, David Schoeman, and Mark John Costello. "Marine Life Is Fleeing the Equator to Cooler Waters. History Tells Us This Could Trigger a Mass Extinction Event." *The Conversation* (April 7, 2021).

569 Smale, Dan A., Thomas Wernberg, Eric C. J. Oliver, Mads Thomsen, Ben P. Harvey, Sandra C. Straub, Michael T. Burrows et al. "Marine Heatwaves Threaten Global Biodiversity and the Provision of Ecosystem Services." *Nature Climate Change* 9 (March 4, 2019).

570 Cheng, Lijing, John Abraham, Zeke Hausfather, and Kevin E. Trenberth. "How Fast are the Oceans Warming?" *Science* 363, no. 6423 (January 11, 2019).

571 International Union for Conservation of Nature. *Explaining Ocean Warming: Causes, Scale, Effects and Consequences* (September 2016).

572 Ozarslan, Ramazan, and Yadigar Sekerci. "Fractional Order Oxygen—Plankton System under Climate Change." *Chaos: An Interdisciplinary Journal of Nonlinear Science* 30, no. 3 (March 19, 2020).

573 Sekerci, Yadigar, and Sergei Petrovskii. "Mathematical Modelling of Plankton–Oxygen Dynamics under the Climate Change." *Bulletin of Mathematical Biology* 77, no. 12 (December 2015).

574 Sekerci, Yadigar, and Sergei Petrovskii. "Global Warming Can Lead to Depletion of Oxygen by Disrupting Phytoplankton Photosynthesis: A Mathematical Modelling Approach." *Geosciences* 8, no. 6 (June 3, 2018).

575 Schmidtko, Sunke, Lothar Stramma, and Martin Visbeck. "Decline in Global Oceanic Oxygen Content during the Past Five Decades." *Nature* 542 (February 15, 2017).

576 Li, Guancheng, Lijing Cheng, Jiang Zhu, Kevin E. Trenberth, Michael E. Mann, and John P. Abraham. "Increasing Ocean Stratification over the Past Half-Century." *Nature Climate Change* 10 (September 28, 2020).

577 Sallée, Jean-Baptiste, Violaine Pellichero, Camille Akhoudas, Etienne Pauthenet, Lucie Vignes, Sunke Schmidtko, Alberto Naveira Garabato, Peter Sutherland, and Mikael Kuusela. "Summertime Increases in Upper-Ocean Stratification and Mixed-Layer Depth." *Nature* 591 (March 24, 2021).

578 Wishner, K.F., B. A. Seibel, C. Roman, C. Deutsch, D. Outram, C. T. Shaw, M. A. Birk, K. A. S. Mislan, T. J. Adams, D. Moore, and S. Riley. "Ocean Deoxygenation and Zooplankton: Very Small Oxygen Differences Matter." *Science Advances* 4, no. 12 (December 19, 2018).

579 Helmholtz Centre for Ocean Research Kiel (GEOMAR). "Global Ocean De-Oxygenation Quantified." ScienceDaily (February 15, 2017).

580 Breitburg, Denise, Lisa A. Levin, Andreas Oschlies, Marilaure Grégoire, Francisco P. Chavez, Daniel J. Conley, Véronique Garçon et al. "Declining Oxygen in the Global Ocean and Coastal Waters." *Science* 359, no. 6371 (January 5, 2018).

581 Welch, Craig. "Climate Change Is Suffocating Large Parts of the Ocean." *National Geographic* (January 4, 2018).

582 Watson, Andrew J. "Oceans on the Edge of Anoxia." *Science* 354, no. 6319 (December 23, 2016).

583 NOAA. Ocean Acidification.

584 Sosdian, S.M., R. Greenop, M. P. Hain, G. L. Foster, P. N. Pearson, and C. H. Lear. "Constraining the Evolution of Neogene Ocean Carbonate Chemistry Using the Boron Isotope pH Proxy." *Earth and Planetary Science Letters* 49 (September 15, 2018).

585 Dutkiewicz, Stephanie, J. Jeffrey Morris, Michael J. Follows, Jeffery Scott, Orly Levitan, Sonya T. Dyhrman, and Ilana Berman-Frank. "Impact of Ocean Acidification on the Structure of Future Phytoplankton Communities." *Nature Climate Change* 5 (July 20, 2015).

586 Chu, Jennifer. "Ocean Acidification May Cause Dramatic Changes to Phytoplankton," MIT (July 20, 2015).

587 Bednaršek, Nina, Richard A. Feely, Marcus W. Beck, Simone R. Alin, Samantha A. Siedlecki, Piero Calosie, Emily L.Norton et al. "Exoskeleton Dissolution with Mechanoreceptor Damage in Larval Dungeness Crab Related to Severity of Present-Day Ocean Acidification Vertical Gradients." *Science of the Total Environment* 716 (January 22, 2020).

588 Barton, Alan, Burke Hales, George G. Waldbusser, Chris Langdon, and Richard A. Feely. "The Pacific Oyster, *Crassostrea Gigas*, Shows Negative Correlation to Naturally Elevated Carbon Dioxide Levels; Implications for Near-Term Ocean Acidification Effects." *Limnology and Oceanography* 57, no. 3 (April 16, 2012).

589 Bednaršek, Nina, R. A. Feely, J. C. P. Reum, B. Peterson, J. Menkel, S. R. Alin, and B. Hales. "*Limacina Helicina* Shell Dissolution as an Indicator of Declining Habitat Suitability Owing to Ocean Acidification in the California Current Ecosystem." *Proceedings of the Royal Society B* (April 30, 2014).

590 Kintisch, Eli. "Snails Are Dissolving in Pacific Ocean." *Science* (May 1, 2014).

591 O'Donnell, Michael J., Matthew N. George, and Emily Carrington. "Mussel Byssus Attachment Weakened by Ocean Acidification." *Nature Climate Change* 3 (March 10, 2013).

592 Jellison, Brittany M., Aaron T. Ninokawa, Tessa M. Hill, Eric Sanford and Brian Gaylord. "Ocean Acidification Alters the Response of Intertidal Snails to a Key Sea Star Predator." *Proceedings of the Royal Society B* (June 29, 2016).

593 Fox, Caleb P., Jessica H. Whiteside, Paul E. Olsen, Xingqian Cui, Roger E. Summons, Erdem Idiz, and Kliti Grice. "Two-Pronged Kill Mechanism at the End-Triassic Mass Extinction." *Geology* 50 no.4 (January 5, 2022).

594 Miller, Seth H., Denise L. Breitburg, Rebecca B. Burrell, and Andrew G. Keppel. "Acidification Increases Sensitivity to Hypoxia in Important Forage Fishes." *Marine Ecology Progress* 549 (May 10, 2016).

595 Six, Katharina D., Silvia Kloster, Tatiana Ilyina, Stephen D. Archer, Kai Zhang, and Ernst Maier-Reimer. "Global Warming Amplified by Reduced Sulphur Fluxes as a Result of Ocean Acidification." *Nature Climate Change* 3 (August 25, 2013).

596 Hubbard, Jule. Road Repairs Continuing; Fall Creek Road Is Biggest Job Left." *Wilkes Journal-Patriot* (July 31, 2013).

597 Risser, Mark D. and Michael F. Wehner. "Attributable Human-Induced Changes in the Likelihood and Magnitude of the Observed Extreme Precipitation during Hurricane Harvey," *Geophysical Research Letters* 44, no. 24 (December 12, 2017).

598 Mach, Katharine, and Miyuki Hinosept. "What Climate Scientists Want You to See in the Floodwaters." *The New York Times* (September 2, 2017).

599 Summers, Hannah. "Floods and Devastation in India, Nepal and Bangladesh—in Pictures." *The Guardian* (August 16, 2017).

600 Carlowicz, Michael. "Tracking 30 Years of Sea Level Rise." NASA Earth Observatory (August 19, 2022).

601 Tebaldi, Claudia, Roshanka Ranasinghe, Michalis Vousdoukas, D. J. Rasmussen, Ben Vega-Westhoff, Ebru Kirezci, Robert E. Kopp, Ryan Sriver, and Lorenzo Mentaschi. "Extreme Sea Levels at Different Global Warming Levels." *Nature Climate Change* 11 (August 30, 2021).

602 The Royal Society. *Climate Updates: What Have We Learnt since the ipcc 5th Assessment Report?* (2017).

603 IPCC. *Climate Change 2021: The Physical Science Basis, Summary for Policymakers.* From: *Climate Change 2021: The Physical Science Basis* (August 7, 2021).

604 Arctic Mapping and Assessment Programme. *Snow, Water, Ice and Permafrost. Summary for Policy-makers* (2017).

605 Jevrejeva, Svetlana, Luke P. Jackson, Riccardo E. M. Riva, Aslak Grinsted, and John C. Moore. "Coastal Sea Level Rise with Warming Above 2°C," *Proceedings of the National Academy of Sciences* 113, no. 47 (November 22, 2016).

606 Nauels, Alexander, Joeri Rogelj, Carl-Friedrich Schleussner, Malte Meinshausen, and Matthias Mengel. "Linking Sea Level Rise and Socioeconomic Indicators under the Shared Socioeconomic Pathways." *Environmental Research Letters* 12, no. 11 (November 11, 2017).

607 Bamber, Jonathan L., Michael Oppenheimer, Robert E. Kopp, Willy P. Aspinall, and Roger M. Cooke. "Ice Sheet Contributions to Future Sea-Level Rise from Structured Expert Judgment." *Proceedings of the National Academy of Sciences* 116 no. 23 (May 20, 2019).

608 Horton, Benjamin P., Nicole S. Khan, Niamh Cahill, Janice S. H. Lee, Timothy A. Shaw, Andra J. Garner, Andrew C. Kemp, Simon E. Engelhart, and Stefan Rahmstorf. "Estimating Global Mean Sea-Level Rise and Its Uncertainties by 2100 and 2300 from an Expert Survey." *npj Climate and Atmospheric Sciences* 3 (May 8, 2020).

609 NOAA et al. *2022 Sea Level Rise Technical Report* (February 2022).

610 Jevrejeva, S., L. P. Jackson, A. Grinsted, D. Lincke, and B. Marzeion. "Flood Damage Costs under the Sea Level Rise with Warming of 1.5°C And 2°C." *Environmental Research Letters*, 13, no. 7 (July 4, 2018).

611 Doyle, Alister, Elizabeth Culliford, and Lucas Jackson. "The Hunt for Better Climate Science." Reuters (September 19, 2018).

612   Koppe, Robert E., Robert M. DeConto, Daniel A. Bader, Carling C. Hay, Radley M. Horton, Scott Kulp, Michael Oppenheimer, David Pollard, and Benjamin H. Strauss. "Evolving Understanding of Antarctic Ice-Sheet Physics and Ambiguity in Probabilistic Sea-Level Projections." *Earth's Future* 5 no. 12 (December 14, 2017).
613   EPA. *Climate Change Indicators in the United States 2016 Fourth Edition.*
614   Nerem, R. S., B. D. Beckley, J. T. Fasullo, B. D. Hamlington, D. Masters, and G. T. Mitchum. "Climate-Change–Driven Accelerated Sea-Level Rise Detected in the Altimeter Era," *Proceedings of the National Academy of Sciences* 115 No. 9 (February 12, 2018).
615   Hoffman, Jeremy S., Peter U. Clark Andrew C. Parnell and Feng He. "Regional and Global Sea-Surface Temperatures during the Last Interglaciation." *Science* 355, no. 6322 (January 20, 2017).
616   Rohling, Eelco J., Fiona D. Hibbert, Katharine M. Grant, Eirik V. Galaasen, Nil Irvalı, Helga F. Kleiven, Gianluca Marino et al. "Asynchronous Antarctic and Greenland Ice-Volume Contributions to the Last Interglacial Sea-Level Highstand." *Nature Communications* 10 (November 6, 201)9.
617   Hibbert, Fiona, Eelco Rohling, and Katharine Grant. "Scientists Looked At Sea Levels 125,000 Years in the Past. The Results are Terrifying." *The Conversation* (November 6, 2019).
618   Levermann, Anders et al., "The Multimillennial Sea-Level Commitment of Global Warming," *Proceedings of the National Academy of Sciences* 110, no. 34, August 20, 2013.
619   Fischer, Hubertus, Katrin J. Meissner, Alan C. Mix, Nerilie J. Abram, Jacqueline Austermann, Victor Brovkin, Emilie Capron et al. "Palaeoclimate Constraints on the Impact of 2°C Anthropogenic Warming and Beyond." *Nature GeoScience* 11 (June 25, 2018).
620   Storlazzi, Carl, Stephen B. Gingerich, A. P. Van Dongeren, Olivia M. Cheriton, Peter W. Swarzenski, Ellen Quataert, Clifford I. Voss, Donald W. Field, Hariharasubramanian Annamalai, Greg A. Piniak, and Robert McCall. "Most Atolls Will be Uninhabitable by the Mid-21st Century Because of Sea-Level Rise Exacerbating Wave-Driven Flooding." *Science Advances* 4, no. 4 (April 25, 2018).
621   Kulp, Scott A. and Benjamin H, Strauss. "New Elevation Data Triple Estimates Of Global Vulnerability to Sea-Level Rise and Coastal Flooding." *Nature Communications* 10 (October 29, 2019).
622   Sallenger, Asbury H., Jr., Kara S. Doran, and Peter A. Howd. "Hotspot of Accelerated Sea-Level Rise on the Atlantic Coast of North America." *Nature Climate Change* 2 (June 24, 2012).
623   Jevrejeva, Svetlana, Luke P. Jackson, Riccardo E. M. Riva, Aslak Grinsted, and John C. Moore. "Coastal Sea Level Rise with Warming Above 2°C," *Proceedings of the National Academy of Sciences* 113, no. 47 (November 22, 2016).

624 Holder, John, Niko Kommenda, and Jonathan Watts. "The Three-Degree World: The Cities That Will Be Drowned By Global Warming." *The Guardian* (November 3, 2017).

625 Climate Central. "Mapping Choices: Carbon, Climate, and Rising Seas—Our Global Legacy" (November 2015).

626 Hallegatte, Stephane, Colin Green, Robert J. Nicholls, and Jan Corfee-Morlot. "Future Flood Losses in Major Coastal Cities." *Nature Climate Change* 3 (August 18, 2013).

627 Strauss, Benjamin, Scott Kulp, and Anders Levermann. "Carbon Choices Determine US Cities Committed To Futures below Sea Level." *Proceedings of the National Academy of Sciences*" 112, no. 44 (November 3, 2015).

628 Environmental Protection Agency. Climate Change Indicators: Oceans.

629 Union of Concerned Scientists. *Underwater: Rising Seas, Chronic Floods, and the Implications for us Coastal Real Estate* (June, 2018).

630 Union of Concerned Scientists. *When Rising Seas Hit Home: Hard Choices Ahead for Hundreds of us Coastal Communities* (July 2017).

631 Zillow. "Climate Change and Housing: Will a Rising Tide Sink all Homes?" (August 2, 2016).

632 Grinsted, Aslak, John Moore, and Svetlana Jevrejeva. "Projected Atlantic Hurricane Surge Threat from Rising Temperatures." *Proceedings of the National Academy of Sciences* 110, no. 14 (April 2, 2013).

633 National Weather Service. Hurricane Harvey Info (2017).

634 NOAA. The State of High Tide Flooding and Annual Outlook.

635 Sweet, William V. and Joseph Park. "From the Extreme to the Mean: Acceleration and Tipping Points of Coastal Inundation from Sea-level Rise" *Earth's Future* 2, no. 12 (December 2014).

636 Sweet, William V., Greg Dusek, Jayantha Obeysekera, and John J. Marra. *Patterns and Projections of High Tide Flooding Along the U.S. Coastline Using a Common Impact Threshold.* NOAA (February 2018).

637 Willner, Sven N., Anders Levermann, Fang Zhao, and Katja. "Adaptation Required to Preserve Future High-End River Flood Risk at Present Levels." *Science Advances* 4, no. 1 (January 10, 2018).

638 NOAA. "Spring Outlook: Historic, Widespread Flooding to Continue through May" (March 21, 2019).

639 Dottori, Francesco, Wojciech Szewczyk, Juan-Carlos Ciscar, Fang Zhao, Lorenzo Alfieri, Yukiko Hirabayashi, Alessandra Bianchi et al. "Increased Human and Economic Losses from River Flooding with Anthropogenic Warming." *Nature Climate Change* 8 (September 11, 2018).

640 Hoegh-Guldberg, Ove. *BCG Economic Valuation: Methodology and Sources, Reviving the Ocean Economy the Case for Action 2015.*

641 Setter, Renee, and Camilo Mora. "Impacts of Climate Change on Site Selection for Coral Restoration." AGU Ocean Sciences Meeting (February 17, 2020).

642 Dietzel, Andreas, Michael Bode, Sean R. Connolly, and Terry P. Hughes. "Long-Term Shifts in the Colony Size Structure of Coral Populations along the Great Barrier Reef." *Proceedings of the Royal Society B* (October 14, 2020).

643 NOAA. Coral Reef Watch.

644 NOAA. Coral Reef Futures.

645 Frieler, K., M. Meinshausen, A. Golly, M. Mengel, K. Lebek, S. D. Donner, and O. Hoegh-Guldberg. "Limiting Global Warming to 2°C Is Unlikely to Save Most Coral Reefs." *Nature Climate Change* 3 (September 16, 2012).

646 King, Andrew, David Karoly, Mitchell Black, Ove Hoegh-Guldberg, and Sarah Perkins-Kirkpatrick. "Great Barrier Reef Bleaching Would be Almost Impossible without Climate Change." *The Conversation* (April 28, 2016).

647 van Hooidonk, Ruben, Jeffrey Maynard, Jerker Tamelander, Jamison Gove, Gabby Ahmadia, Laurie Raymundo, Gareth Williams, Scott F. Heron, and Serge Planes. "Local-Scale Projections of Coral Reef Futures and Implications of the Paris Agreement." *Scientific Reports* 6 (December 21, 2016).

648 Dixon, Adele M., Piers M. Forster, Scott F. Heron, Anne M. K. Stoner, and Maria Beger. "Future Loss of Local-Scale Thermal Refugia in Coral Reef Ecosystems." PLOS *Climate* (February 1, 2022).

649 Hughes, Terry P., Kristen D. Anderson, Sean R. Connolly, Scott F. Heron, James T. Kerry, Janice M. Lough, Andrew H. Baird et al. "Spatial and Temporal Patterns of Mass Bleaching of Corals in the Anthropocene." *Science* 359, no. 6371 (January 5, 2018).

650 Hughes, Terry P., James T. Kerry, Andrew H. Baird, Sean R. Connolly, Andreas Dietzel, C. Mark Eakin, Scott F. Heron et al. "Global Warming Transforms Coral Reef Assemblages." *Nature* 556 (April 18, 2018).

651 Ainsworth, Tracy D., Scott F. Heron, Juan Carlos Ortiz, Peter J. Mumby, Alana Grech, Daisie Ogawa, C. Mark Eakin, and William Leggat. "Climate Change Disables Coral Bleaching Protection on the Great Barrier Reef." *Science* 352, no. 6283 (April 15, 2016).

652 Muehllehner, Nancy, Chris Langdon, Alyson Venti, and David Kadko. "Dynamics of Carbonate Chemistry, Production, and Calcification of the Florida Reef Tract (2009–2010): Evidence for Seasonal Dissolution." *Global Biogeochemical Cycles* 30, no. 5 (May 2, 2016).

653 Perry, Chris T., Lorenzo Alvarez-Filip, Nicholas A. J. Graham, Peter J. Mumby, Shaun K. Wilson, Paul S. Kench, Derek P. Manzello et al. "Loss of Coral Reef Growth Capacity to Track Future Increases in Sea Level." *Nature* 558 (June 14, 2018).

654 NOAA. Estuary Habitat.

655 Florida Department of Environmental Protection. Benefits of Mangroves.

656 Menéndez, Pelayo, Iñigo J. Losada, Saul Torres-Ortega, Siddharth Narayan, and Michael W. Beck. "The Global Flood Protection Benefits of Mangroves." *Scientific Reports*, 10 (March 10, 2020).

657 Blankespoor, Brian, Susmita Dasgupta, and Glenn-Marie Lange. *Mangroves as Protection from Storm Surges in a Changing Climate.* World Bank Group (March 2016).

658 Alongi, Daniel M. "Carbon Sequestration in Mangrove Forests." *Carbon Management* (April 2014).

659 Jerath, Meenakshi, Mahadev Bhat, Victor H. Rivera-Monroy, Edward Castañeda-Moya, Marc Simard, and Robert R. Twilley. "The Role of Economic, Policy, and Ecological Factors in Estimating the Value of Carbon Stocks in Everglades Mangrove Forests, South Florida, USA," *Environmental Science & Policy* 66 (December 2016).

660 Kirwan, Matthew, L. and Simon M., Mudd. "Response of Salt-Marsh Carbon Accumulation to Climate Change." *Nature* 489 (September 26, 2012).

661 Lovelock, Catherine E., Donald R. Cahoon, Daniel A. Friess, Glenn R. Guntenspergen, Ken W. Krauss, Ruth Reef, Kerrylee Rogers, et al. "The Vulnerability of Indo-Pacific Mangrove Forests to Sea-Level Rise." *Nature* 526 (October 22, 2015).

662 Saintilan, Neil, Catherine Lovelock, and Kerrylee Rogers. "Rising Seas Threaten to Drown Important Mangrove Forests, Unless We Intervene." *The Conversation* (October 14, 2015).

663 ABCTV Catalyst. "The Secret Life of Krill" (March 24, 2015).

664 Kawaguchi, S., A. Ishida, R. King, B. Raymond, N. Waller, A. Constable, S. Nicol, M. Wakita, and A. Ishimatsu. "Risk Maps for Antarctic Krill under Projected Southern Ocean Acidification." *Nature Climate Change* 3 (July 7, 2013).

665 Piñones, Andrea, and Alexey Fedorov. "Projected Changes of Antarctic Krill Habitat by the End of the 21st Century." *Geophysical Research Letters* 43, no. 16 (August 28, 2016).

666 Lamb, Joleah B., Jeroen A. J. M. Van De Water, David G. Bourne, Craig Altier, Margaux Y. Hein, Evan A. Fiorenza, Nur Abu, Jamaluddin Jompa, and C. Drew Harvell. "Seagrass Ecosystems Reduce Exposure to Bacterial Pathogens of Humans, Fishes, and Invertebrates." *Science* 355, no. 6326 (February 17, 2017).

667 Short, Frederick T., Beth Polidoro, Suzanne R. Livingstone, Kent E. Carpenter, Salomão Bandeira, Japar Sidik Bujang, Hilconida P.Calumpon et al. "Extinction Risk Assessment of the World's Seagrass Species." *Biological Conservation* 144, no. 7 (July 2011).

668 Fourqurean, James W., Carlos M. Duarte, Hilary Kennedy, Núria Marbà, Marianne Holmer, Miguel Angel Mateo, Eugenia T. Apostolaki et al. "Seagrass

Ecosystems as a Globally Significant Carbon Stock." *Nature GeoScience* 5 (May 20, 2012).

669 Krumhansl, Kira A., Daniel K. Okamoto, Andrew Rassweiler, Mark Novak, John J. Bolton, Kyle C. Cavanaugh, Sean D. Connell et al. "Global Patterns of Kelp Forest Change Over the Past Half-Century." *Proceedings of the National Academy of Sciences* 119, no. 48 (November 29, 2016).

670 UN Food and Agriculture Organization. *The State of World Fisheries and Aquaculture 2020* (2020).

671 Cheung, William L., Gabriel Reygondeau, and Thomas L. Frölicher. "Large Benefits to Marine Fisheries of Meeting the 1.5°C Global Warming Target." *Science* 354, no. 6319 (December 23, 2016).

672 Free, Christopher M., James T. Thorson, Malin L. Pinsky, Kiva L. Oken, John Wiedenmann, and Olaf P. Jensen. "Impacts of Historical Warming on Marine Fisheries Production." *Science* 363 no. 6430 (March 1, 2019).

673 Rutgers University. "Climate Change Shrinks Many Fisheries Globally, Rutgers-Led Study Finds" (February 27, 2019).

674 Lam, Vicky W. Y., William W. L. Cheung, Gabriel Reygondeau, and U. Rashid Sumaila. "Projected Change in Global Fisheries Revenues under Climate Change." *Scientific Reports* 6 (September 7, 2016).

675 Moore, J. Keith, Weiwei Fu, Francois Primeau, Gregory L. Britten, Keith Lindsay, Matthew Long, Scott C. Doney, Natalie Mahowald, Forrest Hoffman, and James T. Randerson. "Sustained Climate Warming Drives Declining Marine Biological Productivity." *Science* 359, no. 6380 (March 9, 2018).

676 Moore, Jefferson Keith. "Climate Change Could Alter Ocean Food Chains, Leading to Far Fewer Fish in the Sea." *The Conversation* (April 19, 2018).

677 World Wildlife Fund et al., *The World's Forgotten Fishes* (2021).

678 Dahlke, Flemming T., Sylke Wohlrab, Martin Butzin, and Hans-Otto Pörtner. "Thermal Bottlenecks in the Life Cycle Define Climate Vulnerability of Fish." *Science* 369, no. 6499 (July 3, 2020).

679 Perry, Allison L., Paula J. Low, Jim R. Ellis, and John D. Reynolds. "Climate Change and Distribution Shifts in Marine Fishes." *Science* 308, no. 5730 (June 24, 2005).

680 Anon. "Warming Spells Trouble for Fish," *Science* (July 10, 2008).

681 Pauly, Daniel, and William W. L. Cheung. "Sound Physiological Knowledge and Principles in Modeling Shrinking of Fishes under Climate Change." *Global Change Biology* 24 no. 1 (August 21, 2017).

682 Gong, Hongjing, Chao Li, and Yuntao Zhou. "Emerging Global Ocean Deoxygenation across the 21st Century," *Geophysical Research Letters* 48, no. 23 (November 19, 2021).

683 Pershing, Andrew J., Michael A. Alexander, Christina M. Hernandez, Lisa A. Kerr, Arnault Le Bris, Katherine E. Mills, Janet A. Nye et al. "Slow Adaptation in the Face of Rapid Warming Leads to Collapse of the Gulf of Maine Cod Fishery." *Science* 350, no. 6262 (November 13, 2015).

684 World Wildlife Fund. Living Planet Report 2016 (2016).

685 National Center for Atmospheric Research. "How Melting Arctic Ice Affects Ocean Currents."

686 Delworth, Thomas L., Peter U. Clark, Marika Holland, William E. Johns, Till Kuhlbrodt, Jean Lynch-Stieglitz, Carrie Morrill, Richard Seager, Andrew J. Weaver, and Rong Zhang. "The Potential for Abrupt Change in the Atlantic Meridional Overturning Circulation, Chapter 4, *Abrupt Climate Change*."

687 Caesar, L., G. D. McCarthy, D. J. R. Thornalley, N. Cahill, and S. Rahmstorf. "Current Atlantic Meridional Overturning Circulation Weakest in Last Millennium." *Nature GeoScience* 14 (February 25, 2021).

688 Potsdam Institute for Climate Impact Research. "Gulf Stream System at Its Weakest in over a Millennium" (February 25, 2021).

689 Berwyn, Bob, "Scientists Say Ocean Circulation Is Slowing. Here's Why You Should Care." Inside Cliamte News (May 7, 2018).

690 Liu, Wei, Alexey Fedorov, and Florian Sévellec. "The Mechanisms of the Atlantic Meridional Overturning Circulation Slowdown Induced by Arctic Sea Ice Decline," *Journal of Climate* 32, no. 4 (February 15, 2019).

691 Boers, Niklas."Observation-Based Early-Warning Signals for a Collapse of the Atlantic Meridional Overturning Circulation." *Nature Climate Change* 11 (August 5, 2021).

692 Carrington, Damien. "Climate Crisis: Scientists Spot Warning Signs of Gulf Stream Collapse." *The Guardian* (August 5, 2021).

693 IPCC. *Climate Change 2022: Impacts, Adaptation and Vulnerability: Summary for Policymakers*. From: IPCC Sixth Assessment Report: Impacts, Adaptation and Vulnerability (February 27, 2022).

694 US Global Change Research Program, *Fourth National Climate Assessment, Chapter 15: Potential Surprises: Compound Extremes and Tipping Elements*. From: *Fourth National Climate Assessment Volume 1* (2018).

695 Pecl, Gretta T., Miguel B. Araújo, Johann D. Bell, Julia Blanchard, Timothy C. Bonebrake, I-Ching Chen, Timothy D. Clark et al. "Biodiversity Redistribution under Climate Change: Impacts on Ecosystems and Human Well-Being." *Science* 355, no., 6332 (March 31, 2017).

696 Climate Health Action. U.S. Call to Action on Climate, Health, and Equity: A Policy Action Agenda (2019).

697 *The Lancet*. "The Lancet Countdown on Health and Climate Change." (2020).

698 Romanello, Marina, Alice McGushin, Claudia Di Napoli, Paul Drummond, Nick Hughes, Louis Jamart, Harry Kennard et al. "The 2021 Report of the Lancet Countdown on Health and Climate Change: Code Red for a Healthy Future." *The Lancet* 398, no. 10311 (October 30, 2021).

699 DARA. "*Climate Vulnerability Monitor: A Guide to the Cold Calculus of a Hot Planet*" (2012).

700 World Health Organization. "Climate Change and Health." (October 30, 2021).

701 Hallegatte, Stephane, Mook Bangalore, Laura Bonzanigo, Marianne Fay, Tamaro Kane, Ulf Narloch, Julie Rozenberg, David Treguer, and Adrien Vogt-Schilb. *Shock Waves: Managing the Impacts of Climate Change on Poverty*. World Bank Group (2016).

702 World Bank Group. "Decline of Global Extreme Poverty Continues but Has Slowed: World Bank" (September 19, 2018).

703 Kaiman, Jonathan. "Chinese Struggle through 'Airpocalypse' Smog." *The Guardian* (February 16, 2013).

704 NASA. "Smog Shuts down Harbin." Earth Observatory (October 21, 2013).

705 Yu, Katrina. "The Good News (And Not So Good News) About China's Smoggy Air." NPR (December 18, 2018).

706 Kintisch, Eli. "Why is China's Smog So Bad? Researchers Point Far Away to a Melting Arctic." *Science* (March 15, 2017).

707 Zou, Yufei, Yuhang Wang, Yuzhong Zhang, and Ja-Ho Koo. "Arctic Sea Ice, Eurasia Snow, and Extreme Winter Haze in China." *Science Advances* 3, no. 3 (March 15, 2017).

708 Cai, Wenju, Ke Li, Hong Liao, Huijun Wang, and Lixin Wu. "Weather Conditions Conducive To Beijing Severe Haze More Frequent under Climate Change." *Nature Climate Change* 7 (March 20, 2017).

709 American Lung Association. *The State of the Air 2020* (2020).

710 EPA. "Persistent Organic Pollutants: A Global Issue, A Global Response" (2009).

711 Wang, XioPing, DianChao Sun, and TanDong Yao. "Climate Change and Global Cycling of Persistent Organic Pollutants: A Critical Review." *Science China Earth Sciences* 59 (September 6, 2016).

712 Tabuchi, Hiroko, Nadja Popovich, Blacki Migliozzi, and Andrew W. Lehren. "Floods are Getting Worse, and 2,500 Chemical Sites Lie in the Water's Path." *The New York Times* (February 6, 2018).

713 Balbus, John M., Alistair B. A. Boxall, Richard A. Fenske, Thomas E. McKone, and Lauren Zeise. "Implications of Global Climate Change for the Assessment and Management of Human Health Risks of Chemicals in the Natural Environment." *Environmental Toxicology and Chemistry* 32, no. 1 (January 2013).

714 Obrist, Daniel, Yannick Agnan, Martin Jiskra, Christine L. Olson, Dominique P. Colegrove, Jacques Hueber, Christopher W. Moore, Jeroen E. Sonke, and Detlev Helmig. "Tundra Uptake of Atmospheric Elemental Mercury Drives Arctic Mercury Pollution." *Nature* 547 (July 12, 2017).

715 Schuster, Paul F., Kevin M. Schaefer, George R. Aiken, Ronald C. Antweiler, John F. Dewild, Joshua D. Gryziec, Alessio Gusmeroli et al. "Permafrost Stores a Globally Significant Amount of Mercury." *Geophysical Research Letters* 45 (February 5, 2018).

716 St. Pierre, Kyra A., Scott Zolkos, Sarah Shakil, Suzanne E. Tank, Vincent L. St. Louis, and Steven V. Kokelj. "Unprecedented Increases in Total and Methyl Mercury Concentrations Downstream of Retrogressive Thaw Slumps in the Western Canadian Arctic." *Environmental Science & Technology* 52, No 24 (November 26, 2018).

717 EPA, "Basic Information about Mercury."

718 Government of Canada. Mercury in the Food Chain.

719 Genchi, Giuseppe, Maria Stefania Sinicropi, Alessia Carocci, Graziantonio Lauria, and Alessia Catalano. "Mercury Exposure and Heart Diseases." *International Journal of Environmental Research and Public Health* 14, no. 1 (January 12, 2017).

720 Jonsson, Sofi, Agneta Andersson, Mats B. Nilsson, Ulf Skyllberg, Erik Lundberg, Jeffra K. Schaefer, Staffan Åkerblom, and Erik Björn. "Terrestrial Discharges Mediate Trophic Shifts and Enhance Methylmercury Accumulation in Estuarine Biota." *Science Advances* 3, no. 1 (January 27, 2017).

721 Sever, Megan. "Inner Workings: Big Wildfires Mobilize Mercury. What Are the Risks to Surface Water?" *Proceedings of the National Academy of Sciences* 118, no. 27 (July 6, 2021).

722 Kudela, R. M., E. Berdalet, S. Bernard, M. Burford, L. Fernand, S. Lu, S. Roy et al. "Harmful Algal Blooms: A Scientific Summary for Policymakers." IOC/UNESCO (2015).

723 Gobler, Christopher J., Owen M. Doherty, Theresa K. Hattenrath-Lehmann, Andrew W. Griffith, Yoonja Kang, and R. Wayne Litaker. "Ocean Warming since 1982 Has Expanded the Niche Of Toxic Algal Blooms In The North Atlantic And North Pacific Oceans." *Proceedings of the National Academy of Sciences* 114, no. 9 (May 9, 2017).

724 Stony Brook University. "Research Shows Global Warming Making Oceans More Toxic." Phys.org(April 27, 2017).

725 McKibben, S. Morgaine, William Peterson, A. Michelle Wood, Vera L. Trainer, Matthew Hunter, and Angelicque E. White. "Climatic Regulation of the Neurotoxin Domoic Acid." *Proceedings of the National Academy of Sciences* 114, no. 2 (January 10, 2017).

726 UN Environment Programme. *UNEP Frontiers 2016 Report: Emerging Issues of Environmental Concern* (2016).

727 Mora, Camilo, Tristan McKenzie, Isabella M. Gaw, Jacqueline M. Dean, Hannah von Hammerstein, Tabatha A. Knudson et al. "Over Half of Known Human Pathogenic Diseases can be Aggravated by Climate Change." *Nature Climate Change* (August 8, 2022).

728 US Global Change Research Program, *The Impacts of Climate Change on Human Health in the United States*, April 2016).

729 Centers for Disease Control and Prevention. "Vital Signs: Trends in Reported Vectorborne Disease Cases—United States and Territories, 2004–2016" (May 4, 2018).

730 Carlson, Colin J., Gregory F. Albery, Cory Merow, Christopher H. Trisos, Casey M. Zipfel, Evan A. Eskew, Kevin J. Olival, Noam Ross, and Shweta Bansal. "Climate Change Increases Cross-Species Viral Transmission Risk." *Nature* (April 28, 2022).

731 Hummel, Michelle, Matthew Berry, and Mark T. Stacey. "Sea-level Rise Impacts on Wastewater Treatment Systems along the US Coasts." American Geophysical Union meeting (2017).

732 World Health Organization. *Quantitative Risk Assessment of the Effects of Climate Change on Selected Causes of Death 2030s and 2050s* (2014.)

733 Capinha, César, Jorge Rocha, and Carla A. Sousa. "Macroclimate Determines the Global Range Limit of *Aedes aegypti*." *EcoHealth* 11, no. 3 (March 19, 2014).

734 World Health Organization. Dengue and Severe Dengue.

735 IPCC. *Climate Change 2022: Impacts, Adaptation and Vulnerability: Summary for Policymakers.* From: IPCC Sixth Assessment Report: Impacts, Adaptation and Vulnerability (February 27, 2022).

736 Knowlton, Kim. "Zika Goes Viral in the US." Natural Resources Defense Council (August 3, 2015).

737 Ginty, Molly M. "Climate Change Bites." Natural Resources Defense Council (December 31, 2015).

738 Rochlin, Ilia, Dominick V. Ninivaggi, Michael L. Hutchinson, and Ary Farajollahi. "Climate Change and Range Expansion of the Asian Tiger Mosquito (Aedes albopictus) in Northeastern USA: Implications for Public Health Practitioners." *PLOS ONE* 8, no. 4 (April 2, 2013).

739 Langer, Julia, Abbey Dufoe, and Jen Brady. *US Faces a Rise in Mosquito "Disease Danger Days".* Climate Central (August 8, 2018).

740 Hoberg, Eric P. and David R. Brooks. "Evolution in Action: Climate Change, Biodiversity Dynamics and Emerging Infectious Disease," *Philosophical Transactions of the Royal Society B* 370 (April 5, 2015).

741 Parham, Paul E., Joanna Waldock, George K. Christophides, and Edwin Michael. "Climate Change and Vector-Born Diseases of Humans." *Philosophical Transactions of the Royal Society B* 370 (April 5, 2015).

742 Revich, Boris A. and Marina A. Podolnaya. "Thawing of Permafrost May Disturb Historic Cattle Burial Grounds in East Siberia." *Global Health Action* 4 (November 21, 2011).

743 Doucleff, Michaeleen. "Anthrax Outbreak in Russia Thought to be Result of Thawing Permafrost." NPR (August 3, 2016).

744 Centers for Disease Control and Prevention. Candida auris (2021).

745 Morales-López, Soraya E., Claudia M. Parra-Giraldo, Andrés Ceballos-Garzón, Heidys P. Martínez, Gerson J. Rodríguez, Carlos A. Álvarez-Moreno, and José Y. Rodríguez. "Invasive Infections with Multidrug-Resistant Yeast *Candida auris*, Colombia." *Emerging Infectious Diseases* 23 no. 1 (January 2017).

746 Casadevall, Arturo, Dimitrios P. Kontoyiannis, and Vincent Robert. "On the Emergence of *Candida auris*: Climate Change, Azoles, Swamps, and Birds." *mBio* (July 23, 2019).

747 American Society of Microbiology. "Rise of *Candida auris* Blamed on Global Warming," ScienceDaily (July 23, 2019).

748 Centers for Disease Control and Prevention. Vibrio Species Causing Vibriosis (May 13, 2016).

749 Vezzuli, Luigi, Chiara Grande, Philip C. Reid, Pierre Hélaouët, Martin Edwards, Manfred G. Höfle, Ingrid Brettar, Rita R. Colwell, and Carla Pruzzo. "Climate Influence on Vibrio and Associated Human Diseases during the Past Half-Century in the Coastal North Atlantic." *Proceedings of the National Academy of Sciences* 113, no. 34 (August 23, 2016).

750 Baker-Austin, Craig, Joaquin A. Trinanes, Nick G. H. Taylor, Rachel Hartnell, Anja Siitonen, and Jaime Martinez-Urtaza. "Emerging Vibrio Risk at High Latitudes in Response to Ocean Warming." *Nature Climate Change* 3 (July 22, 2012).

751 Chestney, Nina. "Bacteria Outbreak in Northern Europe Due to Ocean Warming, Study Says." Reuters (July 22, 2012).

752 Lamb, Joleah B., Jeroen A. J. M. Van De Water, David G. Bourne, Craig Altier, Margaux Y. Hein, Evan A. Fiorenza, Nur Abu, Jamaluddin Jompa, and C. Drew Harvell. "Seagrass Ecosystems Reduce Exposure to Bacterial Pathogens of Humans, Fishes, and Invertebrates." *Science* 355, no. 6326 (February 17, 2017).

753 Zimmer, Carl. "Disappearing Seagrass Protects Against Pathogens, Even Climate Change, Scientists Find." *The New York Times* (February 16, 2017).

754 Blauw, Lisanne L., N. Ahmad Aziz, Martijn R. Tannemaat, C. Alexander Blauw, Anton J. de Craen, Hanno Pijl, and Patrick C. N. Rensen. "Diabetes Incidence and Glucose Intolerance Prevalence Increase with Higher Outdoor Temperature." *BMJ Open Diabetes Research & Care* 5, no. 1 (January 2017).

755 American Psychological Association. *Mental Health and Our Changing Climate: Impacts, Implications, and Guidance* (March 29, 2017).

756 Climate Psychiatry Alliance.

757 Bowles, Devin, Colin Butler, and Sharon Friel. "Climate Change and Health in Earth's Future." *Earth's Future* 2, no. 2 (February 2014).

758 Reeping, Paul M. and David Hemenway. "The Association between Weather and the Number of Daily Shootings in Chicago (2012–2016)." *Injury Epidemiology* 7 (June 22, 2020).

759 Ranson, Matthew. "Crime, Weather, and Climate Change." *Journal of Environmental Economics and Management* 67, no. 3 (May 2014).

760 Costello, Anthony, Mustafa Abbas, Adriana Allen, Sarah Ball, Sarah Bell, Richard Bellamy, Sharon Friel, Nora Groce et al. "Managing the Health Effects of Climate Change." *The Lancet* 373, no. 9676 (May 16, 2009).

761 Hill, Alice C. and Leonardo Martinez-Diaz. *Building a Resilient Tomorrow: How to Prepare for the Coming Climate Disruption.* Oxford University Press, 2022.

762 FAO, IFAD, UNICEF, WFP, and WHO. *The State of Food Security and Nutrition in the World 2022.* (July 15, 2022).

763 Global Network against Food Crises. *2020 Global Report on Food Crises* (2020).

764 Global Network against Food Crises. *Global Report on Food Crises—2022* (May 4, 2022).

765 Ray, Deepak K., Paul C. West, Michael Clark, James S. Gerber, Alexander V. Prishchepov, and Snigdhansu Chatterjee. "Climate Change Has Likely Already Affected Global Food Production," *PLOS ONE* (May 31, 2019).

766 Ray, Deepak. "Climate Change is Affecting Crop Yields and Reducing Global Food Supplies." *The Conversation* (July 9, 2019).

767 World Resources Institute. *Creating a Sustainable Future.* (December 2018).

768 Ray, Deepak K., Nathaniel D. Mueller, Paul C. West, and Jonathan A. Foley. "Yield Trends Are Insufficient to Double Global Crop Production by 2050." *PLOS ONE* 8, no. 6 (June 2013).

769 Hallegatte, Stephane, Mook Bangalore, Laura Bonzanigo, Marianne Fay, Tamaro Kane, Ulf Narloch, Julie Rozenberg, David Treguer, and Adrien Vogt-Schilb. *Shock Waves: Managing the Impacts of Climate Change on Poverty.* World Bank Group (2016).

770 Haile, Mekbib G., Tesfamicheal Wossen, Kindie Tesfaye, and Joachim von Braun. "Impact of Climate Change, Weather Extremes, and Price Risk on Global Food Supply." *Economics of Disasters and Climate Change* 1, no., 1 (May 6, 2017).

771 Challinor, A.J., J. Watson, D. B. Lobell, S. M. Howden, D. R. Smith, and N. Chhetri. "A Meta-Analysis of Crop Yield under Climate Change and Adaptation." *Nature Climate Change* 4 (March 16, 2014).

772 Intergovernmental Science-Policy Platform on Biodiversity and Ecosystem Services. "Worsening Worldwide Land Degradation Now 'Critical', Undermining Well-Being of 3.2 Billion People" (March 2018).

773 Tigchelaar, Michelle, David S. Battisti, Rosamond L. Naylor, and Deepak K. Ray. "Future Warming Increases Probability of Globally Synchronized Maize Production Shocks." *Proceedings of the National Academy of Sciences* 115, no 26 (June 11, 2018).

774 Wang, Xuhui, Chuang Zhao, Christoph Müller, Chenzhi Wang, Philippe Ciais, Ivan Janssens, Josep Peñuelas et al. "Emergent Constraint on Crop Yield Response to Warmer Temperature from Field Experiments." *Nature Sustainability* 3 (June 29, 2020).

775 Reed, Sarah. "Climate Change Will Reduce Crop Yields Sooner Than We Thought." University of Leeds (March 16, 2014).

776 UN Food and Agriculture Organization. *Adapting Agriculture to Climate Change* (2016).

777 Moore, Caitlin E., Katherine Meacham-Hensold, Pauline Lemonnier, Rebecca A Slattery, Claire Benjamin, Carl J Bernacchi, Tracy Lawson, and Amanda P Cavanagh. "The Effect Of Increasing Temperature on Crop Photosynthesis: From Enzymes to Ecosystems." *Journal of Experimental Botany* 72, no. 8 (February 23, 2021).

778 Cook, Benjamin I., Jason E. Smerdon, Richard Seager, and Sloan Coats. "Global Warming and 21st Century Drying." *Climate Dynamics* 43, no. 9 (March 6, 2014).

779 Lesk, Corey, Pedram Rowhani, and Navin Ramankutty. "Influence of Extreme Weather Disasters on Global Crop Production." Nature 529 (January 6, 2016).

780 Zhao, Chuang, Shilong Piao, Xuhui Wang, David B. Lobell, Yao Huang, Mengtian Huang, Yitong Yao et al. "Temperature Increase Reduces Global Yields of Major Crops in Four Independent Estimates." *Proceedings of the National Academy of Sciences* 114, no. 35 (August 29, 2017).

781 Schauberger, Bernhard, Sotirios Archontoulis, Almut Arneth, Juraj Balkovic, Philippe Ciais, Delphine Deryng, Joshua Elliott et al. "Consistent Negative Response of US Crops to High Temperatures in Observations and Crop Models." *Nature Communications* 8 (January 19, 2017).

782 Battisti, David S. and Rosamond L. Naylor. "Historical Warnings of Future Food Insecurity with Unprecedented Seasonal Heat." *Science* 323, no. 5911 (January 9, 2009).

783 Tigchelaar, Michelle, David S. Battisti, Rosamond L. Naylor, and Deepak K. Ray. "Future Warming Increases Probability of Globally Synchronized Maize Production Shocks". *Proceedings of the National Academy of Sciences* 115, no. 26 (June 26, 2018).

784 Challinor, A. J., A.-K. Koehler, J. Ramirez-Villegas, S. Whitfield, and B. Das. "Current Warming Will Reduce Yields Unless Maize Breeding and Seed Systems Adapt Immediately." *Nature Climate Change* 6 (June 20, 2016).

785 Liu, Bing, Senthold Asseng, Christoph Müller, Frank Ewert, Joshua Elliott, David B. Lobell, Pierre Martre et al. "Similar Estimates of Temperature Impacts on Global Wheat Yield by Three Independent Methods." *Nature Climate Change* 6 (October 20, 2016).

786 Zhao, Chuang, Shilong Piao, Xuhui Wang, Yao Huang, Philippe Ciais, Joshua Elliott, Mengtian Huang et al. "Plausible Rice Yield Losses under Future Climate Warming." *Nature Plants* 3 (December 19, 2016).

787 Lustgarten, Abrahm. "How Russia Wins the Climate Crisis." *The New York Times* (December 16, 2020).

788 Parfenova, Elena, Nadezhda Tchebakova1, and Amber Soja. "Assessing Landscape Potential for Human Sustainability and 'Attractiveness' Across Asian Russia in a Warmer 21st Century." *Environmental Research Letters* 14, no. 6 (June 7, 2019).

789 Evich, Helena Bottemiller. "The Great Nutrient Collapse."*Politico* (September 13, 2017).

790 Loladze, Irene. "Hidden Shift of the Ionome of Plants Exposed to Elevated CO_2 Depletes Minerals at the Base of Human Nutrition." *eLife* (May 7, 2014).

791 Myers, Samuel S., Antonella Zanobetti, Itai Kloog, Peter Huybers, Andrew D. B. Leakey, Arnold J. Bloom, Eli Carlisle et al. "Increasing CO_2 Threatens Human Nutrition." *Nature* 510 (May 7, 2014).

792 Medek, Danielle E., Joel Schwartz, and Samuel Myers. "Estimated Effects of Future Atmospheric CO_2 Concentrations on Protein Intake and the Risk of Protein Deficiency by Country and Region." *Environmental Health Perspectives* 125, no. 8 (August 2017).

793 Zhu, Chunwu, Kazuhiko Kobayashi, Irakli Loladze, Jianguo Zhuqian Jiangxi Xugang Liu et al. "Carbon Dioxide (CO_2) Levels This Century Will Alter the Protein, Micronutrients, and Vitamin Content of Rice Grains with Potential Health Consequences for the Poorest Rice-Dependent Countries." *Science Advances* 4, no. 5 (May 23, 2018).

794 Springmann, Marco, Daniel Mason-D'Croz, Sherman Robinson, Tara Garnett, H. Charles J Godfray, Douglas Gollin, Mike Rayner, Paola Ballon, and Peter Scarborough. "Global and Regional Health Effects of Future Food Production under Climate Change: A Modelling Study." *The Lancet* 387, no. 10031 (May 2016).

795 Ziska, Lewis H., Jeffery S. Pettis, Joan Edwards, Jillian E. Hancock, Martha B. Tomecek, Andrew Clark, Jeffrey S. Dukes, Irakli Loladze and H. Wayne Polley. "Rising Atmospheric CO_2 Is Reducing the Protein Concentration of a Floral Pollen

Source Essential for North American Bees." *Proceedings of the Royal Society B* 283 (April 13, 2016).

796 Zhu, Zaichun, Shilong Piao, Ranga B. Myneni, Mengtian Huang, Zhenzhong Zeng, Josep G. Canadell, Philippe Ciais et al. "Greening Of the Earth and Its Drivers." *Nature Climate Change* 6 (April 25, 2016).

797 Sneed, Annie. "Ask the Experts: Does Rising CO_2 Benefit Plants?" *Scientific American* (January 23, 2018).

798 Wang, Songhan, Yongguang Zhang, Weimin, Jing M. Chen, Philippe Ciais, Alessandro Cescatti et al. "Recent Global Decline of CO_2 Fertilization Effects on Vegetation Photosynthesis," *Science* 370, no. 6522 (December 11, 2020).

799 Cowan, Tim, Sabine Undorf, Gabriele C. Hegerl, Luke J. Harrington, and Friederike E. L. Otto. "Present-Day Greenhouse Gases Could Cause More Frequent and Longer Dust Bowl Heat waves." *Nature Climate Change* 10 (May 18, 2020).

800 Achakulwisu, Ploy Pattanun, Loretta Mickley, and Susan Anenberg. "Increased Deaths and Illnesses from Inhaling Airborne Dust: An Understudied Impact of Climate Change." *The Conversation* (June 11, 2018).

801 Maki, Teruya, Kevin C. Lee, Kei Kawai, Kazunari Onishi, Chun Sang Hong, Yasunori Kurosaki, Masato Shinoda et al. "Aeolian Dispersal of Bacteria Associated With Desert Dust and Anthropogenic Particles Over Continental and Oceanic Surfaces." *Journal of Geophysical Research* 124, no.10 (April 9, 2019).

802 Lambert, Andrew, A. Gannet Hallar, Maria Garcia, Courtenay Strong,Elisabeth Andrews, Jenny L. Hand. "Dust Impacts of Rapid Agricultural Expansion on the Great Plain." *Geophysical Research Letters* (October 12, 2020).

803 Pease, Roland. "Dust Bowl 2.0? Rising Great Plains Dust Levels Stir Concerns." *Science* (October 20, 2020).

804 Glotter, Michael, and Joshua Elliott. "Simulating US Agriculture in a Modern Dust Bowl Drought." *Nature Plants* 3 (December 12, 2016).

805 Mitchum, Robert. "Dust Bowl Would Devastate Today's Crops, Study Finds." University of Chicago (December 19, 2016).

806 Heslin, Alison, Michael J. Puma, Philippe Marchand, Joel A. Carr, Jampel Dell'Angelo, Paolo D'Odorico, Jessica A. Gephart et al. "Simulating the Cascading Effects of an Extreme Agricultural Production Shock: Global Implications of a Contemporary US Dust Bowl Event." *Frontiers in Sustainable Food Systems* (March 20, 2020).

807 Richey, Alexandra, Brian F. Thomas, Min-Hui Lo, John T. Reager, James S. Famiglietti, Katalyn Voss, Sean Swenson, and Matthew Rodell. "Quantifying Renewable Groundwater Stress with GRACE." *Water Resources Research* 15 (July 14, 2015).

808 DeGraaf, Inge. "Groundwater Resources around the World Could Be Depleted by 2050s." American Geophysical Union (December 15, 2016).

809 Katz, Cheryl. "As Groundwater Dwindles, a Global Food Shock Looms." *National Geographic* (December 22, 2016).

810 Hofste, Rutger Willem, Paul Reig, and Leah Schleifer. "17 Countries, Home to One-Quarter of the World's Population, Face Extremely High Water Stress." World Resources Institute (August 6, 2019).

811 Kimmelman, Michael. "Mexico City, Parched and Sinking, Faces a Water Crisis." *The New York Times* (February 17, 2017).

812 Pathak, Sushmita. "No Drips, No Drops: A City of 10 Million Is Running Out Of Water." National Public Radio (June 25, 2019).

813 Indian Water Ministries. *Composite Water Management Index* (June 2018).

814 Farinosi, F., C. Giupponi, A. Reynaud, G. Ceccherini, C. Carmona-Moreno, A. De Roo, D. Gonzalez-Sanchez, and G.Bidoglio. "An Innovative Approach to the Assessment of Hydro-Political Risk: A Spatially Explicit, Data Driven Indicator of Hydro-Political Issues." *Global Environmental Change* 52 (September 2018).

815 Pearce, Fred. "Salt Scourge: The Dual Threat of Warming and Rising Salinity." *Yale Environment360* (May 10, 2022).

816 Hassani, Amirhossein, Adisa Azapagic, and Nima Shokri. "Predicting Long-Term Dynamics of Soil Salinity and Sodicity on a Global Scale." *Proceedings of the National Academy of Sciences* 117, no. 52 (December 22, 2020).

817 Bailey, Rob, and Laura Wellesley. *Chokepoints and Vulnerabilities in Global Food Trade.* Chatham House Report (June 2017).

818 Tigchelaar, Michelle, David S. Battisti, Rosamond L. Naylor, and Deepak K. Ray. "Future Warming Increases Probability of Globally Synchronized Maize Production Shocks." *Proceedings of the National Academy of Sciences* 115, no. 26 (June 26, 2018).

819 UN Food and Agriculture Organization. *How to Feed the World in 2050* (2009).

820 Myers, Samuel S., Matthew R. Smith, Sarah Guth, Christopher D. Golden, Bapu Vaitla, Nathaniel D. Mueller, Alan D. Dangour, and Peter Huybers. "Climate Change and Global Food Systems: Potential Impacts on Food Security and Undernutrition." *Annual Review of Public Health* 38 (January 6, 2017).

821 UN Population Division, Department of Economic and Social Affairs of the United Nations Secretariat. *World Population Prospects 2022* (2022).

822 Mills, Michael. "How to Avoid Population Overshoot and Collapse." *Psychology Today* (November 2, 2011).

823 Wackernagel, Mathis and William E. Rees. *Our Ecological Footprint: Reducing Human Impact on the Earth.* New Society Publishers (1996).

824 Wackernagel, Mathis, Niels B. Schulz, Diana Deumling, Alejandro Callejas Linares, Martin Jenkins, Valerie Kapos, Chad Monfreda, Jonathan Loh, Norman Myers, Richard Norgaard, and Jørgen Randers. "Tracking the Ecological Overshoot

of the Human Economy." *Proceedings of the National Academy of Sciences* 99, no. 4 (July 9, 2002).

825 Global Footprint Network. Ecological Footprint.

826 Barnosky, Anthony A., Elizabeth A. Hadly, Jordi Bascompte, Eric L. Berlow, James H. Brown, Mikael Fortelius, Wayne M. Getz et al. "Approaching a State Shift in Earth's Biosphere." *Nature* 486, no. 7401 (June 6, 2012).

827 Keim, Brandon. "Is Humanity Pushing Earth Past a Tipping Point?" *Wired* (June 6, 2016).

828 Newland, Kathleen. *Climate Change and Migration Dynamics*. Migration Policy Institute (September 2011).

829 International Organization for Migration. *Migration, Environment and Climate Change: Assessing the Evidence* (2009).

830 Brown, Oli. *Migration and Climate Change*. International Organization for Migration (2008).

831 Christian Aid Society. *Human Tide: The Real Migration Crisis* (May 2007).

832 Nicholls, Robert J., Natasha Marinova, Jason A. Lowe, Sally Brown, Pier Vellinga, Diogo de Gusmão, Jochen Hinkel, and Richard S. J. Tol. "Sea-Level Rise and its Possible Impacts Given a 'Beyond 4°C World' in the Twenty-First Century." *Philosophical Transactions of the Royal Society B* 369, no. 1934 (November 29, 2011).

833 Weerasinghe, Sanjula. "What We Know About Climate Change and Migration." Institute for the Study of International Migration (February 2021).

834 de Sherbinin, Alex. "Climate Impacts as Drivers of Migration" Migration Policy Institute (October 23, 2020).

835 Intergovernmental Science-Policy Platform on Biodiversity and Ecosystem Services. "Worsening Worldwide Land Degradation Now 'Critical', Undermining Well-Being of 3.2 Billion People" (March 2018).

836 World Bank. *Groundswell Part 2: Acting on Internal Climate Migration* (September 13, 2021).

837 Nicholls, Robert J., Natasha Marinova, Jason A. Lowe, Sally Brown, Pier Vellinga, Diogo de Gusmão, Jochen Hinkel, and Richard S. J. Tol. "Sea-Level Rise and its Possible Impacts Given a 'Beyond 4°C World' in the Twenty-First Century." *Philosophical Transactions of the Royal Society B* 369, no. 1934 (November 29, 2011).

838 Hauer, Matthew E., Jason M. Evans, and Deepak R. Mishra. "Millions Projected to be at Risk from Sea-Level Rise in the Continental United States." *Nature Climate Change* 6 (March 14, 2016).

839 Lelieveld, J., Y. Proestos, P. Hadjinicolaou, M. Tanarhte, E. Tyrlis, and G. Zittis. "Strongly Increasing Heat Extremes in the Middle East and North Africa (MENA) in the 21st Century," *Climatic Change* 137 (April 23, 2016).

840 Hsiang, Solomon M. and Adam H. Sobel. "Potentially Extreme Population Displacement and Concentration in the Tropics under Non-Extreme Warming." *Scientific Reports* 6 (June 9, 2016).

841 Missirian, Anouch and Wolfram Schlenker. "Asylum Applications Respond to Temperature Fluctuations." *Science* 358, no. 6370 (December 22, 2017).

842 Freedman, Andrew. "Global Warming Could Spark Future Refugee Crises as Crops Fail." *Mashable* (December 22, 2017).

843 National Intelligence Council. *Implications for US National Security of Anticipated Climate Change* (September 21, 2016).

844 Cohn, D'vera, Jeffrey S., Passel, and Ana Gonzalez-Barrera. "Rise in U.S. Immigrants from El Salvador, Guatemala and Honduras Outpaces Growth from Elsewhere." Pew Research Center (December 7, 2017).

845 UN Food and Agriculture Organization. *Dry Corridor—Situation Report June 2016* (June 2016).

846 Markham, Lauren. "How Climate Change Is Pushing Central American Migrants to the US." *The Guardian* (April 6, 2019).

847 Blitzer, Jonathan. "How Climate Change Is Fuelling the US Border Crisis." *The New Yorker* (April 3, 2019).

848 Semple, Kirk. "Central American Farmers Head to the US, Fleeing Climate Change." *The New York Times* (April 13, 2019).

849 Lakhani, Nina. "'People Are Dying': How the Climate Crisis Has Sparked an Exodus to the US." *The Guardian* (July 29, 2019).

850 Hallett, Miranda Cady. "How Climate Change is Driving Emigration from Central America." *The Conversation* (September 6, 2019).

851 Seay-Fleming, Carrie. "Beyond Violence: Drought and Migration in Central America's Northern Triangle." NewSecurity Beat (April 12, 2018).

852 Davis, Joseph A. "Backgrounder: Climate Crisis May Quickly Confront US, World with National Security Threats." Society of Environmental Journalists (February 23, 2022).

853 Selby, Jan. "On Blaming Climate Change for the Syrian Civil War." Middle East Research and Information Project 296 (Fall 2020).

854 National Intelligence Council. *Implications for US National Security of Anticipated Climate Change* (September 21, 2016).

855 CNA Military Advisory Board. *National Security and the Accelerating Risks of Climate Change 2014* (May 2014).

856 US Department of Defense. *Quadrennial Defense Review 2014* (2014)

857 Coats, Daniel R. *Worldwide Threat Assessment of the US Intelligence Community* (January 29, 2019).

858 The National Security, Military, and Intelligence Panel on Climate Change. *A Security Threat Assessment of Global Climate Change* (February 2020).

859 Levy, Barry S.; Sidel, Victor W.; and Patz, Jonathan A., "Climate Change and Collective Violence," *Annual Review of Public Health*, 38, January 11, 2017.

860 Welzer, Harald. *Climate Wars: What People Will Be Killed For in the 21st Century.* Wiley (2012).

861 Elwert, Georg. "Intervention in Markets of Violence.

862 Hsiang, Solomon H., Kyle C. Meng, and Mark A. Cane. "Civil Conflicts are Associated with the Global Climate." *Nature* 476 (August 24, 2011).

863 Hsiang, Solomon, Marshall Burke, and Edward Miguel. "Quantifying the Influence of Climate on Human Conflict." *Science* 341, no. 6151 (September 13, 2013).

864 Schleussner, Carl-Friedrich, Jonathan F. Donges, Reik V. Donner, and Hans Joachim Schellnhuber. "Armed-Conflict Risks Enhanced By Climate-Related Disasters in Ethnically Fractionalized Countries." *Proceedings of the National Academy of Sciences* 113, no. 33 (August 16, 2016).

865 Werrell, Caitlin, Francesco Femia, and Troy Sternberg. "Did We see It Coming? State Fragility, Climate Vulnerability, and the Uprisings in Syria and Egypt." *SAIS Review of International Affairs* 35, no. 1 (Winter–Spring 2015).

866 Schkoda. Catherine M., Shawna G. Cuan, and E. D. McGrady. "Proceedings and Observations from a Climate Risk Event." CNA Analysis & Solutions (December 2015).

867 Hill, Alice C. and Leonardo Martinez-Diaz. *Building a Resilient Tomorrow: How to Prepare for the Coming Climate Disruption.* Oxford University Press, 2022.

868 Orr, David W. *Down to the Wire: Confronting Climate Collapse* Oxford University Press, 2009.

869 Welzer, Harald. *Climate Wars: What People Will Be Killed for in the 21st Century.* Wiley, 2012.

870 Motesharrei, Safa, Jorge Rivas, and Eugenia Kalnay. "Human and Nature Dynamics (HANDY): Modeling Inequality and Use of Resources in the Collapse or Sustainability of Societies." *Ecological Economics* 101 (May 2014).

871 Oxfam. "5 Shocking Facts about Extreme Global Inequality and How to Even It Up."

872 Inequality.org. Global Inequality.

873 Inequality.org. Income Inequality in the United States.

874 Diamond, Jared. *Collapse: How Societies Choose to Fail or Succeed* 2011, Penguin Books.

875 Campbell, Kurt M., Jay Gulledge, J. R. McNeill, John Podesta, Peter Ogden, Leon Fuerth, R. James Woolsey, Julianne Smith, Richard Weitz, Derek Mix, and

Alexander T. J. Lennon. *The Age of Consequences: The Foreign Policy and National Security Implications of Global Climate Change* (November 2007).

876 Lent, Jeremy. "The Cruel, Topsy-Turvy Economics of Collapse." Patterns of Meaning (October 31, 2017).

877 Mian, Zia. "Kashmir, Climate Change, and Nuclear War." *Bulletin of the Atomic Scientists* (December 7, 2016).

878 Johnson, Keith. "Are India and Pakistan on the Verge of a Water War?" *Foreign Policy* (February 25, 2019).

879 Wester Philippus, Arabinda Mishra, Aditi Mukherji, Arun Bhakta Shrestha, eds. *The Hindu Kush Himalaya Assessment—Mountains, Climate Change, Sustainability and People.* Springer Nature Switzerland AG, 2019.

880 Federation of American Scientists. "Status of World Nuclear Forces" (2022).

881 Mills, Michael, Owen B. Toon, Julia Lee-Taylor, and Alan Robock. "Multidecadal Global Cooling and Unprecedented Ozone Loss Following a Regional Nuclear Conflict." *Earth's Future* 2, no. 4 (April 1, 2014).

882 Jägermeyr, Jonas, Alan Robock, Joshua Elliott, Christoph Müller, Lili Xia, Nikolay Khabarov, Christian Folberth et al. "A Regional Nuclear Conflict Would Compromise Global Food Security." *Proceedings of the National Academy of Sciences* 117, no. 13 (March 31, 2020).

883 Duncombe, Janessa. "Nuclear War Would Spawn a "Nuclear" El Niño." *Eos* (March 2, 2020).

884 Coiupe, Joshua, Charles G. Bardeen, Alan Robock, and Owen B. Toon. "Nuclear Winter Responses to Nuclear War between the United States and Russia in the Whole Atmosphere Community Climate Model Version 4 and the Goddard Institute for Space Studies ModelE." *Journal of Geophysical Research* 124, no. 15 (July 23, 2019).

885 Federation of American Scientists. "Status of World Nuclear Forces" (2022).

886 Covering Climate Now. "More Climate Reporting, At Last" (February 3, 2022).

887 UN Climate Change Conference COP26.

888 Visram, Talib. "The Language of Climate Is Evolving, from 'Change' to 'Catastrophe'." *Fast Company* (December 6, 2021).

889 Corbett, Julia B. "Media Power and Climate Change." *Nature Climate Change* 5 (April 2015).

890 Monbiot, George. "The Climate Crisis Is Already Here—But No One's Telling Us." *The Guardian* (August 3, 2016).

891 The New York Times Company. T Brand Studio.

892 *The New York Times.* "Algae May be Small—But Its Impact Could be Big."

893 *The New York Times.* "How Our Energy Needs Are Changing, in a Series of Interactive Charts."

894 Atkin, Emily. "The NYT Stopped Shilling for Cigarettes. Why Won't It Stop Shilling for Fossil Fuels?" (August 30, 2021).

895 Pew Research Center. State of the News Media.

896 Climate Central. Climate Central website.

897 Climatewire. Climatewire website

898 DeSmog. DeSmog website.

899 Inside Climate News. Inside Climate News website.

900 Covering Climate Now. Covering Climate Now website.

901 Society of Environmental Journalists. Society of Environmental Journalists website.

902 Hertsgaard, Mark, and Kyle Pope. "The Media are Complacent While the World Burns," *Columbia Journalism Review* (April 22, 2019).

903 Hertsgaard, Mark, and Kyle Pope. "The Media's Climate Coverage Is Improving, But Time Is Very Short." *Columbia Journalism Review* (September 23, 2020).

904 Leiserowitz, Anthony, Edward Maibach, Seth Rosenthal, John Kotcher, Jennifer Carman, Liz Neyens, Jennifer Marlon, Karine Lacroix and Matthew Goldberg. *Climate Change in the American Mind, September 2021.* Yale Program on Climate Change Communication and George Mason University Center for Climate Change Communication (September 2021).

905 Leiserowitz, A., E. Maibach, S. Rosenthal, J. Kotcher, J. Carman, L. Neyens, M. Goldberg, K. Lacroix, and J. Marlon. *Politics & Global Warming,* Yale Program on Climate Change Communication and George Mason University Center for Climate Change Communication (September 2021).

906 Johnson, Will. "Exclusive Poll: Amid COVID-19, Americans Don't Care about Climate Change Anymore." *Fortune* (August 10, 2020).

907 Hertsgaard, Mark, and Kyle Pope. "The Media Is Still Mostly Failing To Convey the Urgency of the Climate Crisis." *The Guardian* (June 3, 2021).

908 Taft, Molly. "Why TV Is So Bad at Covering Climate Change," Gizmodo, July 14, 2020.

909 Teirstein, Zoya, "Is Climate Change a "Ratings Killer," or is Something Wrong with For-Profit Media?" *Grist* (July 25, 2018).

910 Gustafson, Abel, Anthony Leiserowitz, Edward Maibach, John Kotcher, Seth Rosenthal, and Matthew Goldberg. *Climate Change in the Minds of US News Audiences.* Yale Program on Climate Change Communication and George Mason University Center for Climate Change Communication (October 6, 2020).

911 Dunwoody, Sharon. "Science Journalism: Prospects in the Digital Age." *Routledge Handbook of Public Communication of Science and Technology* (June 19, 2014).

912 Grieco, Elizabeth. "US Newspapers Have Shed Half of Their Newsroom Employees since 2008." Pew Research Center (April 20, 2020).

913 Union of Concerned Scientists. "Science or Spin?: Assessing the Accuracy of Cable News Coverage of Climate Science" (April 2014).

914 Haskins, Justin. "Sleep Well, Ocasio-Cortez, and Consider Having a Family. Here's the Truth about Our Planet." Fox News (September 7, 2019).

915 Grynbaum, Michael, and Tiffany Hsu. "'Nothing to Do with Climate Change': Conservative Media and Trump Align on Fires." *The New York Times* (September 15, 2020).

916 Harvey, Fiona. "Truthful Climate Reporting Shifts Viewpoints, but Only Briefly, Study Finds." *The Guardian* (June 20, 2022).

917 Nyhan, Brendan, Ethan Porter, and Thomas J. Wood. "Time and Skeptical Opinion Content Erode the Effects of Science Coverage on Climate Beliefs and Attitudes." *Proceedings of the National Academy of Sciences* 119, no. 6 (June 21, 2022).

918 Atkin, Emily. "May 26 Was Good. The News Made It Bad." Heated (June 14, 2021).

919 Upton, John. "Media Contributing to 'Hope Gap' on Climate Change." Climate Central (March 28, 2015).

920 Macdonald, Ted. "Solutions to Climate Change Get Short Shrift on Broadcast TV News." Media Matters for America (January 28, 2019).

921 Revkin, Andrew C. "Vanishing Frogs, Climate, and the Front Page." *The New York Times* (March 24, 2008).

922 NOAA. NOAA Ship Ronald H. Brown.

923 AntarcticGlaciers.org. "Ice Core Basics."

924 National Academy of Sciences. "Climate Modeling 101."

925 Leiserowitz, Anthony, Edward Maibach, Connie Roser-Renouf, Geoff Feinberg, and Seth Rosenthal. "Majorities of Americans Trust Climate Scientists, Family and Friends," *Climate Change in the American Mind*. Yale Program on Climate Change Communication and George Mason University Center for Climate Change Communication (March 2015).

926 Pew Research Center. *The Politics of Climate* (October 4, 2016).

927 Revkin, Andrew C. "Climate Experts Tussle over Details. Public Gets Whiplash." *The New York Times* (July 29, 2008).

928 Weart, Spencer. *The Discovery of Global Warming: Rapid Climate Change* (January 2017).

929 Voosen, Paul. "Joint Research Push Targets Fast-Melting Antarctic Ice." *Science* 354, no. 6309 (September 14, 2016).

930 EPA. *Inventory of US Greenhouse Gas Emissions and Sinks: 1990–2014* (April 15, 2016).

931 Mooney, Chris. "The US Has Been Emitting a Lot More Methane Than We Thought, Says EPA." *The Washington Post* (April 15, 2016).

932 Brandt, A.R., G. A. Heath, E. A. Kort, F. O'Sullivan, G. Pétron, S. M. Jordaan, P. Tans et al. "Methane Leaks from North American Natural Gas Systems." *Science* 343, no 6172 (February 14, 2014).

933 Alvarez, Ramón A., Daniel Zavala-Araiza, David R. Lyon, David T. Allen, Zachary R. Barkley, Adam R. Brandt, Kenneth J. Davis, Scott C. Herndon et al. "Assessment of Methane Emissions from the US Oil and Gas Supply Chain." *Science* 361, no. 6398 (June 21, 2018).

934 Deemer, Bridget R., John A. Harrison, Siyue Li, Jake J. Beaulieu, Tonya DelSontro, Nathan Barros, José F. Bezerra-Neto et al. "Greenhouse Gas Emissions from Reservoir Water Surfaces: A New Global Synthesis." *BioScience* 66, no. 11 (October 4, 2016).

935 Cornwall, Warren. "Hundreds of New Dams Could Mean Trouble for Our Climate," *Science* (September 28, 2016).

936 Coral Bleaching Task Force. "Coral Bleaching Taskforce Documents Most Severe Bleaching on Record." ARC Centre of Excellence for Coral Reef Studies, James Cook University (March 29, 2016).

937 Urban, M.C., G. Bocedi, A. P. Hendry, J.-B. Mihoub, G. Pe'er, A. Singer, J. R. Bridle et al. "Improving the Forecast for Biodiversity under Climate Change." *Science* 353, no. 6304 (September 9, 2016).

938 Shepherd, Theodore G. "Effects of a Warming Arctic." *Science* 353, no. 6303 (September 2, 2016).

939 Parazoo, Nicholas C., Roisin Commane, Steven C. Wofsy, Charles D. Koven, Colm Sweeney, David M. Lawrence, Jakob Lindaas, Rachel Y.-W. Chang, and Charles E. Miller. "Detecting Regional Patterns of Changing A Process for Capturing CO_2 from the Atmosphere Flux in Alaska." *Proceedings of the National Academy of Sciences* 113, no. 28 (July 12, 2016).

940 Rasmussen, Carol. "Growing Arctic Carbon Emissions Could Go Unobserved." NASA Global Climate Change News (June 27, 2016).

941 McGuire, Bill. *Hothouse Earth: An Inhabitant's Guide.* Icon Books (2022).

942 Dunlap, Riley E. and Robert J. Brulle, eds. *Climate Change and Society: Sociological Perspectives.* Oxford University Press, 2015.

943 Carleton, Tamma A. and Solomon M. Hsiang. "Social and Economic Impacts of Climate." *Science* 353, no. 6304 (September 9, 2016).

944 Zaringhalam, Maryam. "Failure in Science Is Frequent and Inevitable—and We Should Talk More about It." *Scientific American*, June 30, 2016.

945 Is This How You Feel? website.

946 Anderson, Kevin. "Duality in Climate Science," *Nature GeoScience* 8 (October 12, 2015).

947 Hansen, James. "Dangerous Scientific Reticence." Earth Institute, Columbia University (March 23, 2016).

948 Hansen, James. "Congressional Testimony of Dr. James Hansen" (June 23, 1988).

949 Climate Science Awareness and Solutions, Earth Institute, Columbia University.

950 Lewandowsky, Stephan, Naomim Oreskes, James S. Risbey, Ben R.Newell, and Michael Smithson. "Seepage: Climate Change Denial and Its Effect on the Scientific Community." *Global Environmental Change* 33 (July 2015).

951 Oreskes, Naomi, Michael Oppenheimer, and Dale Jamieson. "Scientists Have Been Underestimating the Pace of Climate Change." *Scientific American* (August 19, 2019).

952 Brysse, Keynyn, Naomi Oreskes, Jessica O'Reilly, and Michael Oppenheimer. "Climate Change Prediction: Erring on the Side of Least Drama?" *Global Environmental Change* 23, no. 1 (February 2013).

953 Schwartz, John. "Will We Survive Climate Change?" *The New York Times* (November 19, 2018).

954 Myers, Krista F., Peter T. Doran, John Cook, John E. Kotcher, and Teresa A Myers. "Consensus Revisited: Quantifying Scientific Agreement on Climate Change and Climate Expertise among Earth Scientists 10 Years Later." *Environmental Research Letters* 16, no. 10 (October 20, 2021).

955 Leiserowitz, Anthony, Edward Maibach, Seth Rosenthal, John Kotcher, Jennifer Carman, Liz Neyens, Jennifer Marlon, Karine Lacroix, and Matthew Goldberg. *Climate Change in the American Mind, April 2022.* Yale Program on Climate Change Communication and George Mason University Center for Climate Change Communication (April 2022).

956 American Association for the Advancement of Science. "Thirty-One Top Scientific Societies Speak With One Voice on Global Climate Change." Eurekalert! (June 28, 2016).

957 NCCS. Discover Supercomputer: NCCS' Primary Computing Platform.

958 CarbonBrief. "Q&A: How Do Climate Models Work?" (January 15, 2018).

959 Pielke, Roger Jr. and Justin Ritchie. "How Climate Scenarios Lost Touch with Reality." *Issues* 37, no. 4 (Summer 2021).

960 Hausfather, Zeke, and Glen P. Peters. "Emissions—the 'Business as Usual' Story Is Misleading." *Nature* 577 (January 29, 2020).

961 Hausfather, Zeke. "Explainer: How 'Shared Socioeconomic Pathways' Explore Future Climate Change," Carbon Brief (April 19, 2018).

962 Jamieson, Kathleen Hall, Dan Kahan, and Dietram E. Scheufele. "Introduction: Why Science Communication?" in Jamieson, Kathleen Hall, Dan Kahan, and Dietram E. Scheufele, eds, *The Oxford Handbook of the Science of Science Communication*, Oxford University Press, June 16, 2017.

963 Voosen, Paul. "Climate Scientists Open up Their Black Boxes to Scrutiny." *Science* 354, no. 6311 (October 28, 2016).

964 Oppenheimer, Michael, Christopher M. Little, and Roger M. Cooke. "Expert Judgement and Uncertainty Quantification for Climate Change." *Nature Climate Change* 6 (April 27, 2016).

965 Kelly, Morgan. "New Tool Puts a Consistent Value on Experts' Uncertainty on Climate Change Models." Princeton University News (April 27, 2016).

966 NASA. "Climate Change: How Do We Know?"

967 Hawkins, Ed. "Reconciling Estimates of Climate Sensitivity." Climate Lab Book blog (June 27, 2016).

968 Tierney, Jessica E., Christopher J. Poulsen, Sabel P. Montañez, Tripti Bhattacharya, Ran Feng, Heather L. Ford, and Bärbel Hönisch. "Past Climates Inform Our Future." *Science* 370, no. 6517 (November 6, 2020).

969 US Global Change Research Program. *Fourth National Climate Assessment, Executive Summary.* From: *Fourth National Climate Assessment Volume 1* (2018).

970 Drijfhout, Sybren. "What Climate 'Tipping Points' are—and How They Could Suddenly Change Our Planet." *The Conversation* (December 9, 2015).

971 IPCC. *Climate Change 2021: The Physical Science Basis. Chapter 9: Ocean, Cryosphere, and Sea Level Change.* From: *Climate Change 2021: The Physical Science Basis* (August 9, 2021).

972 Zandt, Michiel H.in 't, Susanne Liebner; and Cornelia U. Welte. "Roles of Thermokarst Lakes in a Warming World." *Trends in Microbiology* 28, no. 9 (September 2020).

973 Schneider von Deimling, T., G. Grosse, J. Strauss, L. Schirrmeister, A. Morgenstern, S. Schaphoff, M. Meinshausen, and J. Boike. "Observation-Based Modelling of Permafrost Carbon Fluxes with Accounting for Deep Carbon Deposits and Thermokarst Activity." *Biogeosciences* 12, no. 11 (June 5, 2015).

974 Crowther, T.W., K. E. O. Todd-Brown, C. W. Rowe, W. R. Wieder, J. C. Carey, M. B. Machmuller, B. L. Snoek et al. "Quantifying Global Soil Carbon Losses in Response to Warming." *Nature* 540, no. 7631 (November 30, 2016).

975 Mooney, Chris. "Scientists Have Long Feared This 'Feedback' To the Climate System. Now They Say It's Happening." *The Washington Post* (November 30, 2016).

976 Hausfather, Zeke, and Richard Betts. "Analysis: How 'Carbon-Cycle Feedbacks' Could Make Global Warming Worse." CarbonBrief (April 14, 2020).

977 American Association for the Advancement of Science 2018 Annual Meeting, "National Climate Assessment Scientists Present Latest Developments." News conference (February 18, 2018).

978 US Global Change Research Program. *Fourth National Climate Assessment, Chapter 15: Potential Surprises: Compound Extremes and Tipping Elements.* From: *Fourth National Climate Assessment Volume 1* (2018).

979 Mora, Camilo, Daniele Spirandelli, Erik C. Franklin, John Lynham, Michael B. Kantar, Wendy Miles, Charlotte Z. Smith, et al. "Broad Threat to Humanity

from Cumulative Climate Hazards Intensified by Greenhouse Gas Emissions." *Nature Climate Change* 8 (November 19, 2018).

980 Schwartz, John. "'Like a Terror Movie': How Climate Change Will Cause More Simultaneous Disasters." *The New York Times* (November 19, 2018).

981 Motesharrei, Safa, Jorge Rivas, Eugenia Kalnay, Ghassem R. Asrar, Antonio J. Busalacchi, Robert F. Cahalan, Mark A. Cane et al. "Modeling Sustainability: Population, Inequality, Consumption, and Bidirectional Coupling of the Earth and Human Systems." *National Science Review* 3 (December 11, 2016).

982 Sato, Yousuke, Hiroaki Miura, Hisashi Yashiro, Daisuke Goto, Toshihiko Takemura, Hirofumi Tomita, and Teruyuki Nakajima. "Unrealistically Pristine Air in the Arctic Produced by Current Global Scale Models." *Scientific Reports* 6 (May 25, 2016).

983 Wilkinson, Jen. "Current Atmospheric Models Underestimate the Dirtiness of Arctic Air," EurekAlert! (May 25, 2016).

984 Liu, Heping, Qianyu Zhang, Gabriel G Katul, Jonathan J Cole, F Stuart Chapin III, and Sally MacIntyre. "Large CO_2 Effluxes at Night and During Synoptic Weather Events Significantly Contribute To CO_2 Emissions from A Reservoir," *Environmental Research Letters* 11, no. 6 (May 24, 2016).

985 IPCC. *Climate Change 2021: The Physical Science Basis, Chapter 7: Clouds and Aerosols*. From: *Climate Change 2021: The Physical Science Basis* (August 9, 2021).

986 CarbonBrief. "While Global Climate Models Do a Good Job of Simulating the Earth's Climate, They are Not Perfect" (January 17, 2018).

987 Highwood, Ellie. "Guest Post: Why Clouds Hold the Key to Better Climate Models." CarbonBrief (January 1, 2018).

988 Schneider, Tapio, Colleen M. Kaul, and Kyle G. Pressel. "Possible Climate Transitions from Breakup of Stratocumulus Decks under Greenhouse Warming." *Nature GeoScience* 12 (February 25, 2019).

989 Voosen, Paul. "Use of 'Too Hot' Climate Models Exaggerates Impacts of Global Warming." *Science* (May 4, 2022).

990 Hausfather, Zeke, Kate Marvel, Gavin A. Schmidt, John W. Nielsen-Gammon, and Mark Zelinka. "Climate Simulations: Recognize the 'Hot Model' Problem." Nature 605 (May 4, 2022).

991 Cesana, Grégory V. and Anthony D. Del Genio. "Observational Constraint on Cloud Feedbacks Suggests Moderate Climate Sensitivity." *Nature Climate Change* 11 (February 15, 2021).

992 Myers, Timothy A., Ryan C. Scott, Mark D. Zelinka, Stephen A. Klein, Joel R. Norris, and Peter M. Caldwell. "Observational Constraints on Low Cloud Feedback Reduce Uncertainty of Climate Sensitivity." *Nature Climate Change* 11 (May 13, 2021).

993 Ceppi, Paulo, and Peer Nowack. "Observational Evidence That Cloud Feedback Amplifies Global Warming." *Proceedings of the National Academy of Sciences* 118, no. 30 (July 27, 2021).

994 Harvey, Chelsea. "Clouds May Speed up Global Warming." *Scientific American* (July 26, 2021).

995 Hausfather, Zeke, Henri F. Drake, Tristan Abbott, and Gavin A. Schmidt. "Evaluating the Performance of Past Climate Model Projections." *Geophysical Research Letters* 47, no. 1 (December 4, 2019).

996 Meredith, Dennis. "Please Explain: Training Scientists to Be Better Communicators." *Chronicle of Higher Education* (May 16, 2010).

997 Climate Science Legal Defense Fund. Resources for Scientists.

998 Mann, Michael E., Raymond S. Bradley, and Malcolm K., Hughes. "Global-Scale Temperature Patterns and Climate Forcing Over the Past Six Centuries." *Nature* 392 (April 23, 1998).

999 Mann, Michael. "I'm A Scientist Who Has Gotten Death Threats. I Fear What May Happen under Trump." *The Washington Post* (December 16, 2016).

1000 Climate Science Legal Defense Fund. "Perspectives of Scientists Who Become Targets: Michael Mann" (July 20, 2017).

1001 McKibben, Bill. "Embarrassing Photos of Me, Thanks to My Right-Wing Stalkers." *The New York Times* (August 5, 2016).

1002 Hayhoe, Katharine. *Saving Us: A Climate Scientist's Case for Hope and Healing in a Divided World*. Simon & Schuster, 2021.

1003 Gleick, Peter. "From Scientists to Policymakers: Communicating on Climate, Scientific Integrity, and More." Significant Figures by Peter Gleick (December 1, 2016).

1004 National Science Board. *Science & Engineering Indicators 2016, Chapter 7, Science and Technology: Public Attitudes and Understanding, p. 31*. From: *Science & Engineering Indicators 2016* (2016).

1005 Funk, Cary and Lee Rainie. "AAAS Scientists' Views on the Scientific Enterprise." Pew Research Center (January 29, 2015).

1006 Rainie, Lee, Cary Funk, and Monica Anderson. "Scientists' Views: Most Approve of Active Role in Public Debates about Science and Technology." Pew Research Center (February 15, 2015).

1007 March for Science website.

1008 Niemeier, Ulrike, and Simone Tilmes. "Sulfur Injections for a Cooler Planet." *Science* 357, no. 6348 (July 21, 2017).

1009 ResponsibleScientists.org. "An Open Letter Regarding Climate Change From Concerned Members of the US National Academy of Sciences." (September 20, 2016).

1010   Center for Research on Environmental Decisions. *The Psychology of Climate Change Communication* (October 2009).

1011   Committee on the Science of Science Communication, National Academies of Sciences, Engineering, and Medicine. *Communicating Science Effectively: A Research Agenda* (December 13, 2016).

1012   Nyhan, Brendan. "Why the Backfire Effect Does Not Explain the Durability of Political Misperceptions." *Proceedings of the National Academy of Sciences* 118, no. 15 (April 13, 2021).

1013   Freise, Amanda. "It's Time for Scientists to Stop Explaining So Much." *Scientific American* (July 19, 2016).

1014   Kahan, Dan M., Ellen Peters, Maggie Wittlin, Paul Slovic, Lisa Larrimore Ouellette, Donald Braman, and Gregory Mandel. "The Polarizing Impact of Science Literacy and Numeracy on Perceived Climate Change Risks." *Nature Climate Change* 2 (May 27, 2012).

1015   American Association for the Advancement of Science. Office of Government Relations.

1016   COMPASS website.

1017   American Geophysical Union. Share and Advocate for Earth and Space Science.

1018   Union of Concerned Scientists. The Science Network Workshop Series.

1019   Risbey, James S. "The New Climate Discourse: Alarmist or Alarming." *Global Environmental Change* 18, no. 1 (February 2008).

1020   McGuire, Bill. *Hothouse Earth: An Inhabitant's Guide.* Icon Books (2022).

1021   Bradshaw, Corey J. A., Paul R. Ehrlich, Andrew Beattie, Gerardo Ceballos, Eileen Crist, Joan Diamond, Rodolfo Dirzo et al. "Underestimating the Challenges of Avoiding a Ghastly Future," *Frontiers in Conservation Science* (January 13, 2021).

1022   Ripple, William J., Christopher Wolf, Thomas M. Newsome, Jillian W. Gregg, Timothy M. Lenton, Ignacio Palomo, Jasper A. J. Eikelboom et al. "World Scientists' Warning of a Climate Emergency 2021." *BioScience* 71, no. 9 (July 28, 2021).

1023   Hassol, Susan. "Improving How Scientists Communicate About Climate Change," *EOS* 89, no. 11 (March 11, 2008).

1024   Somerville, Richard, and Susan Joy Hassol. "Communicating the Science of Climate Change." *Physics Today* (October 2011).

1025   Center for Research on Environmental Decisions. *The Psychology of Climate Change* (October 2009).

1026   IPCC. *Climate Change 2021: The Physical Science Basis, Summary for Policymakers* From: *Climate Change 2021: The Physical Science Basis* (August 7, 2021).

1027 IPCC, *Climate Change 2021: The Physical Science Basis, Chapter 1: Framing, context, methods* From: *Climate Change 2021: The Physical Science Basis* (August 7, 2021).

1028 Budescu, David, Stephen Broomell, and Han-Hui Por. "Effective Communication of Uncertainty in the IPCC Reports." *Climatic Change* 13, no. 2 (November 23, 2011).

1029 Plass, Gilbert N. "The Carbon Dioxide Theory of Climatic Change." *Tellus* 8, no. 2 (May 1956).

1030 Broecker, Wallace. "Climatic Change: Are We on the Brink of a Pronounced Global Warming?" *Science* 189, no. 4201 (August 8, 1975).

1031 Ehrlich, Paul R. and Anne H. Ehrlich. "Can a Collapse of Global Civilization be Avoided?" *Proceedings of the Royal Society B* (January 9, 2013).

1032 Holdren, John P. "Global Climate Disruption What Do we Know? What Should we Do?" Speech at Harvard Kennedy School (November 6, 2007).

1033 Pimm, Stuart L. "Climate Disruption and Biodiversity." *Current Biology* 19 (July 28, 2009).

1034 Weyler, Rex. "Global Heating Revisited." Greenpeace International (January 5, 2013).

1035 Marshall, George. *Don't Even Think About It: Why Our Brains are Wired to Ignore Climate Change* Bloomsbury, 2014.

1036 Alcindor, Yamiche. "In Sweltering South, Climate Change is Now a Workplace Hazard." *The New York Times* (August 3, 2017).

1037 Center for Research on Environmental Decisions. *The Psychology of Climate Change Communication* (October 2009).

1038 Gore, Al. "Al Gore: Climate of Denial." *Rolling Stone* (June 22, 2011).

1039 Klein, Naomi. *This Changes Everything: Capitalism vs. The Climate.* Simon & Shuster, August 4, 2015.

1040 The Nature Conservancy. Working with Companies.

1041 The Nature Conservancy. JPMorgan Chase & Co. Transforming the Way We Protect Natural Capital.

1042 Orr, David W. *Down to the Wire: Confronting Climate Collapse.* Oxford University Press, 2009.

1043 BP. The BP Brand.

1044 Ridgeway, James. "BP's Slick Greenwashing." *Mother Jones* (May 4, 2010).

1045 NOAA. Deepwater Horizon.

1046 Urbina, Ian. "Workers on Doomed Rig Voiced Concern about Safety." *The New York Times* (July 21, 2010).

1047 Oil and Gas Climate Initiative. "Taking Action: Accelerating a Low Emissions Future." (November 2016).

1048 Haszeldine, Stuart. "Oil Companies' Climate Initiative Lacks Initiative." Energy and Carbon blog (July 11, 2016).

1049 Shankleman, Jess and Rakteem Katakey. "Big Oil to Invest $1 Billion in Carbon-Capture Technology." *Bloomberg Markets* (November 4, 2016).

1050 Ceres. "Investing in the Clean Trillion: Closing the Clean Energy Investment Gap." (January 2014).

1051 Christen, Caroline. "Investigation: How the Meat Industry is Climate-Washing its Polluting Business Model." DeSmog (July 18, 2021).

1052 Banerjee, Neela. "Exxon: The Road Not Taken." Inside Climate News (September-December 2015).

1053 Jerving, Sara, Kattie Jennings, Masako Melissa Hirsch, and Susanne Rust. "What Exxon Knew About the Earth's Melting Arctic." *Los Angeles Times* (October 9, 2015).

1054 Jennings, Kattie, Dino Grandoni, and Susanne Rust. "How Exxon Went from Leader to Skeptic on Climate Change Research." *Los Angeles Times* (October 23, 2015).

1055 Lieberman, Amy and Susanne Rust. "Big Oil Braced for Global Warming While it Fought Regulations." *Los Angeles Times* (December 31, 2015).

1056 Edge, Dan, Jane McMullen, Gesbeen Mohammad, and Robin Barnwell, producers. "The Power of Big Oil." PBS Frontline (April 19, April 26, and May 3, 2022).

1057 Supran, Geoffrey, and Naomi Oreskes. "Assessing ExxonMobil's Climate Change Communications (1977–2014)," *Environmental Research Letters* 12 (August 23, 2017).

1058 Supran, Geoffrey, and Naomi Oreskes. "The Forgotten Oil Ads That Told Us Climate Change Was Nothing." *The Guardian* (November 18, 2021).

1059 Cook, John, Geoffrey Supran, Stephan Lewandowsky, Naomi Oreskes, and Edward Maibach. *America Misled: How the Fossil Fuel Industry Deliberately Misled Americans about Climate Change.* Center for Climate Change Communication, George Mason University et al. (October 2019.)

1060 Thomson, Alex. "Revealed: ExxonMobil's Lobbying War on Climate Change Legislation." 4 News (June 30, 2021).

1061 JPMorgan Chase & Co. "Our Paris-Aligned Financing Commitment." (October 2020).

1062 Oil Change International, Rainforest Action Network, BankTrack, Indigenous Environmental Network, Reclaim Finance, Sierra Club, and Urgewald. *Banking on Climate Chaos* (2022).

1063 Flitter, Emily. "Think the Big Banks Have Abandoned Coal? Think Again." *The New York Times* (May 28, 2018).

1064 Accountable. US. *Over 50 Major Corporations That Claim To Be Concerned About Climate Issues Help Lead The Very Trade Groups Fighting The "Biggest Climate Change Bill Ever" – The Reconciliation Package In Congress* (September 21, 2021).

1065 Milman, Oliver. "Apple and Disney among Companies Backing Groups Against US Climate Bill." *The Guardian* (October 1, 2021).

1066 InfluenceMap. "The CA100+ Target Companies Scoring and Analysis of Climate Lobbying." (2021).

1067 Union of Concerned Scientists. *The Climate Deception Dossiers* (2015).

1068 Union of Concerned Scientists. *A Climate of Corporate Control: How Corporations Have Influenced the US Dialogue on Climate Science and Policy* (May 31, 2012).

1069 Ekwurzel, B., J. Boneham, M. W. Dalton, R. Heede, R. J. Mera, M. R. Allen, and P. C. Frumhoff. "The Rise in Global Atmospheric CO_2, Surface Temperature, and Sea Level from Emissions Traced to Major Carbon Producers." *Climatic Change* (September 7, 2017).

1070 Black, Richard, Kate Cullen, Byron Fay, Dr Thomas Hale, John Lang, Saba Mahmood, and Steve Smith. *Taking Stock: A Global Assessment Of Net Zero Targets.* The Energy & Climate Intelligence Unit and Oxford Net Zero (March 2021).

1071 Science Based Targets. Companies Taking Action website.

1072 Evans, Peter, and Clifford Krauss. "What's Really behind Corporate Promises on Climate Change?" *The New York Times* (February 24, 2021).

1073 MSCI. *The MSCI Net-Zero Tracker* (July 2021).

1074 Wright, Christopher, and Daniel Nyberg. "How Bold Corporate Climate Change Goals Deteriorate Over Time." *Harvard Business Review* (November 22, 2017).

1075 Wright Christopher, and Daniel Nyberg. "An Inconvenient Truth: How Organizations Translate Climate Change into Business as Usual." *Academy of Management Journal* 60, no. 5. (November 7, 2016).

1076 Kasser, Tim, Emilie Tricarico, David Boyle, and Andrew Simms. *Advertising's Role in Climate and Ecological Degradation*, New Weather Institute, Possible, and KR Foundation (November 2020).

1077 Harvey, Fiona. "Fossil Fuel Firms 'Have Humanity by the Throat', Says UN Head in Blistering Attack." *The Guardian* (June 17, 2022).

1078 American Petroleum Institute. Multimedia Content.

1079 Climate Investigations Center. Trade Associations and the Public Relations Industry.

1080 Brulle Robert J. Melissa Aronczyk, and Jason Carmichael. "Corporate Promotion and Climate Change: An Analysis of Key Variables Affecting Advertising Spending by Major Oil Corporations, 1986–2015." *Climatic Change* 159 (December 11, 2019).

1081   Brulle, Robert J. and Carter Werthman. "The Role of Public Relations Firms in Climate Change Politics." *Climatic Change* 169 (November 30, 2021).

1082   Cunningham, Nick. "The PR Industry Has Been a 'Major' But 'Overlooked' Influence in Climate Politics for Decades, Says Study." DeSmog (November 20, 2021).

1083   McMullen, Jane. "The Audacious PR Plot that Seeded Doubt about Climate Change." BBC News (July 23, 2022).

1084   Sustainability Accounting Standards Board. *Climate Risk Technical Bulletin* (October 2016).

1085   Goldstein, Allie, Will R. Turner, Jillian Gladstone, and David G. Hole. "The Private Sector's Climate Change Risk and Adaptation Blind Spots." *Nature Climate Change* (December 10, 2018).

1086   Asset Owners Disclosure Project. *Got it Covered? Insurance in a Changing Climate* (May 2018).

1087   Ceres. "Business Call to Action: Build Back Better" (2020).

1088   Oreskes, Naomi, and Auden Schendler. "Corporations Will Never Solve Climate Change." *Harvard Business Review* (November 4, 2015).

1089   Espiner, Tom. "JPMorgan Warns of Climate as a Threat to 'Human Life as We Know It'." BBC News (February 21, 2020).

1090   Swiss Re Institute. *The Economics of Climate Change* (April 22, 2021).

1091   The Investor Agenda. "477 Investors with USD $34 Trillion in Assets Urge G20 Leaders to Keep Global Temperature Rise to 1.5 Degrees Celsius" (June 26, 2019).

1092   Gelles, David and Hiroko Tabuchi. "How an Organized Republican Effort Punishes Companies for Climate Action." *The New York Times* (May 27, 2022).

1093   Vadén, T., V. Lähde, A. Majava, P. Järvensivu, T. Toivanen, E. Hakala, and J. T. Eronen. "Decoupling For Ecological Sustainability: A Categorisation and Review of Research Literature." *Environmental Science & Policy* 112 (October 2020).

1094   Hickel, Jason and Giorgos Kallis. "Is Green Growth Possible?" *New Political Economy* 25, no. 4 (April 17, 2019).

1095   DARA, Climate Vulnerability Forum. *Climate Vulnerability Monitor A Guide to the Cold Calculus of a Hot Planet* (2012.

1096   Dietz, Simon, Alex Bowen, Charlie Dixon, and Philip Gradwell. "'Climate Value at Risk' of Global Financial Assets." *Nature Climate Change* 6 (April 4, 2016).

1097   The Economist Intelligence Unit. "The Cost of Inaction: Recognising the Value at Risk from Climate Change." (2015).

1098   US Global Change Research Program. *Fourth National Climate Assessment Volume 1* (2018).

1099   Climate-Related Market Risk Subcommittee, Market Risk Advisory Committee of the US Commodity Futures Trading Commission. *Managing Climate Risk in the US Financial System* (September 9, 2020).

1100   Universal Ecological Fund. *The Economic Case for Climate Action in the United States* (September 2017).

1101   The Global Commission on the Economy and Climate. *The New Climate Economy: The 2018 Report of the Global Commission on the Economy and Climate* (August 2018).

1102   Morgan Stanley Institute for Sustainable Investing. "Sustainable Reality: Analyzing the Risk and Returns of Sustainable Funds." (2019).

1103   Oreskes, Naomi, and Auden Schendler. "Corporations Will Never Solve Climate Change." *Harvard Business Review* (November 4, 2015).

1104   White House. "Fact Sheet: The American Jobs Plan." (March 31, 2021).

1105   Davenport, Coral, Noam Scheiber, and Lisa Friedman. "Biden's Big Bet: Tackling Climate Change Will Create Jobs, Not Kill Them." *The New York Times* (April 2, 2021).

1106   White House. "Fact Sheet: President Biden Sets 2030 Greenhouse Gas Pollution Reduction Target Aimed at Creating Good-Paying Union Jobs and Securing U.S. Leadership on Clean Energy Technologies." (April 22, 2021).

1107   Orr, David W. *Down to the Wire: Confronting Climate Collapse.* Oxford University Press, 2009.

1108   Stoknes, Per Espen. *What We Think About When We Try Not To Think About Global Warming: Toward a New Psychology of Climate Action.* Chelsea Green Publishing, 2015.

1109   White House. "Executive Order on Tackling the Climate Crisis at Home and Abroad." (January 27, 2021).

1110   Ritter, Bill, Jr. "Biden Plans to Fight Climate Change in a Way No U.S. President Has Done Before." *The Conversation* (January 12, 2021).

1111   Congress.gov. *H.R.3684 – Infrastructure Investment and Jobs Act* (2021).

1112   White House. "Fact Sheet: The Bipartisan Infrastructure Deal" (November 6, 2021).

1113   Congress.gov. "H.R.5376 – Inflation Reduction Act of 2022." (2022).

1114   Brown, Matthew and Michael Phillis. "Climate Bill's Unlikely Beneficiary: US Oil and Gas Industry." Associated Press (August 19, 2022).

1115   Bardoff, Jason. "Sorry, but the Virus Shows Why There Won't Be Global Action on Climate Change." *Foreign Policy* (March 27, 2020).

1116   Marshall, George. *Don't Even Think About It: Why Our Brains are Wired to Ignore Climate Change.* Bloomsbury, 2014.

1117   Bremmer, Ian. *The Power of Crisis: How Three Threats—and Our Response—Will Change the World.* Simon & Schuster, 2022.

1118   Yale Program on Climate Change Communication, Climate Nexus, and George Mason University Center for Climate Change Communication. "New Poll: Voters Support Stimulus for Clean Energy, Not Fossil Fuels." (June 29, 2020).

1119   Pew Research Center. "Important Issues in the 2020 Election." (August 13, 2020).

1120   Drutman, Lee, and Steve Teles. "Why Congress Relies on Lobbyists Instead of Thinking for Itself." *The Atlantic* (March 10, 2015).

1121   OpenSecrets.org. Lobbying Database, Industries.

1122   Congressional Research Service. *Legislative Branch: fy 2021 Appropriations* (February 26, 2021).

1123   Drutman, Lee. "How Corporate Lobbyists Conquered American Democracy." *The Atlantic* (April 20, 2015).

1124   Lau, Tim. "Citizens United Explained." Brennan Center for Justice (December 12, 2019).

1125   OpenSecrets.org. Coal Mining: Long-Term Contribution Trends.

1126   OpenSecrets.org. Oil & Gas: Long-Term Contribution Trends.

1127   Whitehouse, Sheldon. "Republicans Want to Fight Climate Change, but Fossil-Fuel Bullies Won't Let Them." *The Washington Post* (January 10, 2017).

1128   Whitehouse, Sheldon. "The Climate Movement Needs More Corporate Lobbyists." *Harvard Business Review* (February 26, 2016).

1129   Thomson, Alex. "Revealed: ExxonMobil's Lobbying War on Climate Change Legislation." 4 News (June 30, 2021).

1130   Aronoff, Kate. "The Biden White House Has an Exxon Problem." *The New Republic* (July 2, 2021).

1131   Quote Investigator. "The Golden Rule: Whoever Has the Gold Makes the Rules."

1132   McCarthy, Tom, and Lauren Gambino. "The Republicans Who Urged Trump to Pull out of Paris Deal are Big Oil Darlings." *The Guardian* (June 1, 2017).

1133   Goodwin, Alec. "A Climate of Cash in Votes on Global Warming." Center for Responsive Politics (August 29, 2016).

1134   OpenSecrets.org. Revolving Door.

1135   Weisman, Jonathan, and Lisa Friedman. "Behind Manchin's Opposition, a Long History of Fighting Climate Measures." *The New York Times* (December 20, 2021).

1136   Flavelle, Christopher, and Julie Tate. "How Joe Manchin Aided Coal, and Earned Millions." *The New York Times* (March 27, 2022).

1137   Boguslaw, Daniel. "Joe Manchin's Dirty Empire." *The Intercept* (September 3, 2021).

1138   Leiserowitz, A., E. Maibach, S. Rosenthal, J. Kotcher, J. Carman, L. Neyens, M. Goldberg, K. Lacroix, and J. Marlon. *Politics & Global Warming, April 2022,* Yale Program on Climate Change Communication and George Mason University Center for Climate Change Communication (July 7, 2022).

1139   Chait, Jonathan. "Why Do Republicans Always Say 'I'm Not a Scientist'?" *New York Magazine* (May 30, 2014).

1140   Paulos, John Allen. "Why Don't Americans Elect Scientists?" *The New York Times* (February 13, 2012).

1141   Levitan, Dave. *Not a Scientist: How Politicians Mistake, Misrepresent, and Utterly Mangle Science.* W. W. Norton & Company, 2017.

1142   Tigue, Kristoffer. "Experts Debunk Viral Post Claiming 1,100 Scientists Say 'There's No Climate Emergency'." Inside Climate News (August 23, 2022).

1143   Davenport, Coral, and Mark Landler. "Trump Administration Hardens Its Attack on Climate Science." *The New York Times* (May 27, 2019).

1144   Davenport, Coral, Lisa Friedman, and Christopher Flavelle. "Biden's Climate Plans Are Stunted after Dejected Experts Fled Trump." *The New York Times* (August 1, 2021).

1145   White House. "FACT SHEET: President Biden Sets 2030 Greenhouse Gas Pollution Reduction Target Aimed at Creating Good-Paying Union Jobs and Securing US Leadership on Clean Energy Technologies." (April 22, 2021).

1146   House Select Committee on the Climate Crisis. *Solving the Climate Crisis: The Congressional Action Plan for a Clean Energy Economy and a Healthy, Resilient, and Just America* (June 2020).

1147   Davenport, Coral. "The Case is a Crucial Moment in the GOP Drive to Tilt Courts against Climate Action." *The New York Times* (June 19, 2022).

1148   Supreme Court of the United States. "West Virginia et al. v. Environmental Protection Agency et al." October term 2021.

1149   Friedman, Lisa. "Democrats Designed the Climate Law to Be a Game Changer. Here's How." *The New York Times* (August 23, 2022).

1150   Joselow, Maxine. "Court Ruling on Social Cost of Carbon Upends Biden's Climate Plans." *The Washington Post* (February 21, 2022).

1151   Gelles, David. "How Republicans Are 'Weaponizing' Public Office against Climate Action." *The New York Times* (August 5, 2022).

1152   Tankersley, Jim and Lisa Friedman. "US and China Restart Climate Talks." *The New York Times* (November 15, 2022).

1153   Stafford, Rick and Peter J. S. Jones. "How to Stop Climate Change: Six Ways to Make the World a Better Place." *The Conversation* (May 1, 2019).

1154   University of Oxford/UN Development Programme. *Peoples' Climate Vote* (January 2021).

1155   *The Washington Post. Washington Post*-ABC News Poll (November 7–10, 2021).

1156   Stoddard, Isak, Kevin Anderson, Stuart Capstick, Wim Carton, Joanna Depledge, Keri Facer, and Clair Gough. "Three Decades of Climate Mitigation:

Why Haven't We Bent the Global Emissions Curve?" *Annual Review of Environment and Resources* (June 29, 2021).

1157 Carrington, Damian. "'Blah, Blah, Blah': Greta Thunberg Lambasts Leaders over Climate Crisis." *The Guardian* (September 28, 2021).

1158 Dunlap, Riley E. and Robert J. Brulle, eds. *Climate Change and Society: Sociological Perspectives*. Oxford University Press, 2015.

1159 McKie, Robin. "Climate Change Deniers' New Battle Front Attacked." *The Observer* (November 9, 2019).

1160 Supran, Geoffrey, and Naomi Oreskes. "Rhetoric and Frame Analysis of ExxonMobil's Climate Change Communications." *OneEarth* 4, no. 5 (May 21, 2021).

1161 Hardisty. David J. and Elke U. Weber. "Discounting Future Green: Money Versus the Environment." *Journal of Experimental Psychology: General* 138 no. 3 (2009).

1162 Gilbert, Daniel. "If Only Gay Sex Caused Global Warming." *Los Angeles Times* (July 2, 2006).

1163 Gilbert, Daniel. "Global Warming and Psychology." Harvard Thinks Big (2010).

1164 Campbell, Troy H. and Aaron C, Kay. "Solution Aversion: On the Relation between Ideology and Motivated Disbelief." *Journal of Personality and Social Psychology* 107 (November 2014).

1165 Society for Personality and Social Psychology. "Facts, Beliefs, and Identity: The Seeds of Science Skepticism." Phys.org (January 22, 2017).

1166 Schaffner, Brian, and Samantha Luks. "This is What Trump Voters Said When Asked to Compare his Inauguration Crowd with Obama's." *The Washington Post* (January 27, 2017).

1167 Schaffner, Brian F. and Samantha Luks. "Misinformation or Expressive Responding? What an Inauguration Crowd Can Tell Us about the source of Political Misinformation in Surveys." *Public Opinion Quarterly* 82, no. 1 (Spring 2018).

1168 CSPAN, Sen. James Inhofe (R-OK). Snowball in the Senate (February 26, 2015).

1169 Kauffmann, Robert Michael L. Mann, Sucharita Gopal, Jackie A. Liederman, Peter D. Howe, Felix Pretis, Xiaojing Tang, and Michelle Gilmore. "Spatial Heterogeneity of Climate Change as an Experiential Basis for Skepticism." *Proceedings of the National Academy of Sciences* Vol.114, no. 1 (January 3, 2017).

1170 Waldman, Scott. "Climate Change Skepticism Fueled by Gut Reaction to Local Weather." *Scientific American* (December 20, 2016).

1171 Scopelliti, Irene, Carey K. Morewedge, Erin McCormick, H. Lauren Min, Sophie Lebrecht, asnd Karim S. Kassam. "Bias Blind Spot: Structure, Measurement, and Consequences." *Management Science* 61, no. 10 (October 2015).

1172   Rea, Shilo. "Researchers Find Everyone Has a Bias Blind Spot," Carnegie Mellon University (June 8, 2015).

1173   Hart, P. Sol, and Erik C. Nisbet. "Boomerang Effects in Science Communication: How Motivated Reasoning and Identity Cues Amplify Opinion Polarization About Climate Mitigation Policies." *Communication Research* 39, no. 6 (August 11, 2011).

1174   Kahan, Dan M., Ellen Peters, Maggie Wittlin, Paul Slovic, Lisa Larrimore Ouellette, Donald Braman, and Gregory Mandel. "The Polarizing Impact of Science Literacy and Numeracy on Perceived Climate Change Risks." *Nature Climate Change* 2 (May 27, 2012).

1175   Kopf, Dan, "Data Shows That Using Science in an Argument Just Makes People More Partisan," *Quartz* (December 23, 2016).

1176   Marshall, George. *Don't Even Think About It: Why Our Brains are Wired to Ignore Climate Change*. Bloomsbury, 2014.

1177   Gertner, Jon. "Why Isn't the Brain Green?" *The New York Times* (April 16, 2009).

1178   Weber, Elke U., "Experience-Based and Description-Based Perceptions of Long-Term Risk: Why Global Warming Does Not Scare us (Yet)." *Climatic Change* 77 (2006).

1179   Moser, Susanne C. and Lisa Dilling. "Making Climate HOT." *Environment* 46, no. 10 (December 2004).

1180   O'Neill, Saffron, and Sophie Nicholson-Cole. "'Fear Won't Do It' Promoting Positive Engagement With Climate Change through Visual and Iconic Representations." *Science Communication* 30, no. 3 (March 2009).

1181   Osaka, Shannon. "Going numb: Why We're Ignoring the Rising Death Toll from COVID-19." *Grist* (December 11, 2020.)

1182   Lewandowsky, Stephan, Naomi Oreskes, James S.Risbey, Ben R.Newell, and Michael Smithson. "Seepage: Climate Change Denial and Its Effect on the Scientific Community," *Global Environmental Change* 33 (July 2015).

1183   Tversky, Amos, and Daniel Kahneman. "Loss Aversion in Riskless Choice: A Reference-Dependent Model." *The Quarterly Journal of Economics* (1991).

1184   Kahneman, Daniel, Jack L. Knetsch, and Richard Thaler. "Experimental Tests of the Endowment Effect and the Coase Theorem." *Journal of Political Economy* (1990).

1185   Goode, Erica. "A Conversation with Daniel Kahneman; On Profit, Loss and the Mysteries of the Mind." *The New York Times* (November 5, 2002).

1186   Marshall, George. "Understanding Faulty Thinking to Tackle Climate Change." *New Scientist* (August 13, 2014).

1187   Konisky, David, Llewelyn Hughes, and Charles H. Kaylor. "Extreme Weather Events and Climate Change Concern." *Climatic Change* 134, no. 4 (February 2016).

1188 Slovic, Paul, and Elke Weber. "Perception of Risk Posed by Extreme Events." Conference paper delivered at "Risk Management strategies in an Uncertain World" (April 12–13, 2002).

1189 Erikson Erik. *Identity and the Life Cycle*. W.W. Norton & Company, Inc., 1994.

1190 Marshall, George. *Don't Even Think About It: Why Our Brains are Wired to Ignore Climate Change*. Bloomsbury, 2014.

1191 Ray, Sarah Jaquette. *A Field Guide to Climate Anxiety: How to Keep Your Cool on a Warming Planet*. University of California Press, 2020.

1192 Voelk, Tom. "Rise of S.U.V.s: Leaving Cars in Their Dust, With No Signs of Slowing." *The New York Times* (May 21, 2020).

1193 Housel, Morgan. "How the Average American Home Has Changed in the Last 40 Years." *The Motley Fool* (September 13, 2013).

1194 University of Chicago Energy Policy Institute and the Associated Press-NORC Center for Public Affairs Research. "Is the Public Willing to Pay to Help Fix Climate Change?" (November 2018).

1195 Tverberg, Gail. "World Energy Consumption since 1820 in Charts." Our Finite World (March 12, 2012).

1196 International Energy Agency. *Global Energy & CO_2 Status Report*, 2019.

1197 Kyba, Christopher C. M., Theres Kuester, Alejandro Sánchez De Miguel, Kimberly Baugh, Andreas Jechow, Franz Hölker, Jonathan Bennie, Christopher D. Elvidge, Kevin J. Gaston, and Luis Guanter. "Artificially Lit Surface of Earth at Night Increasing in Radiance and Extent." *Science Advances* 3, no. 11 (November 22, 2017).

1198 Leiserowitz, Anthony, Edward Maibach, Seth Rosenthal, John Kotcher, Liz Neyens, Jennifer Marlon, Jennifer Carman, Karine Lacroix, and Matthew Goldberg. "Global Warming's Six Americas, September 2021." Yale Program on Climate Change Communication and George Mason University Center for Climate Change Communication (September 2021).

1199 Gleick, Peter. "Joint Statements on Climate Change from National Academies of Science around the World." Significant Figures by Peter Gleick blog (January 17, 2017).

1200 American Association for the Advancement of Science. "Thirty-One Top Scientific Societies Speak With One Voice on Global Climate Change" EurekAlert! (June 28, 2016).

1201 Myers, Krista F., Peter T Doran, John Cook, John E Kotcher, and Teresa A Myers. "Consensus Revisited: Quantifying Scientific Agreement on Climate Change and Climate Expertise among Earth Scientists 10 Years Later." *Environmental Research Letters* 16, no. 10 (October 20, 2021).

1202   Oreskes, Naomi, and Erik Conway. *Merchants of Doubt: How a Handful of Scientists Obscured the Truth on Issues from Tobacco Smoke to Global Warming.* Bloomsbury Press, 2010.

1203   Fears, Darryl, and Emily Guskin. "The Strong Winds of Climate Change Have Failed To Move the Opinions of Many Americans." *The Washington Post* (November 12, 2021).

1204   Saas, Lydia. "Global Warming Attitudes Frozen since 2016." Gallup (April 5, 2021).

1205   Leiserowitz, A., E. Maibach, S. Rosenthal, J. Kotcher, J. Carman, L. Neyens, M. Goldberg, K. Lacroix, and J. Marlon. *Politics & Global Warming, April 2022,* Yale Program on Climate Change Communication and George Mason University Center for Climate Change Communication (July 7, 2022).

1206   Pew Research Center. "After Seismic Political Shift, Modest Changes in Public's Policy Agenda" (January 24, 2017).

1207   Lockwood, Ben, and Matthew Lockwood. "How Do Right-Wing Populist Parties Influence Climate and Renewable Energy Policies? Evidence from OECD Countries." *Global Environmental Politics* (April 6, 2022).

1208   University of Warwick. "New Research into Threat Posed to Climate Change Policies by the Rise of the Populist Right" Phys.org (April 14, 2022).

1209   Markandya, Anil, Jon Sampedro, Steven J Smith, Rita Van Dingenen, Cristina Pizarro-Irizar, Iñaki Arto, Mikel González-Eguino, K. E. O. Todd-Brown, C. W. Rowe, W. R. Wieder, J. C. Carey, M. B. Machmuller, and B. L. Snoek. "Health Co-Benefits from Air Pollution and Mitigation Costs of the Paris Agreement: A Modelling Study." *The Lancet* 2, no. 3 (March 2018).

1210   Landrigan, Philip. "The Health and Economic Benefits of Climate Mitigation and Pollution Control." *The Lancet*, 2, no. 3 (March 2018).

1211   UN Environment Programme. *Global Environment Outlook.* Cambridge University Press, 2019.

1212   Krugman, Paul. "Covid-19 Brings Out All the Usual Zombies." *The New York Times* (March 28, 2020).

1213   Bardon, Adrian. *The Truth about Denial: Bias and Self-Deception in Science Politics, and Religion.* Oxford University Press, 2019.

1214   Forgey, Quint. "Trump Cautions Davos against Heeding 'Prophets of Doom' on Climate Change." *Politico* (January 20, 2020).

1215   Milman, Oliver. "Climate Denial Is Waning on the Right. What's Replacing It Might Be Just as Scary." *The Guardian* (November 21, 2021).

1216   Turner, Joe and Dan Bailey. "'Ecobordering': Casting Immigration Control as Environmental Protection." *Environmental Politics* (April 29, 2021).

1217 Brulle, Robert J. "Institutionalizing Delay: Foundation Funding and the Creation of US Climate Change Counter-Movement Organizations." *Climatic Change* (December 21, 2013).

1218 Fischer, Douglas. "'Dark Money' Funds Climate Change Denial Effort." *Scientific American* (December 23, 2013).

1219 Union of Concerned Scientists. Global Warming Skeptic Organizations (2013).

1220 Fitzsimmons, Jill. "Meet the Climate Denial Machine." Media Matters for America (November 28, 2012).

1221 DeSmog. Climate Disinformation Database.

1222 Farrell, Justin. "Corporate Funding and Ideological Polarization about Climate Change." *Proceedings of the National Academy of Sciences* 113, No. 1 (January 5, 2016).

1223 Farrell, Justin. "Network Structure and Influence of the Climate Change Counter-Movement." *Nature Climate Change* 6 (November 30, 2015).

1224 Stoknes, Per Espen. *What We Think About When We Try Not To Think About Global Warming: Toward a New Psychology of Climate Action*. Chelsea Green Publishing, 2015.

1225 Lewandowsky, Stephan, Giles E. Gignac, and Klaus Oberauer. "The Role of Conspiracist Ideation and Worldviews in Predicting Rejection of Science." *PLOS ONE*, 8, no. 10 (October 2013).

1226 Lewandowsky, Stephan, Klaus Oberauer, and Giles E, Gignac. "NASA Faked the Moon Landing—Therefore, (Climate) Science Is a Hoax." *Psychological Science* 24, no. 5 (March 26, 2013).

1227 Khoo, Michael. "Climate, Clicks, Capitalism, and Conspiracists." Friends of the Earth (August 27, 2020).

1228 Hornsey, Matthew J., Emily A. Harris, and Kelly S. Fielding. "Relationships among Conspiratorial Beliefs, Conservatism and Climate Scepticism across Nations." *Nature Climate Change* (May 7, 2018).

1229 Harlos, Christian, Tim C. Edgell, and Johan Hollander. "No Evidence of Publication Bias in Climate Change Science." *Climatic Change* 140 (December 28, 2016).

1230 Hollander, Johan. "We Looked At 1,154 Climate Science Results and Found No Evidence of 'Publication Bias'." *The Conversation* (October 5, 2017).

1231 Dunlap, Riley E. and Aaron M. McCright. "Challenging Climate Change: The Denial Climate Movement," in Dunlap, Riley E. and Robert J Brulle, eds. *Climate Change and Society: Sociological Perspectives*, Oxford University Press, 2015.

1232 Haskins, Justin. "Commentary: The 6 Biggest Reasons I'm a Climate-Change Skeptic—And Why You Should Be a Skeptic Too." Blaze Media (July 23, 2017).

1233   Siegel, Ethan. "Heartland's '6 Reasons To Be A Climate-Change Skeptic' Are Six Demonstrable Falsehoods." *Forbes* (July 2, 2017).

1234 CO_2 Coalition. *What Rising CO_2 Means for Global Food Security* (February, 2019).

1235   Abbot, John, and Jennifer Marohasy. "The Application of Machine Learning for Evaluating Anthropogenic Versus Natural Climate Change." *GeoResJ* 14 (December 2017).

1236   The Climate Modelling Laboratory.

1237   Readfearn, Graham, "Why the IPA's Claim Global Warming is Natural is 'Junk Science'," August 25, 2017.

1238   Benestad, Rasmus. "Learning From Mistakes in Climate Research." *Theoretical and Applied Climatology* 126, no. 3–4 (August 20, 2015).

1239   Foley, Katherine Ellen. "Those 3% of Scientific Papers That Deny Climate Change? A Review Found Them All Flawed." *Quartz* (September 5, 2017).

1240   Abraham, John. "Just Who Are These 300 'Scientists' Telling Trump To Burn The Climate?" *The Guardian* (February 27, 2017).

1241   Wallace, Tim. "Cosmic Ray Theory of Global Warming Gets Cold Response." *Cosmos* (December 22, 2017).

1242   Abraham, John. "More Errors Identified in Contrarian Climate Scientists' Temperature Estimates" *The Guardian* (May 11, 2017).

1243   Spencer, Roy W. *A Guide to Understanding Global Temperature Data* (July 2016).

1244   Nuccitelli, Dana. "These Are the Best Arguments from the 3% of Climate Scientist 'Skeptics.' Really." *The Guardian* (July 25, 2016).

1245   Skeptical Science. Global Warming & Climate Change Myths.

1246   Koonin, Steven E. *Unsettled: What Climate Science Tells Us, What It Doesn't, and Why It Matters.* BenBella Books, 2021.

1247   DeSmog. "Steve Koonin."

1248   Yohe, Gary. "A New Book Manages to Get Climate Science Badly Wrong." *Scientific American* (May 13, 2021).

1249   Center for Countering Digital Hate. *The Toxic Ten: How Ten Fringe Publishers Fuel 69% of Digital Climate Change Denial* (November 2, 2021).

1250   Bensinger, Greg. "Social Media Is Polluted With Climate Denialism." *The New York Times* (November 12, 2021).

1251   Stop Funding Heat. *In Denial—Facebook's Growing Friendship with Climate Misinformation* (November 2021).

1252   Levantesi, Stella, and Giulio Corsion. "Climate Deniers Are Using These Four Major Scare Tactics to Stop Climate Action." DeSmog (November 16, 2021).

1253 Harvey, Jeffrey A., Daphne van den Berg, Jacintha Ellers, Remko Kampen, Thomas W Crowther, Peter Roessingh, Bart Verheggen et al. "Internet Blogs, Polar Bears, and Climate-Change Denial by Proxy." *BioScience* (November 29, 2017).

1254 Franta, Benjamin. "Trump Pulled Out the Oil Industry Playbook and Players for Paris." *The Guardian* (July 26, 2017).

1255 Walker, Joe. "Draft Global Climate Science Communications Plan."

1256 Union of Concerned Scientists. *The Climate Deception Dossiers* (2015).

1257 CNN. "Santorum Claims Climate Scientists 'Driven by Money'" (November 26, 2018).

1258 Sherwood, Anthony. "Scientists Getting Filthy Rich on Climate Change? Here Are The Facts." *Huffington Post* (May 26, 2016).

1259 Mann, Michael. "Open Season on Climate Science." *Undark* (February 17, 2017).

1260 Goldman, Gretchen. "House Science Committee Chairman Lamar Smith Defends ExxonMobil, Subpoenas Union of Concerned Scientists: An FAQ." Union of Concerned Scientists (July 13, 2016).

1261 Kimmel, Ken. "When Subpoenas Threaten Climate Science." *The New York Times* (July 19, 2016).

1262 Climate Science Legal Defense Fund. "Perspectives of Scientists Who Become Targets: Michael Mann" (July 20, 2017).

1263 Mann, Michael. "I'm a Scientist Who Has Gotten Death Threats. I Fear What May Happen under Trump." *The Washington Post* (December 16, 2016).

1264 Marshall, George. *Don't Even Think About It: Why Our Brains are Wired to Ignore Climate Change*. Bloomsbury, 2014.

1265 IPCC. *Climate Change 2022: Mitigation of Climate Change, Summary for Policymakers*. From: *Climate Change 2022: Mitigation of Climate Change* (April 4, 2022).

1266 Borenstein, Seth. "No Obituary for Earth: Scientists Fight Climate Doom Talk." Associated Press (April 4, 2022).

1267 The Global Commission on the Economy and Climate. *The New Climate Economy: The 2018 Report of the Global Commission on the Economy and Climate* (August 2018).

1268 Figueres, Christiana, Hans Joachim Schellnhuber, Gail Whiteman, Johan Rockström, Anthony Hobley, and Stefan Rahmstorf. "Three Years to Safeguard Our Climate." *Nature* 546, no. 7660 (June 28, 2017).

1269 International Energy Agency. *World Energy Outlook 2011* (November 2011).

1270 Kemp, Luke, Chi Xu, Joanna Depledge, Kristie L. Ebi, Goodwin Gibbins, Timothy A. Kohler, Johan Rockström et al. "Climate Endgame: Exploring Catastrophic Climate Change Scenarios." *Proceedings of the National Academy of Sciences* 119, no. 34 (August 23, 2022).

1271   Gates, Bill. *How to Avoid a Climate Disaster: The Solutions We Have and the Breakthroughs We Need*. Knopf, 2021.

1272   Monbiot, George. "We Need Optimism—but Disneyfied Climate Predictions are Just Dangerous." *The Guardian* (May 13, 2022).

1273   Mann, Michael E. *The New Climate War: The Fight to Take Back Our Climate*. Hatchette Book Group, 2021.

1274   Wadhwa, Vivek, and Alex Salkever. "Our Amazing Clean Energy Future Has Arrived." *Foreign Policy* (January 23, 2021).

1275   Wallace-Wells, David. "The Uninhabitable Earth (annotated version)." *New York* (July 9, 2017).

1276   Wallace-Wells, David. *The Uninhabitable Earth: Life After Warming*. Penguin, 2019.

1277   Mooney, Chris. "Scientists Challenge Magazine Story about 'Uninhabitable Earth'." *The Washington Post* (July 12, 2017).

1278   Gore, Al, "Al Gore: The Climate Crisis Is the Battle of Our Time, and We Can Win," *The New York Times* (September 20, 2019).

1279   Dovere, Edward-Isaac. "Al Gore: America Is Close to a 'Political Tipping Point' on Climate Change." *The Atlantic* (January 3, 2019).

1280   Dunlap, Riley E. and Aaron M. McCright. "Challenging Climate Change: The Denial Climate Movement." In Dunlap, Riley E. and Robert J., Brulle, eds. *Climate Change and Society: Sociological Perspectives*. Oxford University Press, 2015.

1281   Stoknes, Per Espen. *What We Think About When We Try Not To Think About Global Warming: Toward a New Psychology of Climate Action*. Chelsea Green Publishing, 2015.

1282   Beattie, Geoffrey. "Optimism Bias and Climate Change," *British Academy Review*, Summer 2018.

1283   UN Framework Convention on Climate Change. *Paris Agreement* (October 5, 2016).

1284   Nordhaus, William D. "Can We Control Carbon Dioxide?" IIASA (June 1975).

1285   Nordhaus, William D. "Strategies for the Control of Carbon Dioxide." Cowles Foundation Discussion Paper no. 443 (January 6, 1977).

1286   Rijsberman, F. R. and Swart, R. J. "Targets and Indicators of Climate Change." Stockholm Environment Institute (1990).

1287   Carbon Brief Staff. "Two degrees: The History of Climate Change's Speed Limit." *Carbon Brief* (August 12, 2014).

1288   Knutti, Reto, Joeri Rogelj, Jan Sedláček, and Erich M. Fischer. "A Scientific Critique of the Two-Degree Climate Change Target." *Nature GeoScience* (December 7, 2015).

1289   Covering Climate Now. "Press Briefing: Countdown to COP26: What's at Stake" (September 2, 2021).

1290   UN Framework Convention on Climate Change. *Paris Agreement text* (2015).

1291   Milman, Oliver. "James Hansen, Father Of Climate Change Awareness, Calls Paris Talks 'A Fraud." *The Guardian* (December 12, 2015).

1292   Gillis, Justin. "James Hansen, Climate Scientist Turned Activist, Criticizes Paris Talks." *The New York Times* (December 2, 2015).

1293   Rockström, Johan, Hans Joachim Schellnhuber,Brian Hoskins,Veerabhadran Ramanathan,Peter Schlosser,Guy Pierre Brasseur,Owen Gaffney,Carlos Nobre,Malte Meinshausen,Joeri Rogelj, and Wolfgang Lucht. "The World's Biggest Gamble." *Earth's Future* 4, no. 10 (October 27, 2016).

1294   Odendahl, Terry. "The Failures of the Paris Climate Change Agreement and How Philanthropy Can Fix Them." *Stanford Social Innovation Review* (January 22, 2016).

1295   International Energy Agency. World Energy Outlook 2018 (November 13, 2018).

1296   Climate Action Tracker. Climate Action Tracker website

1297   UN Environment Programme. *The Emissions Gap Report 2016* (2016).

1298   UN Environment Programme. *The Emissions Gap Report 2017* (2017).

1299   UN Environment Programme. *The Emissions Gap Report 2018* (2018).

1300   UN Environment Programme. *The Emissions Gap Report 2019* (2019).

1301   UN Environment Programme. *The Emissions Gap Report 2020* (2020).

1302   UN Environment Programme. *The Emissions Gap Report 2022* (2022).

1303   Höhne, Niklas Michel den Elzen, Joeri Rogelj, Bert Metz, Taryn Fransen, Takeshi Kuramochi, Anne Olhoff et al. "Emissions: World Has Four Times the Work or One-Third of the Time." *Nature* (March 4, 2020).

1304   UN Environment Programme. *The Emissions Gap Report 2016* (2016).

1305   Rogelj, Joeri Michel den Elzen, Niklas Höhne, Taryn Fransen, Hanna Fekete, Harald Winkler, Roberto Schaeffer, Fu Sha, Keywan Riahi, and Malte Meinshausen. "Paris Agreement Climate Proposals Need a Boost to Keep Warming Well Below 2°C." *Nature* 534 (June 29, 2016).

1306   Climate Interactive. Climate Scoreboard.

1307   UN Environment Programme. *Global Environment Outlook*. Cambridge University Press, 2019.

1308   Universal Ecological Fund. *The Truth about Climate Change* (September 2016).

1309   Schurer, Andrew P. Michael E. Mann, Ed Hawkins, Simon F. B. Tett, and Gabriele C. Hegerl. "Importance of the Pre-Industrial Baseline for Likelihood of Exceeding Paris Goals." *Nature Climate Change* 7 (July 24, 2017).

1310   Pennsylvania State University. "Allowable 'Carbon Budget' Most Likely Overestimated." Phys.org (July 24, 2017).

1311   Gasser T. et al., "Path-Dependent Reductions in CO_2 Emission Budgets Caused by Permafrost Carbon Release, IIASA, September 17, 2018.

1312   IIASA, "Paris Climate Targets Could be Exceeded Sooner Than Expected," September 17, 2018.

1313   Gasser, T. M. Kechiar, P. Ciais, E. J. Burke, T. Kleinen, D. Zhu, Y. Huang et al. "Negative Emissions Physically Needed to Keep Global Warming Below 2°C." *Nature Communications* 6 (August 3, 2015).

1314   Geden, Oliver, and Andreas Löschel. "Define Limits for Temperature Overshoot Targets." *Nature GeoScience* 10 (November 27, 2017).

1315   International Energy Agency. *Energy and Climate Change: World Energy Outlook Special Briefing for COP21* (2015).

1316   Rogelj, Joeri, Oliver Fricko, Malte Meinshausen, Volker Krey, Johanna J. J. Zilliacus, and Keywan Riahi. "Understanding the Origin of Paris Agreement Emission Uncertainties." *Nature Communications* 8 (June 6, 2017).

1317   Mooney, Chris Juliet Eilperin, Desmond Butler, John Muyskens, Anu Narayanswamy, and Naema Ahmed. "Countries' Climate Pledges Built On Flawed Data, Post Investigation Finds." *The Washington Post* (November 7, 2021).

1318   Stoknes, Per Espen. *What We Think About When We Try Not To Think About Global Warming: Toward a New Psychology of Climate Action.* Chelsea Green Publishing, 2015.

1319   Sengupta, Somini. "UN Climate Talks End With Few Commitments and a 'Lost' Opportunity." *The New York Times* (December 15, 2019).

1320   UN Framework Convention on Climate Change. *Nationally Determined Contributions under the Paris Agreement. Synthesis Report by the Secretariat* (September 17, 2021).

1321   UN Framework Convention on Climate Change. "Statement by the Secretary-General on the Report by the UN Framework Convention on Climate Change" (September 17, 2021).

1322   UN Conference of the Parties. *Glasgow Climate Pact* (November 2021).

1323   Zhang, Sarah. "A Huge Solar Plant Caught on Fire, and That's the Least of Its Problems." *Wired* (May 23, 2016).

1324   Danelski, David. "Ivanpah Solar Plant, Built to Limit Greenhouse Gases, is Burning More Natural Gas." *The Press-Enterprise* (January 23, 2017).

1325   The Editorial Board. "Ivanpah Solar Plant Still a Disappointment." *The Sun* (January 25, 2017).

1326   Blum, Jordan. "NRG Slims down by Selling Renewable Energy Holdings." *Houston Chronicle* (February 7, 2018).

1327 Haas, Greg. "Solar Plant near Tonopah Producing Power for NV Energy after Stop during Bankruptcy." 8NewsNow.com (October 14, 2021).

1328 International Energy Agency. Renewables 2021 (December 2021).

1329 International Energy Agency. "Renewables Information Overview, Supply" (August 2021).

1330 International Renewable Energy Agency. *Global Renewables Outlook: Energy Transformation 2050* (April 2020).

1331 US Energy Information Administration. "What Is US Electricity Generation by Energy Source?" (February 2022).

1332 US Energy Information Administration. "EIA Projects That Renewable Generation Will Supply 44% of U.S. Electricity by 2050." From: *Annual Energy Outlook 2022* (March 18, 2022).

1333 International Energy Agency. *Global Energy Review 2020, Renewables* (April 2020).

1334 International Energy Agency. *Tracking Clean Energy Progress* (November 2022).

1335 BloombergNEF. *Energy Transition Investment Trends* (January 2022).

1336 International Energy Agency. *World Energy Investment 2022* (2022).

1337 Energy Initiative, Massachusetts Institute of Technology. *The Future of Solar Energy: An Interdiscplinary MIT Study* (2015).

1338 Nathwani, Jatin. "Solar Power Alone Won't Solve Energy or Climate Needs." *The Conversation* (September 25, 2017).

1339 Creutzig, Felix, Peter Agoston, Jan Christoph Goldschmidt, Gunnar Luderer, Gregory Nemet, and Robert C. Pietzcker. "The Underestimated Potential of Solar Energy to Mitigate Climate Change." *Nature Energy* 2 (August 25, 2017).

1340 Jacobson, Mark, Z., Mark A. Delucchi, Zack A. F. Bauer, Jingfan Wang, Eric Weiner, and Alexander S. Yachanin. "100% Clean and Renewable Wind, Water, and Sunlight (WWS) All-Sector Energy Roadmaps for 139 Countries of the World." *Joule* 1, no. 1 (September 6, 2017).

1341 Jacobson, Mark Z., Mark A. Delucchi, Guillaume Bazouin, Zack A. F. Bauer, Christa C. Heavey, Emma Fisher, Sean B. Morris, Diniana J. Y. Piekutowski, Taylor A. Vencilla, and Tim W. Yeskoo. "100% Clean and Renewable Wind, Water, and Sunlight (WWS) All-Sector Energy Roadmaps for the 50 United States." *Energy & Environmental Science* 8 (July 1, 2015).

1342 Solomon, Tom. "Here's How to Build 100% Clean Renewable Energy in the US Before 2040." *Clean Technica* (October 12, 2016).

1343 International Energy Agency. *The Role of Critical Minerals in Clean Energy Transitions* (May 2021).

1344 International Energy Agency. "Clean Energy Demand for Critical Minerals Set To Soar as the World Pursues Net Zero Goals." (May 5 2021).

1345 Elshkaki, Ayman, T. E. Graedel, Luca Ciacci, and Barbara K. Reck. "Copper Demand, Supply, and Associated Energy Use to 2050." *Global Environmental Change* 39 (July 2016).

1346 Earthworks "Mining 101."

1347 Hickel, Jason. "The Limits of Clean Energy." *Foreign Policy* (September 6, 2019).

1348 Arrobas, Dan.ele La Porta Hund, Kirsten Lori, Mccormick, Michael Stephen Ningthoujam, Jagabanta Drexhage, and John Richard. *The Growing Role of Minerals and Metals for a Low Carbon Future (English).* World Bank Group (June 30, 2017).

1349 International Renewable Energy Agency. "End-Of-Life Management: Solar Photovoltaic Panels." (June 2016).

1350 Electric Power Research Institute. "Wind Turbine Blade Recycling: Preliminary Assessment" (April 17, 2020).

1351 Newell, Richard G. and Daniel Raimi. "The New Climate Math: Energy Addition, Subtraction, and Transition." *Resources for the Future* (October 2018).

1352 Smil, Vaclav. "The Long Slow Rise of Solar and Wind." *Scientific American* (January 2014).

1353 International Energy Agency. *System Integration of Renewables* (January 2018).

1354 International Energy Agency. "Will System Integration of Renewables Be a Major Challenge by 2023?" (January 7, 2020).

1355 International Energy Agency. *World Energy Outlook 2020 Executive Summary* (October 2020).

1356 Caspary, Jay, Michael Goggin, Rob Gramlich, and Jesse Schneider. *Disconnected: The Need for a New Generator Interconnection Policy.* Americans for a Clean Energy Grid (January 2021).

1357 Tverberg, Gail. "Renewable Energy's Inconvenient Truth." OilPrice.com (October 26, 2019).

1358 Pfeifenberger, Johannes, Kasparas Spokas, J. Michael Hagerty, John Tsoukalis, Rob Gramlich, Michael Goggin, Jay Caspary, and Jesse Schneider. *Transmission Planning for the 21st Century: Proven Practices that Increase Value and Reduce Costs.* The Brattle Group, Grid Strategies (October 2021).

1359 Kollipara, Puneet. "Better Power Lines Would Help US Supercharge Renewable Energy, Study Suggests." *Science* (January 25, 2016).

1360 ScottMadden Management Consultants. *Informing the Transmission Discussion* (January 2020).

1361 Jacobson, Marc Z., Anna-Katharina von Krauland, Stephen J.Coughlin, Frances C. Palmer, and Miles M. Smith. "Zero Air Pollution and Zero Carbon from All Energy at Low Cost and Without Blackouts in Variable Weather throughout the

U.S. with 100% Wind-Water-Solar and Storage." *Renewable Energy* 184 (January 2022).

1362 Jordan, Rob. "Researchers Show a 100% Renewable US Grid with No Blackouts Is Possible." Stanford Woods Institute for the Environment (December 7, 2021).

1363 Frew, Bethany, Wesley Cole, Paul Denholm, A. Will Frazier, Nina Vincent, and Robert Margolis. "Sunny with a Chance of Curtailment: Operating the US Grid with Very High Levels of Solar Photovoltaics." *iScience* 21 (November 22, 2019).

1364 Energy Initiative, Massachusetts Institute of Technology. *The Future of Solar Energy: An Interdiscplinary MIT Study* (2015).

1365 Hirth, Lion. "The Market Value of Variable Renewables: The Effect of Solar Wind Power Variability on Their Relative Price." *Energy Economics* 38 (July 2013).

1366 Temple, James. "California is Throttling Back Record Levels of Solar—and That's Bad News for Climate Goals." *MIT Technology Review* (May 24, 2018).

1367 US Energy Information Administration. "California's Curtailments of Solar Electricity Generation Continue to Increase" (August 24, 2021).

1368 Penn, Ivan. "California Invested Heavily in Solar Power. Now there's so Much That Other States are Sometimes Paid to take it." *Los Angeles Times* (June 22, 2017).

1369 Fowlie, Meredith. "The Duck has Landed." UC Berkeley Energy Institute at Haas (May 2, 2016).

1370 Sivaram, Varun and Shayle Kann. "Solar Power Needs a More Ambitious Cost Target." *Nature Energy* 1 (April 7, 2016).

1371 Feldman, David, Vignesh Ramasamy, Ran Fu, Ashwin Ramdas, Jal Desai, and Robert Margolis. *U.S. Solar Photovoltaic System and Energy Storage Cost Benchmark: Q1 2020*. National Renewable Energy Laboratory (January 2021).

1372 Sivaram, Varun and Shayle Kann. "To Become Truly Mainstream, Solar Will Need to Cost 25 Cents per Watt by 2050." Greentech Media (April 7, 2016).

1373 van Kooten, G. Cornelis. "The Economics of Wind Power." *Annual Review of Resource Economics* 8 (July 22, 2016).

1374 Deign, Jason. "Germany's Maxed-Out Grid Is Causing Trouble across Europe." Green Tech Media (March 31, 2020).

1375 Reed, Stanley. "Power Prices Go Negative in Germany, a Positive for Energy Users." *The New York Times* (December 25, 2017).

1376 Goff, Michael. "The Role of Baseload Low-Carbon Electricity in Decarbonization." Breakthrough Blog (December 5, 2016).

1377 Mills, Mark P. "The Tesla and Solar City Merger Is Rooted In Battery Derangement Syndrome." *Forbes* (June 25, 2016).

1378 International Energy Agency. *Technology Roadmap: Energy Storage* (2014).

1379 International Energy Agency. "Energy Storage" (June 2020).

1380 Temple, James. "Relying on Renewables Alone Significantly Inflates the Cost of Overhauling Energy." *MIT Technology Review* (February 26, 2018).

1381 Sepulveda, Nestor A., Jesse D. Jenkins, Aurora Edington, Dharik S. Mallapragada, and Richard K. Lester. "The Design Space for Long-Duration Energy Storage in Decarbonized Power Systems." *Nature Energy* 6 (March 29, 2021).

1382 Roberts, David. "Long-Duration Energy Storage Can Help Clean up the Grid, But Only If It's Super Cheap." Canary Media (June 10, 2021).

1383 US Department of Energy. "Secretary Granholm Announces New Goal to Cut Costs of Long Duration Energy Storage by 90 Percent." Energy.gov (July 14, 2021).

1384 US Department of Energy. Energy Storage Grand Challenge. Energy.gov.

1385 McKinsey & Company. *Net-Zero Power: Long-Duration Energy Storage for a Renewable Grid* (November 22. 2021).

1386 Sivaram, Varun. "Why Moore's Law Doesn't Apply to Clean Energy Technologies." Council on Foreign Relations Energy, Security, and Climate (April 23, 2015).

1387 Schlacter, Fred. "No Moore's Law for Batteries." *Proceedings of the National Academy of Sciences* 110, no. 14 (April 2, 2013).

1388 House, Kurt Zenz. "The Limits of Energy Storage Technology." *Bulletin of the Atomic Scientists* (January 20, 2009).

1389 International Energy Agency. "How Solar Energy Could Be the Largest Source of Electricity by Mid-Century" (2014).

1390 Manoli, Gabriele. "Delay-Induced Rebounds in CO_2 Emissions and Critical Time-Scales to Meet Global Warming Targets." *Earth's Future* 4, no. 12 (December 2016).

1391 *The Engineer.* "Are Renewables Rising Fast Enough to Combat Climate Change?" (January 4, 2017).

1392 Louwen, Atse, Wilfried G. J. H. M. van Sark, André P. C. Faaij, and Ruud E. I. Schropp. "Re-Assessment of Net Energy Production and Greenhouse Gas Emissions Avoidance after 40 Years of Photovoltaics Development." *Nature Communications* 7 (December 6, 2016).

1393 Musial, Walter. Philipp Beiter, Paul Spitsen, Jake Nunemaker, Vahan Gevorgian, Aubryn Cooperman, Rob Hammond, and Matt Shields. *2019 Offshore Wind Technology Data Update.* National Renewable Energy Laboratory (October 2020).

1394 US Department of Energy, US Department of the Interior. *National Offshore Wind Strategy* (September 2016).

1395 International Energy Agency. "Tracking Clean Energy Progress: Renewable Power." (November 2021).

1396 Mathis, Will, and Ryan Beene. "Wind Power's 'Colossal Market Failure' Threatens Climate Fight." Bloomberg (April 22, 2022).

1397 Karnauskas, Kristopher B., Julie K. Lundquist, and Lei Zhang. "Southward Shift of the Global Wind Energy Resource under High Carbon Dioxide Emissions." *Nature GeoScience* 11 (December 11, 2017).

1398 Bird, Steve. "Review Launched into Onshore Impact of Offshore Wind Farms." *The Telegraph* (November 10, 2019).

1399 Bershidsky, Leonid. "Germany's Giant Windmills are Wildly Unpopular." Bloomberg Opinion (October 30, 2019).

1400 Byce, Robert. "Angry US Landowners are Killing off Renewable Energy Projects." *New York Post* (March 7, 2020).

1401 Dentzer, Bill. "Plans Scrapped For Huge Solar Array North of Las Vegas." *Las Vegas Review-Journal* (July 22, 2021).

1402 Simon, Julia. "Misinformation Is Derailing Renewable Energy Projects across the United States." NPR (March 28, 2022).

1403 Miller, Lee M. and David W. Keith. "Observation-Based Solar and Wind Power Capacity Factors and Power Densities." *Environmental Research Letters* 13, no. 10 (October 4, 2018).

1404 Solar Energy Development Programmatic Environmental Impact Statement. "Solar Energy Development Environmental Considerations."

1405 Shellenberger, Michael. "If Renewables Are So Great for the Environment, Why Do They Keep Destroying It?" *Forbes* (May 17, 2018).

1406 Rulli, Maria Cristina, Davide Bellomi, Andrea Cazzoli, Giulia De Carolis, and Paolo D'Odorico. "The Water-Land-Food Nexus of First-Generation Biofuels." *Scientific Reports* 6 (March 3, 2016).

1407 University of Virginia. "Fuel or Food? Study Sees Increasing Competition for Land, Water Resources." ScienceDaily (March 3, 2016).

1408 Richardson, Meredith, and Praveen Kumar. "Critical Zone Services as Environmental Assessment Criteria in Intensively Managed Landscapes." *Earth's Future* 4 (June 20, 2017).

1409 National Research Council. *Renewable Fuel Standard: Potential Economic and Environmental Impacts of us Biofuel Policy* (2011).

1410 Lark, Tyler J., Nathan P. Hendricks, Aaron Smith, Nicholas Pates, Seth A. Spawn-Lee, Matthew Bougie, Eric G. Booth, Christopher J. Kucharik, and Holly K. Gibbs. "Environmental Outcomes of the US Renewable Fuel Standard." *Proceedings of the National Academy of Sciences* 119, no 9 (March 1, 2022).

1411 International Energy Agency. *Technology Roadmap: Bioenergy for Heat and Power* (May 29, 2012).

1412 International Energy Agency. *Hydropower Special Market Report: Analysis and Forecast to 2030* (June 2021).

1413   Pearce, Fred. "Water Warning: The Looming Threat of the World's Aging Dams." Yale Environment 360 (February 3, 2021).

1414   International Energy Agency. "Tracking Clean Energy Progress: Geothermal" (November 2021).

1415   Eavor Technologies, Inc.

1416   Heinberg, Richard. "Tiptoeing through the Renewable Energy Minefield." Post Carbon Institute (June 13, 2016).

1417   Wilcox, J., B. Kolosz, and J. Freeman, eds. CDR Primer (2021).

1418   Taft, Molly. "The Only Carbon Capture Plant in the US Just Closed." Gizmodo (February 2021).

1419   US Department of Energy/National Energy Technology Laboratory. Final Scientific/Technical Report, Petra Nova (March 31, 2020).

1420   Fountain, Henry. "In Blow to 'Clean Coal,' Flawed Plant Will Burn Gas Instead." The New York Times (June 28, 2017).

1421   Anchondo, Carlos. "CCS 'Red Flag?' World's Sole Coal Project Hits Snag." E&E News (January 10, 2022).

1422   Morton, Adam. "'A Shocking Failure': Chevron Criticised for Missing Carbon Capture Target At WA Gas Project." The Guardian (July 19, 2021).

1423   Bakx, Kyle. "Alberta Carbon Capture Project Hits Another Milestone Ahead of Schedule and Below Cost." CBC (July 10, 2020).

1424   Global Witness. Hydrogen's Hidden Emissions (January 20, 2022).

1425   Harvey, Charles and Kurt House. "Every Dollar Spent on This Climate Technology Is a Waste." The New York Times (August 16, 2022).

1426   Reiner, David M. "Learning through a Portfolio of Carbon Capture and Storage Demonstration Projects" Nature Energy 1 (January 11, 2016).

1427   University of Cambridge. "Global Learning Is Needed to Save Carbon Capture and Storage from Being Abandoned." Phys.org (January 11, 2016).

1428   US Government Accountability Office. Carbon Capture and Storage: Actions Needed to Improve doe Management of Demonstration Projects (December 20, 2021).

1429   International Energy Agency. "Tracking Clean Energy Progress: CCUS in Power" (November 2021).

1430   Gasser, T., C. Guivarch, K. Tachiiri, C. D. Jones, and P. Ciais. "Negative Emissions Physically Needed to Keep Global Warming Below 2°C." Nature Communications 6 (August 3, 2015).

1431   International Energy Agency. 20 Years of Carbon Capture and Storage Accelerating Future Deployment (2016).

1432   International Energy Agency. Technology Roadmap: Carbon Capture and Storage 2013 (2013).

1433   IPCC. *Global Warming of 1.5°C, Chapter 2* From: *Global Warming of 1.5°C* (October 6, 2018).

1434   Mac Dowell, Niall, Paul S. Fennell, Nilay Shah, and Geoffrey C. Maitland. "The Role of CO_2 Capture and Utilization in Mitigating Climate Change." *Nature Climate Change* 7 (April 5, 2017).

1435   Smil, Vaclav. "Global Energy: The Latest Infatuations." *American Scientist* 99 (May–June 2011).

1436   Center for International Environmental Law. *Confronting the Myth of Carbon-Free Fossil Fuels: Why Carbon Capture Is Not a Climate Solution* (July 2021).

1437   International Energy Agency. *CCUS in Clean Energy Transitions* (September 2020).

1438   Global CCS Institute. *Global Status of CCS Report 2021* (2021).

1439   Field, Christopher B. and Katharine J. Mach. "Rightsizing Carbon Dioxide Removal." *Science* 356, no. 6339 (May 19, 2017).

1440   Anderson, Kevin and Glen Peters. "The Trouble with Negative Emissions." *Science* 354, no. 6309 (October 14, 2016).

1441   Stenzel, Fabian, Peter Greve, Wolfgang Lucht, Sylvia Tramberend, Yoshihide Wada, and Dieter Gerten. "Irrigation of Biomass Plantations May Globally Increase Water Stress More Than Climate Change." *Nature Communications* 12 (March 8, 2021).

1442   IPCC. *Climate Change and Land* (August, 2019).

1443   Stokstad, Erik. "Bioenergy Not a Climate Cure-All, Panel Warns." *Science* Vol 365, no. 6453 (August 9, 2019).

1444   Boysen, Lena R., Wolfgang Lucht, Dieter Gerten, Vera Heck, Timothy M. Lenton, and Hans Joachim Schellnhube. "The Limits to Global-Warming Mitigation by Terrestrial Carbon Removal." *Earth's Future* 5, no. 5 (May 17, 2017).

1445   Baik, Ejeong, Daniel L. Sanchez, Peter A. Turner, Katharine J. Mach, Christopher B. Field, and Sally M. Benson. "Geospatial Analysis of Near-Term Potential for Carbon-Negative Bioenergy in the United States." *Proceedings of the National Academy of Sciences* 115, no. 13 (March 27, 2018).

1446   Williams, Eric. *The Economics of Direct Air Carbon Capture and Storage.* Global CCS Institute (July 26, 2022).

1447   Keith, David W., Geoffrey Holmes, David St. Angelo, and Kenton Heidel. "A Process for Capturing CO_2 from the Atmosphere." *Joule* 2, no. 8 (June 7, 2018).

1448   Barnard, Michael. "Chevron's Fig Leaf Part 5: Who Is behind Carbon Engineering, & What Do Experts Say?" *Clean Technica* (April 20, 2019).

1449   Barnard, Michael. "Chevron's Fig Leaf Part 7: Carbon Engineering's Fuel Is At Best 25x The Cost, 35x The CO_2 Emissions Compared To an EV." *Clean Technica* (April 27, 2019).

1450 Barnard, Michael. "Chevron's Fig Leaf Part 4: Carbon Engineering's Only Market Is Pumping More Oil," *Clean Technica* (April 19, 2019).

1451 Neuhauseer, Alan. "Carbon Capture: Boon or Boondoggle?" *US News* (July 26, 2019).

1452 Barnard, Michael. "Air Carbon Capture's Scale Problem: 11 Astrodomes for a Ton of CO_2." *Clean Technica* (March 11, 2019).

1453 Hanna, Ryan, Ahmed Abdulla, Yangyang Xu, and David G. Victor "Emergency Deployment of Direct Air Capture as a Response to the Climate Crisis." *Nature Communications* 12 (January 14, 2021).

1454 Sekera, June and Andreas Lichtenberger. "Assessing Carbon Capture: Public Policy, Science and Societal Need." *Biophysical Economics and Sustainability* 5 (October 6, 2020).

1455 Carbfix. CarbFix Project website.

1456 Renforth, P., B. G. Jenkins, and T. Kruger. "Engineering Challenges of Ocean Liming," *Energy* 60 (October 1, 2013).

1457 Paquay, François S. and Richard E. Zeebe. "Assessing Possible Consequences of Ocean Liming on Ocean pH, Atmospheric CO_2 Concentration and Associated Costs." *International Journal of Greenhouse Gas Control* 17 (September 2013).

1458 Fuel Cell Energy. Fuel Cell Energy website.

1459 Schwartz, John. "Exxon Mobil Backs Fuel Cell Effort to Advance Carbon Capture Technology." *The New York Times* (May 5, 2016).

1460 NET Power. NET Power website.

1461 McMahon, Jeff. "NET Power CEO Announces Four New Zero-Emission Gas Plants Underway." *Forbes* (January 8, 2021).

1462 Chazdon, Robin L., Eben N. Broadbent, Danaë M. A. Rozendaal, Frans Bongers, Angélica María Almeyda, T. Mitchell Aide, Patricia Balvanera et al. "Carbon Sequestration Potential of Second-Growth Forest Regeneration in the Latin American Tropics" *Science Advances* 2, no. 5 (May13, 2016).

1463 Little, Mark G. and Robert B. Jackson. "Potential Impacts of Leakage from Deep CO_2 Geosequestration on Overlying Freshwater Aquifers." *Environmental Science & Technology* 44, no. 23 (October 26, 2010).

1464 Tyne, R. L., P. H. Barry, M. Lawson, D. J. Byrne, O. Warr, H. Xie, D. J. Hillegonds et al. "Rapid Microbial Methanogenesis during CO_2 Storage in Hydrocarbon Reservoirs." *Nature* 600 (December 22, 2021).

1465 Zoback, Mark D. and Steven M. Gorelick. "Earthquake Triggering and Large-Scale Geologic Storage of Carbon Dioxide." *Proceedings of the National Academy of Sciences* 109, No 26 (June 26, 2012).

1466 Teng, Yihua and Dongxiao Zhang. "Long-Term Viability of Carbon Sequestration in Deep-Sea Sediments." *Science Advances* 4, no. 7 (July 4, 2018).

1467 UN Environment Programme. *Global Environment Outlook*. Cambridge University Press, 2019.

1468 Sanderson, Benjamin M., Brian C. O'Neill, and Claudia Tebaldi. "What Would it Take to Achieve the Paris Temperature Targets?" *Geophysical Research Letters* 43, no. 13 (July 16, 2016).

1469 Larkin, Alice, Jaise Kuriakose, Maria Sharmina, and Kevin Anderson. "What If Negative Emission Technologies Fail at Scale? Implications of the Paris Agreement for Big Emitting Nations." *Climate Policy* (August 3, 2017).

1470 European Academies' Science Advisory Council. *Negative Emission Technologies: What Role in Meeting Paris Agreement Targets?* (February 2018).

1471 Keller, David P., Andrew Lenton, Emma W. Littleton, Andreas Oschlies, Vivian Scott, and Naomi E. Vaughan. "The Effects of Carbon Dioxide Removal on the Carbon Cycle." *Current Climate Change Reports* (June 14, 2018).

1472 US Department of Energy Office of Fossil Energy and Carbon Management. Carbon Negative Shot.

1473 The National Academies of Sciences, Engineering, and Medicine. *Negative Emissions Technologies and Reliable Sequestration: A Research Agenda*. National Academies Press, 2019.

1474 Tokarska, Katarzyna, and Kirsten Zickfeld. "The Effectiveness of Net Negative Carbon Dioxide Emissions in Reversing Anthropogenic Climate Change." *Environmental Research Letters* 10, no. 9 (September 10, 2015).

1475 Zickfeld, Kirsten, and Deven Azevedo. "Effectiveness of Carbon Dioxide Removal in Lowering Atmospheric CO_2 and Reversing Global Warming in the Context of 1.5 Degrees." American Geophysical Union Fall Meeting (2017).

1476 Jones, C. D., P. Ciais, S. J. Davis, P. Friedlingstein, T. Gasser, G. P. Peters, J. Rogelj et al. "Simulating the Earth System Response to Negative Emissions." *Environmental Research Letters* 11, no. 9 (September 20, 2016).

1477 Niemeier, Ulrike, and Simone Tilmes. "Sulfur Injections for a Cooler Planet." *Science* 357, no. 6348 (July 21, 2017).

1478 Gao, Ru-Shan, Karen H. Rosenlof, Bernd Kärcher, Simone Tilmes, Owen B. Toon, Christopher Maloney, and Pengfei Yu. "Toward Practical Stratospheric Aerosol Albedo Modification: Solar-Powered Lofting." *Science Advances* 7, no. 20 (May 14, 2021).

1479 Pultarova, Tereza. "Clouds of Self-Levitating Soot Might Help Halt Global Warming." Space.com (May 19, 2021).

1480 Wood, Robert. "Marine Cloud Brightening."

1481 Geoengineering Monitor. "Ocean Fertilization." (January 2021).

1482 Sánchez, Joan-Pau, and Colin R. McInnes. "Optimal Sunshade Configurations for Space-Based Geoengineering near the Sun-Earth L1 Point." *PLOS ONE* (August 26, 2015).

1483   Arctic Ice Project. Arctic Ice Project website.

1484   IPCC. *Climate Change 2022: Impacts, Adaptation and Vulnerability: Summary for Policymakers*. From: IPCC Sixth Assessment Report: Impacts, Adaptation and Vulnerability (February 27, 2022).

1485   National Academies of Sciences, Engineering, and Medicine. *Reflecting Sunlight to Cool Earth*. The National Academies Press, 2015.

1486   Solar Geoengineering Non-Use Agreement. "We Call for an International Non-Use Agreement on Solar Geoengineering."

1487   Pierrehumbert, Raymond T. "Climate Hacking is Barking Mad." *Slate* (February 10, 2015).

1488   McMartin, Douglas, Ben Kravitz, Jane C. S. Long, and Philip J. Rasch. "Geoengineering With Stratospheric Aerosols: What Do We Not Know After A Decade Of Research?" *Earth's Future* 4, no. 11 (November, 18, 2016).

1489   National Academies of Sciences, Engineering, and Medicine. *Reflecting Sunlight: Recommendations for Solar Geoengineering Research and Research Governance*. The National Academies Press, 2021.

1490   Jones, Anthony C., James M. Haywood, Nick Dunstone, Kerry Emanuel, Matthew K. Hawcroft, Kevin I. Hodges, and Andy Jones. "Impacts of Hemispheric Solar Geoengineering on Tropical Cyclone Frequency." *Nature Communications* 8 (November 14, 2017).

1491   Gertier, Charles G., Paul A. O'Gorman, Ben Kravitz, John C. Moore, Steven J. Phipps, and Shingo Watanabe. "Weakening of the Extratropical Storm Tracks in Solar Geoengineering Scenarios." *Geophysical Research Letters* 47, no. 11 (April 23, 2020).

1492   Robock, Alan, Martin Bunzl, Ben Kravitz, and Georgiy L. Stenchikov. "A Test for Geoengineering?" *Science* 327, no. 5965 (January 29, 2010).

1493   Beaumont, Hilary. "Chemtrails Conspiracy Theorists are Sending Death Threats to Climate Scientists." *Vice News* (November 22, 2017).

1494   Rotman, David. "A Cheap and Easy Plan to Stop Global Warming." *Technology Review* (February 8, 2013).

1495   Smith, Wake and Gernot Wagner. "Stratospheric Aerosol Injection Tactics and Costs in the First 15 Years of Deployment." *Environmental Research Letters* 13, no. 12 (November 23, 2018).

1496   Niemeier, Ulrike and Simone Tilmes. "Sulfur Injections for a Cooler Planet." *Science* 357, no. 6348 (July 21, 2017).

1497   Trisos, Christopher H., Giuseppe Amatulli, Jessica Gurevitch, Alan Robock, Lili Xia, and Brian Zambri. "Potentially Dangerous Consequences for Biodiversity of Solar Geoengineering Implementation and Termination." *Nature Ecology & Evolution* (January 22, 2018).

1498 Lohmann, Ulrike and Blaž Gasparini. "A Cirrus Cloud Climate Dial?" *Science* 357, no. 6348 (July 21, 2017).

1499 Arctic Ice Project. Arctic Ice Project website.

1500 Niiler, Eric. "Can Tiny Glass Beads Keep Arctic Ice from Melting? Maaaybe." *Wired* (October 18, 2019).

1501 Stillman, Jana, Timothy M. Lenton, Anders Levermann, Konrad Ott, Mike Hulme, François Benduhn, and Joshua B. Horton. "Climate Emergencies Do Not Justify Engineering the Climate." *Nature Climate Change* 5 (April 2015).

1502 Curwood, Steve. "America's Climate Denial Madhouse: Interview with Michael Mann." Living on Earth (December 30, 2016).

1503 International Atomic Energy Agency. *Climate Change and Nuclear Power 2020* (2020).

1504 Westinghouse. AP1000 Pressurized Water Reactor website.

1505 World Nuclear Association. Small Nuclear Power Reactors website.

1506 Westinghouse. *The Westinghouse Small Modular Reactor.*

1507 NuScale Power. NuScale Power website.

1508 Cho, Adrian. "Smaller, Cheaper Reactor Aims to Revive Nuclear Industry, But Design Problems Raise Safety Concerns." *Science* (August 18, 2020).

1509 Levitan, David. "First US Small Nuclear Reactor Design Is Approved." *Scientific American* (September 9, 2020).

1510 Ramana, M. V. "Eyes Wide Shut: Problems with the Utah Associated Municipal Power Systems Proposal to Construct NuScale Small Modular Nuclear Reactors." Oregon Physicians for Social Responsibility (September 2020).

1511 Krall, Lindsay M., Allison M. Macfarlane, and Rodney C. Ewing. "Nuclear Waste from Small Modular Reactors." *Proceedings of the National Academy of Sciences* 199, no. 23 (May 31, 2022).

1512 Makhijani, Arjun and M. V. Ramana. "Why Small Modular Nuclear Reactors Won't Help Counter the Climate Crisis." Environmental Working Group (March 25, 2021).

1513 Ramana, M. V. "The Impossible Promises of Small Modular Nuclear Reactors." *Peace Magazine* (July 1, 2022).

1514 World Nuclear Association. Molten Salt Reactors website.

1515 Waldrop, Mitchell, M. "Nuclear Goes Retro—With a Much Greener Outlook." *Knowable* (February 22, 2019).

1516 Lyman Edwin. *"Advanced' Isn't Always Better: Assessing the Safety, Security, and Environmental Impacts of Non-Light-Water Nuclear Reactors."* Union of Concerned Scientists (March 18, 2021).

1517 World Nuclear Association. "Fukushima Daiichi Accident."

1518 Union of Concerned Scientists. *The Nuclear Power Dilemma* (October 9, 2018).

1519 Baron, Jonathon and Stephen Herzog. "Public Opinion on Nuclear Energy and Nuclear Weapons: The Attitudinal Nexus in the United States." *Energy Research & Social Science* 68 (October 2020).

1520 Plumer, Brad. "Nuclear Power is Dying. Can Radical Innovation Save It?" *Vox* (March 27, 2017).

1521 International Energy Agency. *Nuclear Power and Secure Energy Transitions.* (June 2022).

1522 Jordans, Frank. "Germany Shuts down Half of its 6 Remaining Nuclear Plants." Associated Press (January 3, 2022).

1523 Union of Concerned Scientists. *The Nuclear Power Dilemma* (2018).

1524 Statista Research Department. "Global Number of Nuclear Reactors under Construction by Country 2022." (June 9, 2022).

1525 International Energy Agency. *Nuclear Power in a Clean Energy System* (May 28, 2019).

1526 MIT Energy Initiative. *The Future of Nuclear Energy in a Carbon-Constrained World.* MIT Energy Initiative (2018).

1527 Morgan, M. Granger, Ahmed Abdulla, Michael J. Ford, and Michael Rath. "US Nuclear Power: The Vanishing Low-Carbon Wedge." *Proceedings of the National Academy of Sciences* 115, no. 28 (July 2, 2018).

1528 World Nuclear Industry Status Report. World Nuclear Industry Status Report 2019 (September 24, 2019).

1529 World Nuclear Industry Status Report. World Nuclear Industry Status Report 2021. (September 28, 2021).

1530 US Energy Information Administration. "Levelized Costs of New Generation Resources in the *Annual Energy Outlook 2022*." From: *Annual Energy Outlook 2022* (March 18, 2022).

1531 International Energy Agency. *The Value of Urgent Action on Energy Efficiency.* (June 2022).

1532 International Energy Agency. *Multiple Benefits of Energy Efficiency* (March 2019).

1533 International Energy Agency. *Energy Efficiency 2018* (2018).

1534 International Energy Agency. *Energy Efficiency 2021* (November 2021).

1535 Grubler, Arnulf, Charlie Wilson, Nuno Bento, Benigna Boza-Kiss, Volker Krey, David L. McCollum, Narasimha D. Rao et al. "A Low Energy Demand Scenario for Meeting the 1.5°C Target and Sustainable Development Goals without Negative Emission Technologies." *Nature Energy* 3 (June 4, 2018).

1536 Johnson, Scott J. "Want to Halt Global Warming and Raise Living Standards? Get Efficient." *Ars Technica* (June 5, 2018).

1537 International Energy Agency. "Tracking Clean Energy Progress: Tracking Buildings" (November 2021).

1538 International Energy Agency. "Tracking Clean Energy Progress: Trucks and Buses" (November 2021).

1539 International Energy Agency. *Energy, Climate Change & Environment 2016 Insights* (November 2016).

1540 United Nations Environment Programme. Transport website.

1541 US Energy Information Administration. Energy Use for Transportation.

1542 International Energy Agency. "Tracking Clean Energy Progress: Tracking Transport" (November 2021).

1543 International Maritime Emission Reduction Scheme. Aviation, Shipping and the Paris Agreement.

1544 International Council on Clean Transportation. *Global Transportation Energy and Climate Roadmap* (2012).

1545 International Energy Agency. *Global EV Outlook 2022.* (May 2022).

1546 Kah, Marianne. Electric Vehicle Penetration and Its Impact on Global Oil Demand: A Survey of 2019 Forecast Trends. Columbia Center on Global Energy Policy (December 17, 2019).

1547 Plumer Brad, Nadja Popovich, and Blacki Migliozzi. "Electric Cars Are Coming. How Long Until They Rule the Road?" *The New York Times* (March 10, 2021).

1548 International Energy Agency. "Tracking Clean Energy Progress: Electric Vehicles" (November 2021).

1549 BloombergNEF. Electric Vehicle Outlook 2021 (2021).

1550 IHS Markit. *Battery Electric Vehicles Whitepaper* (February 2020).

1551 Coltura. Gasoline Vehicle Phaseout Advances around the World.

1552 Gov.uk. "COP26 Declaration on Accelerating the Transition to 100% Zero Emission Cars and Vans" (November 21, 2021).

1553 Congress.gov. *H.R.3684 – Infrastructure Investment and Jobs Act* (2021).

1554 White House. "Fact Sheet: The Bipartisan Infrastructure Deal" (November 6, 2021).

1555 Congress.gov. "H.R.5376 – Inflation Reduction Act of 2022." (2022).

1556 Boudette, Neal E. "G.M. Will Sell Only Zero-Emission Vehicles by 2035." *The New York Times* (January 28, 2021).

1557 Boudette, Neal E. "Tesla Might Finally Have Some Competition. From Ford." *The New York Times* (January 15, 2021).

1558 Carrington, Damian. "Electric Car Batteries with Five-Minute Charging Times Produced." *The Guardian* (January 19, 2021).

1559 Penney, Veronica. "Electric Cars Are Better for the Planet—and Often Your Budget, Too." *The New York Times* (January 15, 2021).

1560 Lienart, Paul, Joseph White, and Ben Klayman. "Detroit's Near Future Based On SUVs, Not EVs, Production Plans Show." Reuters (March 26, 2020).

1561   Deloitte. *2022 Global Automotive Consumer Study* (January 2022).

1562   Zarazua de Rubens, Gerardo, Lance Noel, and Benjamin K. Sovacool. "Dismissive and Deceptive Car Dealerships Create Barriers to Electric Vehicle Adoption at the Point of Sale." *Nature Energy* (May 21, 2018).

1563   Deaton, Jeremy. "Car Companies Aren't Even Trying To Sell Electric Cars." Huffington Post (January 14, 2019).

1564   Hall, Kalea. "Car Dealerships Prepare for Electric Vehicle Future." *Government Technology* (January 5, 2020.

1565   Ewing, Jack. "Electric Cars Too Costly for Many, Even With Aid in Climate Bill." *The New York Times* (August 9, 2022).

1566   Plumer, Brad, "Electric Cars Are Coming, and Fast. Is the Nation's Grid up to It?" *The New York Times*, January 29, 2021).

1567   Natter, Ari, and Keith Laing. "The Coming Electric Car Disruption That Nobody's Talking About." Bloomberg (October 22, 2021).

1568   Congressional Research Service. *Electrification May Disrupt the Automotive Supply Chain* (February 8, 2019).

1569   International Energy Agency. *The Role of Critical Minerals in Clean Energy Transitions* (May 2021).

1570   Rodríguez, José Jr. "EVs Are Gaining Steam. Here's What Will Happen To All Those Dead Batteries." Jalopnik (February 2021).

1571   Gottesfeld, Perry. "Opinion: Electric Cars' Looming Recycling Problem." *Undark* (January 21, 2021).

1572   Bieker, Georg. *A Global Comparison of the Life-Cycle Greenhouse Gas Emissions of Combustion Engine and Electric Passenger Cars.* International Council on Clean Transportation (July 20, 2021).

1573   Wolfram, Paul, Stephanie Weber, Kenneth Gillingham, and Edgar G. Hertwich. "Pricing Indirect Emissions Accelerates Low-Carbon Transition of US Light Vehicle Sector." *Nature Communications* 12 (December 8, 2021).

1574   US Energy Information Administration. Energy Use for Transportation.

1575   Sauer, Natalie. "Electric Cars Won't Stop Rising Oil Demand. *Ecologist* (January 25, 2019).

1576   Betancourt, Mark. "Greening the Friendly Skies." *Eos* (November 4, 2020).

1577   Graver, Brandon, Kevin Zhang, and Dan Rutherford. "CO_2 Emissions from Commercial Aviation, 2018." International Council on Clean Transportation (September 9, 2019).

1578   International Civil Aviation Organization. "ICAO Global Environmental Trends—Present and Future Aircraft Noise and Emissions" (May 7, 2019).

1579   Tyers, Roger. "It's Time to Wake up to the Devastating Impact Flying Has on the Environment." *The Conversation* (January 11, 2017).

1580 Apuzzo, Matt, and Sarah Hurtes, "Tasked to Fight Climate Change, a Secretive UN Agency Does the Opposite." *The New York Times* (June 3, 2021).

1581 International Energy Agency. Transport Biofuels (June 2020).

1582 Center for Climate and Energy Solutions. "Global Emissions website,"

1583 Tubiello, F. N., M. Salvatore, R. D. Cóndor Golec, A. Ferrara, S. Rossi, R. Biancalani, S. Federici, H. Jacobs, and A. Flammini. *Agriculture, Forestry and Other Land Use Emissions by Sources and Removal by Sinks.* UN Food and Agriculture Organization (March 2014).

1584 Clark, Michael A., Nina G. G. Domingo, Kimberly Colgan, Sumil K. Thakrar, David Tilman, John Lynch, Inês L. Azevedo, and Jason D. Hill. "Global Food System Emissions Could Preclude Achieving the 1.5° and 2°C Climate Change Targets." *Science* 370, no. 6517 (November 6, 2020).

1585 Tubiello, Francesco N., Mirella Salvatore, Alessandro F. Ferrara, Jo House, Sandro Federici, Simone Rossi, Riccardo Biancalani et al. "The Contribution of Agriculture, Forestry and other Land Use Activities to Global Warming, 1990–2012." *Global Change Biology* 21, no. 7 (July 2015).

1586 Searchinger, Tim and Richard Waite. "Richard, More Rice, Less Methane." World Resources Institute (December 16, 2014).

1587 Reisinger, Andy and Harry Clark. "How Much Do Direct Livestock Emissions Actually Contribute To Global Warming?" *Global Change Biology* 24, no. 4 (November 6, 2017).

1588 FAO, UNDP, UNEP. *A Multi-Billion-Dollar Opportunity—Repurposing Agricultural Support to Transform Food Systems* (2021).

1589 Wollenberg, Eva, Meryl Richards, Pete Smith, Petr Havlík, Michael Obersteiner, Francesco N. Tubiello, Martin Herold et al. "Reducing Emissions from Agriculture to Meet the 2°C Target." *Global Change Biology* 22, no. 12 (December 2016).

1590 Herrero, Mario, Philip K. Thornton, Daniel Mason-D'Croz, Jeda Palmer, Tim G. Benton, Benjamin L. Bodirsky, Jessica R. Bogard et al. "Innovation Can Accelerate the Transition towards a Sustainable Food System." *Nature Food* 19 (May 19, 2020).

1591 Dunn, Rob. *Never Out of Season: How Having the Food We Want When We Want It Threatens Our Food Supply and Our Future.* Little, Brown, 2017.

1592 Sanderman, Jonathan, Tomislav Hengl, and Gregory Fiske. "Soil Carbon Debt of 12,000 Years of Human Land Use." *Proceedings of the National Academy of Sciences* 114, no. 36 (September 5, 2017).

1593 Carrau, Natalia and Martin Drago. *"Getting into a Bind": How the Trade and Investment Regime Blocks the Development of Agroecology and Access to Land.* Friends of the Earth International (October 2016).

1594 The international "4 per 1000" Initiative. 4 per 1000 initiative website.

1595 Wageningen University. "Paris Soil Carbon Sequestration Goals Called Unrealistic." Phys.org (April 21, 2017).

1596 Popkin, Gabriel. "A Soil-Science Revolution Upends Plans to Fight Climate Change."*Quanta* (July 27, 2021).

1597 Cullenward, Danny, Joseph Hamman, and Jeremy Freeman. "Getting Soil Carbon Right." (carbon) plan, June 1, 2020).

1598 Bajželja, Bojana, Keith S. Richards, Julian M. Allwood, Pete Smith, John S. Dennis, Elizabeth Curmi, and Christopher A. Gilligan. "Importance of Food-Demand Management for Climate Mitigation." *Nature Climate Change* 4 (August 31, 2014).

1599 Heinrich Böll Stiftung, Friends of the Earth Europe, Bund für Umwelt, and Naturschutz. *Meat Atlas: Facts and Figures about the Animals We Eat* (September 2021).

1600 Lucas, Tamra, and Richard Horton. "The 21st Century Great Food Transformation." *The Lancet* 393, no. 10170 (January 16, 2019).

1601 Xu, Xiaoming, Prateek Sharma, Shijie Shu, Tzu-Shun Lin, Philippe Ciais, Francesco N. Tubiello, Pete Smith, Nelson Campbell, and Atul K. JainGlobal. "Greenhouse Gas Emissions from Animal-Based Foods are Twice Those of Plant-Based Foods." *Nature Food* 2 (September 13, 2021).

1602 Kim, Brent, Roni Neff, Raychel Santo, and Juliana Vigorito. "The Importance of Reducing Animal Product Consumption and Wasted Food in Mitigating Catastrophic Climate Change." Johns Hopkins Center for a Livable Future (December 2015).

1603 Gerhardt, Carsten, Gerrit Suhlmann, Fabio Ziemßen, Dave Donnan, Mirko Warschun, and Hans Jochen Kühnle. "How Will Cultured Meat and Meat Alternatives Disrupt the Agricultural and Food Industry?" *Industrial Biotechnology* 16, no.16 (October 2020).

1604 Severson, Kim. "The New Secret Chicken Recipe? Animal Cells." *The New York Times* (February 15, 2022).

1605 Springman, Marco. "Analysis and Valuation of the Health and Climate Change Cobenefits of Dietary Change." *Proceedings of the National Academy of Sciences* 113, no. 5 (April 12, 2016).

1606 Gustavsson Jenny, Christel Cederberg, and Ulf Sonesson. *Global Food Losses and Food Waste.* UN Food and Agriculture Organization (2011).

1607 Bond, David P. and Stephen E. Grasby. "On the Causes of Mass Extinctions." *Palaeogeography, Palaeoclimatology, Palaeoecology* 478 (July 2017).

1608 Deep Carbon Observatory. "Scientists Quantify Global Volcanic CO_2 Venting; Estimate Total Carbon on Earth" (October 1, 2019).

1609 National Academies. *Abrupt Impacts of Climate Change: Anticipating Surprises* (2013).

1610   Steffen, Will, Wendy Broadgate, Lisa Deutsch, Owen Gaffney, and Cornelia Ludwig. "The Trajectory of the Anthropocene: the Great Acceleration." *The Anthropocene Review* 2, no. 1 (January 16, 2015).

1611   Gaffney, Owen, and Will Steffen. "The Anthropocene Equation." *The Anthropocene Review* 4, no. 1 (February 10, 2017).

1612   Gaffney, Owen. "Simple Equation Shows How Human Activity Is Trashing The Planet." *New Scientist* (February 10, 2017).

1613   Folke, Carl, Stephen Polasky, Johan Rockström, Victor Galaz, Frances Westley, Michèle Lamont, Marten Schefferig et al. "Our Future in the Anthropocene Biosphere." *Ambio* (March 14, 2021).

1614   Waters, Colin N., Jan Zalasiewicz, Colin Summerhayes, Anthony D. Barnosky, Clément Poirier, Agnieszka Gałuszka, Alejandro Cearreta et al. "The Anthropocene Is Functionally and Stratigraphically Distinct from the Holocene." *Science* 353, no. 6269 (January 8, 2016).

1615   Corcoran, Patricia L., Charles J. Moore, and Kelly Jazvac. "An Anthropogenic Marker Horizon in the Future Rock Record." *GSA Today* 24, no. 6 (June 2014).

1616   Zalasiewicz, Jan, Colin N. Waters, Juliana A. Ivar do Sul, Patricia L. Corcoran, Anthony D. Barnosky, Alejandro Cearreta, Matt Edgeworth et al. "The Geological Cycle of Plastics and Their Use as a Stratigraphic Indicator of the Anthropocene." *Anthropocene* 13 (March 2016).

1617   Orr, David W. *Down to the Wire: Confronting Climate Collapse.* Oxford University Press. 2009.

1618   Zubrow, Keith. "Sir David Attenborough to 60 Minutes on Climate Change: 'A Crime Has Been Committed." 60 Minutes Overtime (September 27, 2020).

1619   BBC. "Extinction: The Facts" (2020).

1620   Ehgartner, Ulrike, Patrick Gould, and Marc Hudson. "On the Obsolescence of Human Beings in Sustainable Development." *Global Discourse* 7, no. 1 (April 18, 2017).

1621   Kübler-Ross, Elisabeth. *On Death and Dying.* Scribner, reprint edition, 2014.

1622   Gregory, Christina. "The Five Stages of Grief."

1623   Friedman, Thomas, L. "Stampeding Black Elephants." *The New York Times* (November 22, 2014).

1624   Orr, David W. *Down to the Wire: Confronting Climate Collapse.* Oxford University Press, 2009.

1625   Goodman, Max. "Why We Need Climate Stoicism to Overcome Climate Despair." State of the Planet (May 19, 2020).

1626   Extinction Rebellion Hannover. Hope dies—Action begins.

1627   Hayhoe, Katharine. *Saving Us: A Climate Scientist's Case for Hope and Healing in a Divided World.* Simon & Schuster, 2021.

1628   Ray, Sarah Jaquette. *A Field Guide to Climate Anxiety: How to Keep Your Cool on a Warming Planet.* University of California Press, 2020.

1629   Hawken, Paul, ed. *Drawdown: The Most Comprehensive Plan Ever Proposed to Reverse Global Warming.* Penguin Random House, 2017.

1630   Pogue, David. *How to Prepare for Climate Change: A Practical Guide to Surviving the Chaos.* Simon & Schuster, 2021.

1631   Climate Psychology Alliance. Climate Psychology Alliance website.

1632   Project InsideOut. Project InsideOut website.

1633   Climate Awakening. Climate Emotion Conversation website.

1634   Willett, Walter, Johan Rockström, Brent Loken, Marco Springmann, Tim Lang, Sonja Vermeulen, Tara Garnett et al. "Food in the Anthropocene: The EAT-Lancet Commission on Healthy Diets from Sustainable Food Systems." The EAT-Lancet Commission on Food, Planet, Health (2019).

1635   Conceivable Future. Conceivable Future website.

1636   Bill Moyers Reports: Earth on Edge.Environmental Organizations.

1637   Extinction Rebellion. Extinction Rebellion website.

1638   350.org. 350.org website.

1639   Climate Reality Project. Climate Reality Project website.

1640   The Climate Mobilization. The Climate Mobilization website.

1641   Climate Emergency Fund. Climate Emergency Fund website.

1642   Society of Environmental Journalists. Society of Environmental Journalists website.

1643   *Anthropocene* magazine. *Anthropocene* magazine website.

1644   Climate Central. Climate Central website.

1645   Climatewire. Climatewire website.

1646   Covering Climate Now. Covering Climate Now website.

1647   DeSmog. DeSmog website.

1648   Inside Climate News. Inside Climate News website.

1649   The Environmental News Cooperative. Floodlight website.

1650   Emily Atkin. HEATED newsletter.

1651   Wynes, Seth, and Kimberly Nicholas. "The Climate Mitigation Gap: Education and Government Recommendations Miss the Most Effective Individual Actions." *Environmental Research Letters* 12 (July 12, 2017).

1652   Thomas, Dylan. "Do Not Go Gentle Into That Good Night." *In Country Sleep, And Other Poems.* Dent, 1952.

1653   Levy, Nicole. "Jeff Zucker talks CNN's Post-Plane Plans." *Politico* (May 20, 2014).

1654   Arkush, David. "Carbon Omission: How the US Media Underreported Climate Change in 2017." Public Citizen (January 2018).

1655 Kalhoefer, Kevin. "So Far, ABC and NBC are Failing to Note the Link between Harvey and Climate Change." Media Matters for America (August 31, 2017).

1656 Tharoor, Ishaan. "Hurricane Harvey and the Inevitable Question of Climate Change." *The Washington Post* (August 29, 2017).

1657 Niler, Eric. "How Climate Change Fueled Hurricane Harvey." *Wired* (August 29, 2017).

1658 Editorial Board. "Beyond Houston, a World Awash." *The New York Times* (August 31, 2017).

1659 Cooper, Evlondo. "Climate Change Is Fueling Storms Like Hurricane Dorian. But You Wouldn't Know That From Watching Broadcast TV News." Media Matters for America (September 6, 2019).

1660 Cooper, Evlondo. "Sunday Shows' Climate Coverage in 2017 Included Few Women, Fewer Minorities, and Zero Scientists." Media Matters for America (February 22, 2018).

1661 Hymas, Lisa. "Climate Change Is the Story You Missed in 2017. And the Media is to Blame." *The Guardian* (December 7, 2017).

1662 Allsop, Jon. "The Press Won't Let Trump Bury Climate Change. But it is Still Complicit." Columbia Journalism Review (November 26, 2018).

1663 Public Citizen. "Climate Uncovered: Media Fail to Connect Hurricane Florence to Climate Change" (September 18, 2018).

1664 MacDonald, Ted. "How Broadcast TV Networks Covered Climate Change in 2020." Media Matters for America (March 10, 2021).

1665 Fisher, Allison. "National Corporate TV News Largely Failed to Cover Hurricane Ida as a Climate Justice Story." Media Matters for America (September 1, 2021).

1666 MacDonald, Ted. "Broadcast and Cable TV News Shows Mentioned Climate Change in a Combined 36% of Wildfire Segments." Media Matters for America (August 4, 2021).

1667 Leiserowitz, Anthony, Edward Maibach, Seth Rosenthal, John Kotcher, Jennifer Carman, Liz Neyens, Jennifer Marlon, Karine Lacroix, and Matthew Goldberg. *Climate Change in the American Mind, April 2022.* Yale Program on Climate Change Communication and George Mason University Center for Climate Change Communication (April 2022).

1668 Center for Climate Change Communication. "*A 2016 National Survey of Broadcast Meteorologists*" (2016).

1669 Gelles, David. "Weather Channel Goes Into Overdrive Covering Back-to-Back Hurricanes." *The New York Times* (September 9, 2017).

1670 The Weather Channel. Collateral: Climate, Data and Science from the Weather Channel.

1671   Perkins, David R. IV, Kristin Timm, Teresa Myers, and Edward Maibach. "Broadcast Meteorologists' Views on Climate Change: A State-of-the-Community Review." *Weather, Climate and Society* 12, no. 12 (February 24, 2020).

1672   Engelhardt, Tom. "Climate Change as the AntiNews." *Huffington Post* (February 3, 2014).

1673   Langlois, Krista. "Has Environmental Journalism Failed?" *Slate* (April 8, 2015).

1674   Seifter, Andrew. "*USA Today's* Climate Denial Problem Isn't Going Away." Media Matters for America (December 12, 2016).

1675   Geiling, Natasha. "Scott Pruitt Was Even More Selfish and Vengeful Than We Thought." *New Republic* (October 26, 2020).

1676   Public Citizen. "Coverage of Climate Denial by Conservative Think Tanks Has Increased" (July 25, 2019).

1677   Kalhoefer, Kevin, "Networks Covering March for Science Provided Platform for Climate Deniers" (April 24, 2017).

1678   Boykoff, Maxwell T. and Jules M. Boykoff. "Balance as Bias: Global Warming and US Prestige Press." *Global Environmental Change* 14 (2004).

1679   Huertas, Aaron. "Despite Fact-Checking, Zombie Myths about Climate Change Persist." Poynter (December 20, 2016).

1680   Robbins, Denise, Kevin Kalhiefer, and Andrew Seifter. "Study: Newspaper Opinion Pages Feature Science Denial and Other Climate Change Misinformation." Media Matters for America (September 1, 2016).

1681   Singer, Fred. "The Sea Is Rising, but Not Because of Climate Change." *Wall Street Journal* (May 15, 2018).

1682   Drum, Kevin. "Wall Street Journal: Relax, Climate Change is No Big Deal." *Mother Jones* (May 16, 2018).

1683   Jacoby, Jeff. "Why are Climate-Change Models So Flawed? Because Climate Science is So Incomplete." *Boston Globe* (March 14, 2017).

1684   Climate Feedback. "Analysis of 'Why are Climate-Change Models So Flawed? Because Climate Science is So Incomplete'" (March 14, 2017).

1685   Hymas, Lisa. "*USA Today* Publishes Still More Climate Misinformation, Denying a Link between Climate Change and Hurricanes." Media Matters for America (September 14, 2018).

1686   Lomborg, Bjørn. "Don't Buy the Latest Climate-Change Alarmism." *New York Post* (August 9, 2021).

1687   Stiglitz, Joseph E. "Are We Overreacting on Climate Change?" *The New York Times* (July 16, 2020).

1688   Stephens, Brett. "Yes, Greenland's Ice is Melting But. . . ." *The New York Times* (October 28, 2022).

1689   Romm, Joe. "After Hyping Itself as Antidote to Fake News, *New York Times* Hires Extreme Climate Denier." ThinkProgress (April 13, 2017).

1690   Atkin, Emily. "A New York Times Columnist Went to Greenland and Discovered Fossil Fuel Talking Points." Heated (November 3, 2022).

1691   Taylor, James. "As the Consensus among Scientists Crumbles, Global Warming Alarmists Attack Their Integrity." *Forbes* (February 13, 2013).

1692   Lefsrud, Lianne M. and Renate E. Meyer. "Science or Science Fiction? Professionals' Discursive Construction of Climate Change." *Organization Studies* (November 19, 2012).

1693   Robbins, Denise. "Before Joining Trump White House, Steve Bannon Ran a Website That Viciously Attacked Climate Scientists." Media Matters for America (November 15, 2016).

1694   Global Challenges Foundation. Global Catastrophic Risks 2021: Navigating the Complex Intersections (2021).

1695   Centers for Disease Control and Prevention. "Pandemic Influenza" (2017).

1696   Morens, David M. and Anthony S. Fauci. "Emerging Infectious Diseases: Threats to Human Health and Global Stability." *PLoS Pathogens* 9, no. 7 (July 2013).

1697   The Review on Antimicrobial Resistance. *Tackling Drug-Resistant Infections Globally: Final Report and Recommendations* (May 2016).

1698   Gore, A. C., V. A. Chappell, S. E. Fenton, J. A. Flaws, A. Nadal, G. S. Prins, J. Toppari, and R. T. Zoeller. "EDC 2: The Endocrine Society's Second Scientific Statement on Endocrine-Disrupting Chemicals." *Endocrine Reviews* 36, no. 6 (December 1, 2015).

1699   Di Renzo, Gian Carlo, Jeanne A. Conry, Jennifer Blake, Mark S. DeFrancesco, Nathaniel DeNicola, James N. Martin Jr., Kelly A. McCue et al. "International Federation of Gynecology and Obstetrics Opinion on Reproductive Health Impacts of Exposure to Toxic Environmental Chemicals." *International Journal of Gynecology and Obstetrics* 131, no. 3 (October 1, 2015).

1700   Wang, Aolin, Dimitri Panagopoulos Abrahamsson, Ting Jiang, Miaomiao Wang, Rachel Morello-Frosch, June-Soo Park, Marina Sirota, and Tracey J. Woodruff. "Suspect Screening, Prioritization, and Confirmation of Environmental Chemicals in Maternal-Newborn Pairs from San Francisco." *Environmental Science & Technology* (March 16, 2021).

1701   Taylor, Ashley P. "More Than 50 New Environmental Chemicals Detected in People." Live Science (March 22, 2021).

1702   President's Cancer Panel. Reducing Environmental Cancer Risk: What We Can Do Now" (April 2010).

1703   Froelich, Amanda. "Sperm Whales Found Dead In Germany, Stomachs FULL of Plastic and Car Parts." *True Activist* (April 21, 2016).

1704   Jambeck, Jenna R., Roland Geyer, Chris Wilcox, Theodore R. Siegler, Miriam Perryman, Anthony Andrady, Ramani Narayan, and Kara Lavender Law. "Plastic Waste Inputs from Land into the Ocean." *Science* 347, no. 6223 (February 13, 2015).

1705   Boucher, Julien, and Damien Friot. *Primary Microplastics in the Oceans.* IUCN (2017).

1706   Lamb, Joleah Bette L. Willis, Evan A. Fiorenza, Courtney S. Couch, Robert Howard, Douglas N. Rader, and James D. True. "Plastic Waste Associated with Disease on Coral Reefs." *Science* 359, no. 6374 (January 26, 2018).

1707   Eriksen, Marcus. "Plastic Pollution in the World's Oceans: More than 5 Trillion Plastic Pieces Weighing over 250,000 Tons Afloat at Sea." *PLOS ONE* 9, no. 12 (December 10, 2014).

1708   Tyree Chris, and Dan Morrison. "Invisibles: The Plastic inside Us." Orb Media (2017).

1709   Leslie, Heather A., Martin J. M. van Velzen, Sicco H.Brandsma, A. Dick Vethaak, Juan J.Garcia-Vallejo, and Marja H. Lamoree. "Discovery and Quantification of Plastic Particle Pollution in Human Blood." *Environmental International* 163 (March, 2022.

1710   Geyer, Roland, Jenna Jambeck, and Kara Lavender Law. "Production, Use, and Fate of All Plastics Ever Made," *Science Advances* 3 (July 19, 2017).

1711   Lebreton, Laurent, and Anthony Andrady. "Future Scenarios of Global Plastic Waste Generation and Disposal." *Nature* 5 (January 29, 2019).

1712   Rochman, Chelsea M., Anna-Marie Cook, and Albert A. Koelmans. "Plastic Debris and Policy: Using Current Scientific Understanding to Invoke Positive Change." *Environmental Toxicology and Chemistry* 35, no. 7 (June 22, 2016).

Index